Demineralization
by Ion Exchange

DEMINERALIZATION BY ION EXCHANGE

In Water Treatment and Chemical Processing of Other Liquids

SAMUEL B. APPLEBAUM

CONSULTING ENGINEER
    PHILADELPHIA, PENNSYLVANIA
FORMERLY,
    TECHNICAL DIRECTOR
        COCHRANE DIVISION—CRANE COMPANY;
    VICE PRESIDENT
        PERMUTIT COMPANY

 ACADEMIC PRESS   New York and London   1968

ACADEMIC PRESS INC.
111 Fifth Avenue, New York, New York 10003

United Kingdom Edition published by
ACADEMIC PRESS INC. (LONDON) LTD.
Berkeley Square House, London W.1

LIBRARY OF CONGRESSS CATALOG CARD NUMBER: 68-18653

PRINTED IN THE UNITED STATES OF AMERICA

To my wife, Stella

Preface

The technique of demineralization by ion exchange, for the complete removal of dissolved impurities from water and other liquids, has increased in use to such a degree that currently it is the purification method most widely applied.

In the past, this subject has been dealt with only briefly in books on general water treatment. The aim of this book is to discuss demineralization at length, with stress on the latest developments. The engineering and practical aspects are emphasized and enough chemistry is included to explain the processes involved. Further information on the chemical theory of ion exchange may be found in texts listed at the end of Chapter 1.

A great many demineralizers are being specified, installed, and operated today in industrial, municipal, and utility power plants to supply pure water for processing, boiler feed, and other purposes. The equipment is often complex and costly. There is need, therefore, for complete information to help executives, consultants, engineers, and chemists select the method and equipment design that will solve their particular water treatment or chemical processing problem with the greatest reliability and economy. The book should also be of value to engineering students because of the emphasis given to the latest techniques now successfully applied.

Since its introduction early in the century, ion exchange has become increasingly essential to industry. Rayon, nylon, and other synthetic fibers, for example, as well as many plastics could not be produced free from defects without ion exchange treatment of their processing water. Television tubes and other electronic parts are dependent on ultrapure demineralized wash water for their satisfactory performance. Modern power plants, both nuclear and fossil-fuel types, could not be operated free from failure without demineralizing their feed water. These are but a few of the many industrial applications of demineralization.)

During the years that ion exchange has become increasingly important to industry, the art of demineralization itself has been subject to ever-changing innovation. Hardly a year goes by without the introduction of a new exchange resin, a novel process, or an equipment design. For the most part this progress has been dictated by the need to meet the rapid changes and growing complexity of industry itself.)

R. Buckminster Fuller, engineer and philosopher, has suggested recently that our technological revolution involves doing "more with less." In the field of communications, he reminds us, we went from wire to wireless and later to a satellite weighing only one-tenth of a ton which outperformed transatlantic cables weighing seventy-five thousand tons. In water treatment, many developments, although less dramatic, have shown the same trend. To mention but one example, the modern condensate demineralizer now operates at flow rates five times greater than that used ten years ago, thus decreasing the size of the equipment and resin inventory by eighty per cent. The same condensate demineralizer now is operating without the costly prefilters previously used to protect the resin. Omitting these prefilters alone cuts investment costs in half, so that the saving to a single large power station may be over half a million dollars.

Demineralizers remove the ionic impurities. But many natural waters also contain various nonionic impurities (turbidity, color, colloids, and organic matter) that could be harmful in industrial applications. These too must be eliminated and their removal usually precedes the demineralizer, in a pretreatment, because they may form deposits on the ion exchange resins and foul them. Pretreatment equipment design has also shown the same trend of doing "more with less." Settling basins are being omitted ahead of "in-depth" filters and the filters are being operated at higher flow rates, in order to reduce costs. Several early chapters are devoted to the subject of pretreatment, because many demineralizer projects normally include these "primary" preconditioning plants.

However beneficial, these new developments have so increased the complexity of the art of liquid conditioning that today more skill and judgement are required for its successful practice. This book, therefore, is intended to present guide lines for the proper application of the many available resins and equipment designs. The text should aid the reader, for example, in making selections from the following possible options: a demineralizer or an evaporator; a demineralizer or a hot lime zeolite plant or a desilicizer; a two-bed, three-bed, or four-bed demineralizer; a secondary polishing two-bed or mixed bed; a decarbonator or a vacuum deaerator; a demineralizer used alone or preceded by a lime softener; a strong acid cation exchanger used alone or preceded by a weak acid cation exchanger; a strong base anion exchanger used alone or preceded by a weak base anion exchanger; continuous or fixed bed demineralizers; a pretreatment plant using in-depth filters alone or preceded by settling basins; high rate in-depth filters or conventional filters; and many other similar choices.

Data are provided in Chapter 8 on the demineralizer equipment, specifying proper materials of construction and design of the shells, their internal distributors, valves, and piping, the regenerating systems, automatic controls, panel, instrumentation, and monitoring devices for the demineralizer as well as for the pretreatment equipment installed for its protection.

Technical calculations of four typical case histories are included in Chapter 9, showing how the demineralizer system, particularly resins and pretreatment, are selected and how the size of units, amounts of resin and their regenerant levels are determined.

In Chapter 14 on chemical processing of nonaqueous liquids by ion exchange, the designs of many actual full scale plants are described for a number of applications. Recent developments of regeneration without chemicals using water elution as well as liquid exchangers are also included.

For several decades, various aspects of demineralization have been presented in innumerable papers at engineering and chemical society meetings and in technical journals, testifying to the growing importance of the subject and its ever-changing nature. This book endeavors to present an objective summary of the state of the art as it exists today.

Acknowledgment is here made to the four American ion exchange resin manufacturers for helpful information, particularly L. Wirth, Jr. of Nalco Chemical Company, Dr. I. M. Abrams of Diamond Shamrock Corporation, Dr. C. Calmon of Ritter Pfaudler Corporation and Dr. R. Kunin of Rohm and Haas Company. Credit is given to the Cochrane Division of Crane Company for permission to use many photographs and diagrams included in the text.

The author also expresses his appreciation to George Glover for his suggestions on Chemical Processing by Ion Exchange, to Mary Adams for drafting a number of the figures, and to Nancy Kelly for her thoroughness in typing the text. Finally, the author affirms his gratitude to his wife for her encouragement and invaluable aid with the manuscript.

SAMUEL B. APPLEBAUM

Philadelphia
February, 1968

Contents

13. Continuous Ion Exchange

14. Chemical Processing by Ion Exchange

Demineralization
by Ion Exchange

1

Brief History of Ion Exchange and the Industrial Needs That Led to Demineralization

Although the possibility of desalting brackish waters was suggested in the Bible, by the ancient Greeks, and by Sir Francis Bacon, the earliest research work on ion exchange was reported in the mid-nineteenth century in the field of agricultural chemistry. It was well known that fertilizers, when applied to the soil, were dissolved by rain. The question that baffled the agriculturists was why these plant nutrients were not lost after rainfall by escaping into the ground water. How did the dissolved foods reach the plant roots? Chemists suspected that some substances must be present in the soil that react with the dissolved salts and hold them in reserve, until the roots can absorb them. The first demonstration of such a reaction was made by two English chemists, Thompson (1) and Way (2), in 1850. They reported that when a solution of fertilizer containing ammonia was passed through a laboratory column of soil, the soil retained the ammonia in exchange for calcium, which was found in the effluent solution. They thought, however, that the interchange proceeded always in that direction, not the reverse. A German chemist, Eichhorn (3), in 1858 was the first to prove that the exchange reaction was reversible. This suggested the possibility of what we call today "regeneration," which is the restoration of an exhausted exchange material to its original state by contact with a regenerating chemical. Many other chemists did research on ion exchange but their contributions are not included in this brief history. Summaries of their work may be found in the general references listed at the end of this chapter.

No practical application of this discovery was made, however, until 1905, when another German chemist, Gans (4), developed the process of "softening"

1

water with synthetic cation exchange materials, called zeolites*; calcium and magnesium cations in the water, the main cause of its "hardness," were exchanged for the sodium cations in the zeolite. Cheap brine was used for its regeneration. Water softeners were then designed and installed abroad in laundries, textile plants, and boiler plants. They were first introduced into the United States about 1912. The "sodium zeolite" water-softening process has continued in successful use in households and industrial plants.

The earliest synthetic cation exchange material was made by the fusion of kaolin, soda, and sand in a typical glass furnace, but this is no longer in use. Replacing the fusion method, a precipitation process was developed in which a siliceous inorganic exchange material was produced from solutions of sodium aluminate, sodium silicate, and alum sulfate. The precipitates were solid gels, which were partially dried and then decrepitated in water to form irregular granules. The product was a sodium aluminosilicate, the general formula of which is $Na_2O \cdot Al_2O_3 \cdot 5SiO_2 \cdot xH_2O$. It was sensitive to attack from aggressive waters having pH values below 6.8 or containing very little silica. It was therefore used only as a sodium exchanger for the softening of hard, clear, neutral waters, mostly in households. Currently this material is used to a very limited extent.

Later in New Jersey natural inorganic siliceous greensand, or glauconite, deposits were discovered to possess cation exchange properties. After proper cleaning, chemical stabilizing, and hardening, the greensand granules proved to be a satisfactory exchange material. It too was a sodium aluminosilicate, but it was more rugged and less sensitive to aggressive waters, although it had less capacity, than the gel exchangers. It was used for many years in a large number of industrial (not household) softeners. Greensand is still being mined and used for certain applications, but it has generally been replaced with nonsiliceous, organic resins, which have greater capacity for exchange. The present-day zeolites are described in Chapter III.

The sodium zeolite process was highly successful. It had a number of important advantages over the old precipitation lime–soda water-softening method (the latter method is described in Chapter 3, Sections IA, IB). The exchange reaction took place automatically and without the need of feeding chemicals to the water. It formed no precipitates requiring removal by settling and filtration; consequently, there was no sludge-disposal problem. It was

---

* The name *zeolite* was derived from two Greek words *zein* and *lithos*, which together mean *boiling stone*. About two hundred years ago, Cronstedt (*4a*), a Swedish geologist, first used the name for certain natural siliceous minerals which became dehydrated on heating. Eichhorn used such natural zeolites in his ion exchange research work mentioned above. The name *zeolite* was then adopted by Gans even for synthetic exchange materials and continues in use today in water softening practice; but the more general term *cation exchanger* is currently preferred for demineralization.

quite rapid, so that only small zeolite units were required. The operation was so simple that it could be conducted by unskilled help. The softening was much more complete so that the effluent contained only traces of hardness, approaching so-called "zero hardness." Finally, the first cost and operating cost were very low. As a result, many thousands of zeolite softening units were installed in homes and in industrial and power plants during the past fifty years.

The sodium zeolite process had certain limitations, however. It exchanged only calcium and magnesium cations for sodium and left the anions unchanged. The softened water, therefore, contained just as much bicarbonate alkalinity, sulfate, chloride, and silica as were present in the raw water. These anions, particularly the bicarbonate combined with sodium cation ($NaHCO_3$), caused difficulties in some industrial applications. When the soft water was used in the manufacture of ice, the ice cakes cracked. When it was used for making certain carbonated beverages, the desirable tang was destroyed through the neutralization of phosphoric and other acids present; flat-tasting beer also resulted. When zeolite-softened water was used for boiler feed, the sodium bicarbonate decomposed to caustic soda and carbonic acid; the caustic soda was claimed to promote embrittlement of the riveted boiler seams then in use, and the carbonic acid, present in the boiler steam, was redissolved in the condensate returns formed from the steam, decreasing their pH value and causing return-line corrosion. Furthermore, the softened water contained more silica, picked up from the siliceous zeolites, when low-silica raw waters were treated.

These difficulties led to the research and development of a second type of ion exchange, the hydrogen cation exchange process, in which hydrogen took the place of sodium. The process therefore converted all the salts to their corresponding acids; the calcium, magnesium, and sodium bicarbonates were thus changed to carbonic acid. This dissociates to free carbon dioxide and water. The carbon dioxide, being a gas, is removable by aeration. In this way the objectionable bicarbonate alkalinity was entirely removed.

The regenerant of the exchanger, however, now had to be an acid rather than sodium chloride, and the cation exchangers then available were unfortunately soluble in acid. Therefore, a new exchanger had to be found, one suitable for the hydrogen cation exchange process.

The first successful exchanger was developed in Holland by Smit (5) in the middle nineteen-thirties. This Dutch material (later made in the United States by the Permutit Company, under the trade names of Zeo-Karb and Ionac C-150) was produced by sulfonating selected bituminous coal granules with fuming sulfuric acid. The sulfonation attached the active sulfonic acid group to the organic matrix. Some carboxylic acid groups also were present, and these, being weakly acidic, increased the material's efficiency in dealkalization. The zeolite could stand waters of low pH and therefore could be regenerated with acid.

This was the first nonsiliceous, organic ion exchange material and was often called "carbonaceous" zeolite. It was also popular because of its nonsiliceous character, which avoided any increase in the silica content of the soft water. It was, therefore, also used in the sodium cycle for water softening, when the alkalinity in the raw water was not too high, but its chief application remained the hydrogen cycle, for reducing both hardness and alkalinity. Thus for the first time alkalinity could be removed by ion exchange, and most of the above-mentioned limitations of the sodium zeolite process could be overcome.

The effluent of the hydrogen cation exchanger was acid, and the acidity had to be neutralized. This was done either by adding alkali or by blending the acid effluent with sodium cation exchange effluent. The latter practice was called "split-stream" blending, and many such plants were installed for boiler feed and other purposes.

The hydrogen cation exchange process also had limitations: it still left the sulfate, chloride, and silica anions in the treated water. Boiler pressures were being elevated in order to lessen the fuel cost of power generation. The high-pressure boilers were very costly and needed extremely pure feedwater, if deposits in both the boiler and the turbine, and expensive shutdowns for cleaning, were to be avoided. Silica, in particular, became the prime enemy, because it formed a very tenacious, glassy deposit that reduced turbine efficiency quickly. Utility central power plants then began to install expensive evaporators, to make distilled water for the boiler-feed makeup. Research chemists consequently realized that there was an urgent need for economical demineralization that would remove all the cations and anions, including silica, by ion exchange.

An English team of chemists, Adams and Holmes (6), did the pioneer work, which they published in 1935. They developed new cation and anion exchangers and predicted that complete demineralization was on its way. However, the early anion exchangers then developed were of poor quality and only weakly basic, so they could not remove silica. Nevertheless, some nonsilica removing demineralizers that produced water otherwise low in dissolved solids content were installed for certain industrial applications.

The development of the high-capacity cation and anion exchange resins used today in demineralizers was stimulated by the research work in 1944 of D'Alelio (7). Most of the modern resins consist of a matrix or hydrocarbon network, to which are attached the ionizable or active functional groups. The network is formed from various organic materials, such as styrene (often called polystyrene) or one of the acrylic acids, which is copolymerized with divinylbenzene. The latter, present in the copolymer in a minor proportion (about 8 to 20%), provides crosslinks on the long chains of the network. The degree of crosslinking affects the properties of the resins (as described in Chapter 7, Section I,B and Chapter 6, Section I). The type of ionizable groups attached to the network determines whether the resin is a weak or strong acid type of cation exchanger or a weak or strong base type of anion exchanger. Sulfonation of the copolymer attaches the ionizable groups in the strong acid cation exchangers and chloromethylation and amination attaches the ionizable groups in most of the anion exchangers. The method of manufacture of these resins, their chemical formulae, their characteristics, and exchange capacities are described in detail in Chapters 6 and 7.

Since the middle nineteen-forties the resin manufacturers in this country and abroad have turned out a series of tailor-made resins of increasing stability and capacity. The various water-treating equipment firms also have greatly improved the designs of automatic demineralizers. The first demineralizers that used strongly basic anion resin, which could remove silica, were installed for boiler-feed makeup purposes in utility central power stations during the late nineteen-forties. Demineralizers consisting of cation and anion resins mixed together in one unit, called "Monobed" or "mixed-bed," were developed in 1950 (8).

The first condensate mixed-bed units for supercritical-pressure utility boilers were installed in 1957. High-rate mixed-bed units with external regeneration were applied in 1960 in the nuclear field for the demineralization of the main condensate stream. Since then, utilities have installed such condensate mixed-bed demineralizers in many nonnuclear stations. Also, the use of ammoniated cation resin in the mixed bed has been started to avoid removing ammonia from the condensate. A recent development is the treatment of industrial condensate and power heater drains for the removal of dissolved and suspended iron by cation exchangers. The possibility of continuous countercurrent ion exchange (9) as an alternative to the existing fixed-bed designs and the use of nonregenerated powdered-resin units are going through a period of economic and technical evaluation at present. In the field of the chemical processing of nonaqueous liquids the use of ion exchange for the purification of valuable products also is making rapid progress.

All these developments are described in detail in the chapters that follow.

REFERENCES

1. H. S. Thompson, Absorbent power of soils, *J. Roy. Agr. Soc.* **11**, 68 (1850).
2. J. T. Way, Power of soil to absorb manure, *J. Roy. Agr. Soc.* **11**, 313 (1850); also **13**, 123 (1852).
3. H. Eichhorn, On the reactions of silicates with dilute solutions of salts, *Pogendorf's Ann. Phys. Chem.* **105**, 126 (1858).
4. R. Gans, Zeolites and similar compounds, their constitution and significance for technology and agriculture, *Jahrb. Kgl. Preuss. Geol. Landesanstalt (Berlin)* **25**, 2, (1905); also **26**, 179

(1905); Also German Patents 197,111 (1906); 174,097 (1906); U.S. Patents 914,405 (1909); 943,535 (1909); 1,131,503 (1915).

4a. A. F. Cronstedt, "Mineralogie, eller Mineral-Rikets Upställning." Stockholm, 1758.

5. P. Smit, U.S. Patent 2,171,408 (1939).

6. B. A. Adams and E. L. Holmes, Adsorptive powers of synthetic zeolites, *J. Soc. Chem. Ind. (London)* **54**, 1–6 T (1935).

7. G. F. D'Alelio, U.S. Patents 2,340,110 (1944); 2,340,111 (1944); 2,366,007 (1945); 2,366,008 (1945).

8. R. Kunin and F. X. McGarvey, U.S. Patent 2,578,837 (1951); 2,692,244 (1954).

9. I. R. Higgins, U.S. Patent 2,815,322 (1957).

GENERAL REFERENCES

C. Calmon and T. R. E. Kressman, "Ion Exchangers in Organic and Biochemistry." Wiley (Interscience), New York, 1957.

F. Helfserich, "Ion Exchange." McGraw-Hill, New York, 1962.

R. Kunin, "Ion Exchange Resins," 2nd ed. Wiley, New York, 1958.

F. Nachod and J. Schubert, "Ion Exchange Technology." Academic Press, New York, 1957.

G. H. Osborn, "Synthetic Ion Exchangers." Chapman & Hall, London, 1961.

O. Samuelson, "Ion Exchange Separations in Analytical Chemistry." Wiley, New York, 1963.

2

Survey of the Impurities in Water, Their Harmful Effects in Industry, and Methods of Removing Them

Demineralization is the removal of the dissolved *ionic* mineral impurities present in water and other liquids. The ions are the positively charged cations and negatively charged anions that permit the water or solution to conduct electricity and are therefore called "electrolytes." The term "deionization" has been used by some to designate the process of removing these ions, but since "demineralization" has come into more common usage among chemists and engineers in the water-treatment field, it is the term employed in this book.

In addition to the dissolved ions many natural waters contain nonionic impurities, as for instance suspended and colloidal matter, that could be harmful in industrial application. These constituents also must be taken out; their removal usually precedes the demineralization, because they may deposit on and in the ion exchange resins and foul them. When it is considered that the ion exchange takes place between a solid, called the exchanger, and a liquid (the process is often called solid–liquid ion exchange),* it is understandable that the exchanger's surfaces and inner pores, to function efficiently, must be kept clean and unclogged. Therefore, unless the influent to the demineralizer is free from such foulants, prior treatment of the water (or other liquid) must be provided. A great many demineralizer projects normally include such pretreatment, or "primary treatment," plants.

In pretreatment various chemicals, such as chlorine, coagulants, and alkalis, are added. They significantly alter the amounts of the various

---

* Liquid exchangers have recently been developed for liquid–liquid ion exchange in chemical processing applications (see Chapter 14).

7

constituents, particularly of the anions, in the water. In technical design calculations for the demineralizers (Chapter 9) the analysis *after* pretreatment, rather than that of the raw water, must be used.

Before a discussion of demineralization proper it is appropriate that this and several chapters to follow be devoted to a survey of the major impurities in water, their harmful effects, and the methods and equipment used for their removal.

I. Water Supplies

Our natural water supplies are derived chiefly from the oceans. Clouds are formed by solar evaporation and are driven by winds overland, to condense and precipitate as rain, snow, or hail. After these fall to the earth, they either flow over the surface or percolate into the ground. Excess water then returns to the primary source by way of the rivers that flow back to the oceans. This is known as the hydrological cycle.

Our water supplies are therefore classified into two main groups, surface waters and underground waters. The surface supplies are rivers, streams, brooks, creeks, lakes, ponds, and reservoirs; the underground waters are wells and springs.

The water vapor in the clouds is quite pure, but as the rain falls through the atmosphere, it gathers dust and gases. Then when it reaches the earth, it picks up impurities from the ground. The surface supplies contain suspended matter eroded from river banks, such as mud, dirt, and turbidity. In addition they contain dissolved mineral matter, leached from the earth and rocks, and organic matter and color from sewage, trade wastes, and decaying vegetation.

The underground supplies, by virtue of the filtering effect during percolation through the earth, are usually free from suspended matter and low in organic content, but, owing to the presence of gases and longer contact with the soil and rocks, most of them contain more dissolved matter than do the surface supplies. The nature of the dissolved substances is determined by the composition of the rocks encountered. For example, hardness (calcium and magnesium) is derived from limestone and gypsum, silica from quartz, and iron and manganese from metallic constituents of the soil. The deeper wells are usually more highly mineralized than the shallow wells.

Despite their greater dissolved content, well waters have the advantage of clarity and greater freedom from bacterial contamination, making them more suitable as drinking water. They also are of lower temperature, making them preferable for cooling purposes. Moreover, their chemical composition is more constant than that of the surface supplies, which varies with the rainfall, and this facilitates the control of their treatment.

The surface supplies in many locations have the advantage of availability in ample quantity. Lake waters are usually clearer than river waters, because the suspended matter settles out. However, storms can stir up lake bottoms near the shore and increase the turbidity appreciably. The municipal intakes in the Great Lakes are therefore extended a considerable distance off shore. Likewise, the installation of very long, private pipelines may be justified by a desire to reach lake water that is clearer and more constant in composition, instead of having to cope with the treatment of a creek supply close at hand that might contain acid water from mine drainage besides variable and high amounts of dissolved impurities.

II. Impurities in Water

Table 2.1 lists the major impurities of our natural waters, classed in three main groups: first, ionic and dissolved; second, nonionic and undissolved; and third, gaseous. The ionic impurities in the first group are subdivided into cations and anions. Organic matter and color appear in both the first two groups, because there are many types (see the footnote to the table).

Table 2.1
MAJOR IMPURITIES OF WATER

Ionic and dissolved		Nonionic and undissolved	Gaseous
Cationic	Anionic		
Calcium	Bicarbonate	Turbidity, silt, mud, dirt and	Carbon dioxide
Magnesium	Carbonate	other suspended matter	Hydrogen sulfide
Sodium	Hydroxide	Color[a]	Ammonia
Potassium	Sulfate	Organic matter[a]	Methane
Ammonium	Chloride	Colloidal silica	Oxygen
Iron	Nitrate	Microorganisms, plankton	Chlorine
Manganese	Phosphate	Bacteria	
	Silica	Oil	
	Organic Matter[a]	Corrosion products (condensate)	
	Color[a]		

(Bicarbonate, Carbonate, Hydroxide are bracketed under "Alkalinity")

[a] Organic matter and color appear in both columns because there are many types: some dissolved and ionic, such as humates, and others colloidal and nonionic, such as tannins. Also there may be types of organic matter that are dissolved and nonionic, not listed above.

Table 2.2 gives typical analyses of several river, lake, well water, and municipal supplies, showing the range of composition that may be expected. The table is based mainly on United States Geological Survey Water Supply Reports.

Table 2.2

ANALYSES OF TYPICAL RIVERS, LAKES, WELL WATERS, AND MUNICIPAL SUPPLIES (PPM)

Water supply	Location	Content as CaCO₃						SiO₂ as SiO₂	Turbidity	Tot. dissolved solids
		Ca	Mg	Na + K	HCO₃	SO₄	Cl			
Mississippi River	New Orleans, La.									
Average		97	51	43	103	48	40	9	535	247
Maximum		130	99	126	150	97	108	6	1770	436
Ohio River	Cincinnati, O.									
Average		100	30	73	40	111	52	3	70	268
Maximum		161	58	102	39	180	102	5	1100	456
Brazos River	South Bend, Tex.									
Average		364	96	780	93	307	840	3	20	1480
Maximum		1150	305	3907	92	1070	4200	9	1400	6530
Missouri River	Kansas City, Mo.									
Average		147	67	111	145	158	22	10	810	420
Maximum		173	75	149	142	230	25	12	10,000	537
Lake Michigan	Chicago, Ill.	77	40	11	96	22	10	2	8	159
Lake Worth	Fort Worth, Tex.	110	33	48	125	21	45	6	20	228
Well	Lafayette, Ind.	252	150	34	310	100	26	12	1	496
Salty well	Roswell, N. Mex.	1400	650	11,000	170	1800	11,080	—	—	15,500
Delaware River (filtered)	Philadelphia, Pa. (municipal)	67	16	10	26	45	22	6	1	130
Colorado River (softened)	Los Angeles, Cal. (municipal)	130	70	335	115	296	124	9	2	678
Hetch Hetchy Reservoir	San Francisco. Cal. (municipal)	8	2	6	9	2	5	3	1	27
Hillsborough River (filtered)	Tampa, Fla. (municipal)	128	21	15	89	50	25	7	2	212
Wells (filtered)	Lincoln, Neb. (municipal)	140	38	64	158	70	14	35	2	312
Catskill supply	New York, N.Y. (municipal)	14	4	5	6	12	5	3	3	42

III. Forms of Water Analysis

Besides the form of analysis shown in Table 2.2 a number of other forms have been used in the past. Water analysts have attempted, for example, to express the salts present by making hypothetical combinations in order to help predict the character of boiler scale. However, they differed in their preferred modes of forming the combinations; see the accompanying schemes. Going from left to right, some analysts first combined the magnesium with the bicarbonate as in scheme 1. If any magnesium remained it was combined with the sulfate. The remaining sulfate was combined with the calcium, the remaining calcium with the chloride, and the remaining chloride with the sodium. Other analysts first combined the calcium with the sulfate in scheme 2, while in scheme 3, the analysts first combined the calcium with the bicarbonate and then followed the steps described above. The widths of the blocks for each of the ions are made the same in all three schemes to show that the amounts of the ions expressed in equivalents would be the same in any case. But the three methods of combination would give three different analyses expressed as the salts assumed to be present. For this reason analysis expressed by hypothetical combinations of the ions has been largely abandoned.

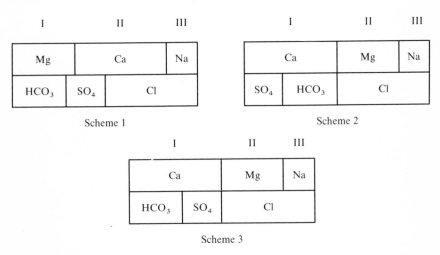

Scheme 1   Scheme 2

Scheme 3

Today most water laboratories state the dissolved impurities in an analysis, not as salts, but as cations and anions actually determined. These may be expressed in terms of the ions themselves or in terms of their equivalent. The preferred method of expression in the water-treatment field is in terms of equivalent calcium carbonate, abbreviated to "as $CaCO_3$." Calcium carbonate is a good common denominator, because it has a molecular weight of 100, which facilitates calculations. Moreover, in this form of analysis the sum of the cations, or "total cations," always equals the "total anions." The method also aids in predicting the comparative analyses after various forms of treatment and the analyses at consecutive steps of a multi-step demineralization. Table 2.3 is the water-analysis form in parts per million (as $CaCO_3$) in general use. It provides the water-composition data needed for demineralization and pretreatment calculations.

Table 2.3
WATER-ANALYSIS FORM

Name _____ Date _____

Address _____

Identification:

	CONSTITUENT		Analysis in PPM as	A	B	C	D	E	F
CATIONS	Calcium	(Ca + +)	CaCO₃						
	Magnesium	(Mg + +)	CaCO₃						
	Sodium	(Na +)	CaCO₃						
	Hydrogen = FMA	(H +)	CaCO₃						
			CaCO₃						
	TOTAL CATIONS		CaCO₃						
ANIONS	Bicarbonate	(HCO₃ -)	CaCO₃						
	Carbonate	(CO₃ - -)	CaCO₃						
	Hydroxide	(OH -)	CaCO₃						
	Sulfate	(SO₄ - -)	CaCO₃						
	Chloride	(Cl -)	CaCO₃						
			CaCO₃						
	TOTAL ANIONS		CaCO₃						
	Total Hardness		CaCO₃						
	Methyl Orange Alkalinity		CaCO₃						
	Iron, Total		Fe						
	Carbon Dioxide, Free		CO₂						
	Silica		SiO₂						
	Turbidity								
	Total Dissolved Solids								
	pH								

OPERATING COST

CHEMICALS	lbs. per 1000 gal.	* Chemical cost cents per lb.	Chemical cost—cents per 1000 gallons

* Based on best available information: Check local supply sources

Some analyses are still being expressed in parts per million in terms of the ions themselves rather than "as $CaCO_3$." Other analyses are being expressed in parts per million in terms of the equivalents of the ions. The latter form is often called either equivalents per million (epm) or milliequivalents per liter (meq/l). The two expressions, epm and meq/l, are synonymous. To convert an analysis, expressed as the ions to their equivalents, the amounts must be divided by the equivalent weight of the ions. The equivalent weight of an ion is its molecular weight divided by its valence, and the equivalent weights of the major cations and anions are:

Cations		Anions	
Ca	20.0	HCO_3	61.0
Mg	12.2	SO_4	48.0
Na	23.0	Cl	35.5

For example, if an analysis shows that there are 40 parts per million of calcium present, expressed in terms of the ion itself (Ca), then it can be divided by 20.0 to obtain 2 epm or 2 meq/l of calcium expressed as the equivalents.

Likewise, if the analysis is expressed in terms of the ions, it can be converted to the form of expression in terms of equivalent calcium carbonate (or as $CaCO_3$) by dividing the figures of the ion amounts by the equivalent weights of the ions and then multiplying by 50 (the equivalent weight of $CaCO_3$). For example, using the same 40 ppm, as Ca, given above:

$$40 \times \tfrac{50}{20} = 100 \text{ ppm, as } CaCO_3.$$

Table 2.4 gives the conversion factors for simplifying the latter calculation.

Expressing an analysis in parts per million as calcium carbonate ("as $CaCO_3$") has the advantage of obtaining larger significant figures, which are easier to use in calculations than the decimal figures often resulting from analyses expressed in equivalents per million or milliequivalents per liter. For all these reasons the preferred analysis is as indicated in Table 2.3.

IV. Units of Measurement

As the water-analysis form (Table 2.3) shows, the preferred *unit* of measurement is parts per million by weight, but occasionally analyses are still expressed in other units such as grains per U.S. gallon, in the United States, or grains per Imperial gallon, in Canada and Britain, or milligrams per liter (metric system).

Table 2.4

FACTORS FOR CONVERSION

FROM PARTS PER MILLION AS THE SUBSTANCE TO PARTS PER MILLION AS $CaCO_3$

Ions	Symbol	Ionic weight	Equivalent weight	Factor[a]
Cations				
Aluminum	Al^{3+}	27.0	9.0	5.56
Ammonium	NH_4^+	18.0	18.0	2.78
Barium	Ba^{2+}	137.4	68.7	0.73
Calcium	Ca^{2+}	40.1	20.0	2.49
Copper	Cu^{2+}	63.6	31.8	1.57
Hydrogen	H^+	1.0	1.0	50.0
Iron (ferrous)	Fe^{2+}	55.8	27.9	1.80
Iron (ferric)	Fe^{3+}	55.8	18.6	2.69
Magnesium	Mg^{2+}	24.3	12.2	4.10
Manganese	Mn^{2+}	54.9	27.5	1.82
Potassium	K^+	39.1	39.1	1.28
Sodium	Na^+	23.0	23.0	2.18
Anions				
Bicarbonate	HCO_3^-	61.0	61.0	0.82
Bisulfate	HSO_4^-	97.1	97.1	0.51
Bisulfite	HSO_3^-	81.1	81.1	0.61
Carbonate	CO_3^{2-}	60.0	30.0	1.67
Chloride	Cl^-	35.5	35.5	1.41
Fluoride	F^-	19.0	19.0	2.63
Hydroxide	OH^-	17.0	17.0	2.94
Nitrate	NO_3^-	62.0	62.0	0.81
Phosphate (primary)	$H_2PO_4^-$	97.0	97.0	0.51
Phosphate (secondary)	HPO_4^{2-}	96.0	48.0	1.04
Phosphate (tertiary)	PO_4^{3-}	95.0	31.7	1.58
Sulfate	SO_4^{2-}	96.1	48.0	1.04
Sulfide	S^{2-}	32.1	16.0	3.12
Sulfite	SO_3^{2-}	80.1	40.0	1.25

[a] Multiply by this factor to convert ppm as the substance to ppm as $CaCO_3$.

One grain per U.S. gallon equals 17.1 ppm, because a U.S. gallon weighs 8.33 pounds and one pound contains 7000 grains. Therefore, to convert from grains per U.S. gallon to parts per million, multiply by 17.1.

One grain per Imperial gallon equals 14.3 ppm, because an Imperial gallon weighs 10 pounds. To convert from grains per Imperial gallon to parts per million, multiply by 14.3.

One milligram per liter equals 1 ppm, because a liter weighs 1,000,000 mg; no conversion factor is required.

Although the unit "grains per gallon" is rarely used today in the water-analysis form itself, it is nevertheless widely used in demineralization calculations. The practice has developed in the United States because the capacity ratings of exchangers have come to be expressed, for convenience, in thousands of grains of ions removed by each cubic foot of exchanger. This is ordinarily abbreviated to "kilograins/cu ft" or "Kgr/cu ft." Then, the parts per million total exchangeable cations and anions given by an analysis are divided by 17.1 to give the grains per U.S. gallon used in demineralizer technical calculations.

Likewise, dosages of chemicals in pretreatment are usually expressed in pounds per thousand gallons of water treated, rather than in parts per million. A dose expressed in parts per million may be converted to pounds per thousand gallons by dividing by 120. A dose expressed in grains per gallon is converted to pounds per thousand gallons by dividing by 7.

V. Harmful Effects of Water Impurities in Industry

In general, the harmful effects may be classified as (a) deposits or scales, formed in boilers and other heat-exchange equipment, which act as insulation, preventing efficient heat transfer and causing boiler tube failures through overheating of the metal, (b) poor-quality boiler steam, which contains impurities that foul steam-using equipment such as turbines and decrease their efficiency rapidly, (c) stains, discoloration, spots, and other surface defects on many industrial products and off-flavors and poor tastes in food and drinks, (d) corrosion of boilers, heaters, and other metal containers and piping, (e) destruction and waste of various chemicals, such as the soap and alkalis used in washing, dyeing, and similar operations, resulting in undesirable precipitates on textiles being produced or laundered, and (f) water unsuitable for drinking and other purposes because of objectionable tastes and odors or bacterial contamination.

VI. Water-Quality Tolerances for Various Applications

Industrial plants use water for a number of purposes: cooling, boiler feed, general services such as drinking and flushing and finally processing of the products manufactured (process water). The limits on the amounts of impurities (tolerances) in the water used for processing in various industries are determined by experience in product quality control. Obviously, with the ever-growing number of new products the water-quality requirements will vary from one plant to another. The cost of treating water to increase its degree of purity must also be considered. For example, ultrapure water, which may contain only traces of dissolved substances (under 0.05 ppm, or 50 parts per billion, ppb) is much more expensive to produce than less pure water, both in first cost, or cost of the more complex demineralizing

Table 2.5

QUALITY TOLERANCES FOR WATER IN VARIOUS INDUSTRIES AND APPLICATIONS

Tolerances, ppm

	Ca and Mg as CaCO₃	HCO₃ as CaCO₃	Fe as Fe	Mn as Mn	Turbidity	Color	Taste and odor	Organics as O₂ consumed	Free Cl as Cl	Total solids	pH
1. Carbonated beverages	250	50	0.2	0.2	0–2	5–10	None	<10	6–8	850	
bottle-washing	0										
2. Breweries	>100; CaSO₄ desirable for yeast	75–100	0.1	0.1	5–10	5–10	None	<10		500–1000; NaCl <275	7.0
3. Ceramics			0.1	0.1	Clear	5–10		<10		Low	
4. Distilleries[a] Deproofing										5–10	
5. Electroplating	0		Low	Low	Low					Low	
6. Food-processing		Water must meet U.S. Public Health Drinking Water Standards (see Table 2.7)									
Baking	25–50	25–50	0.2	0.2	5–10	5–10	None				
Canneries			0.2	0.2	10		None				
Candy			0.2	0.2			None			100	>7.0
Meat-pickling	0										
Starch products	0		0.1	0.1							
Pectin extraction										5–10	

7. Raw-water ice	70	50	0.2	0.2	5	5	None	<10		170	
8. Laundries	0		0.1	0.1	0.1						
9. Leather-tanning	50–135	135	0.2	0.2	20	10–100				5–10; Cl <1	
10. Mirror-silvering	0				2	5					
11. Paper and pulp											
Fine paper	50	75	0.1	0.05	5	5			2.0	200	
Kraft bleached	100	75	0.2	0.1	5	5		0–8	—	300	6.8–7.3
Kraft unbleached	200	150	0.5	0.3	25	80		0–12	—	500	6.5–8.0
Groundwood	200	150	1.0	0.5	50	30			—	300	
Soda and sulfate pulp	100	75	0.1	0.05	25	5				600	
Rayon pulp	8	50			5	5				100	
12. Pharmaceutical products			0	0	0	0	None			1.0	
13. Textile											
General	0–75	70–100	0.1	0.1	5	20				200	
Cotton	10–15	75–100	0.01–0.05	0.01–0.05	1.5	5				200	
Rayon (viscose)	10	75	0.05	0.02	1.0	5				200	
Wool (scour)	0	70	0.1	0.1	5	20				200	
14. Plastics (clear)		70	0.02	0.02	2	2	None	<10		200	

Must also meet U.S. Pharmacopoeia requirements; injection water must be pyrogen-free.

a Same as for breweries, except that $CaSO_4$ is not desirable.

Table 2.6

QUALITY TOLERANCES FOR ULTRAPURE WATER IN SOME APPLICATIONS (IN PPM)

	Fe as Fe	Cu as Cu	Organics as O₂ consumed	Free Cl as Cl	Total solids	Specific resistance, Mohm-cm	pH	Size of particulate matter
				Tolerances, ppm				
Semiconductor	0.005	0.005	1.0	0	trace	18	7.0	Under 0.5 μ
Television tubes	0.005	0.005	0.5	0	trace	2–5	7.0	
Once-through boiler feedwater	0.005	0.005	Silica as SiO₂: 0.01	0	0.05	10	9.3	

equipment required, and in operating cost. These costs must be compared with the benefits to be obtained, before tolerance standards are set.

Tables 2.5 to 2.7 give some suggested water-quality tolerances for various applications. They are based on standards issued from time to time by technical committees of industries and for drinking water, by the U.S. Public Health Service.

Table 2.7 DRINKING WATER STANDARDS, U.S. PUBLIC HEALTH SERVICE (1962 EDITION)

Physical	Desirable limits:	Chemical	Limits for rejection, mg/l.:
Turbidity	5 units	Arsenic (As)	0.05
Color	15 units	Barium (Ba)	1.0
Threshold odor		Cadmium (Cd)	0.01
number	3	Chromium (Cr^{6+})	0.05
		Cyanide (CN)	0.2
		Lead (Pb)	0.05
		Selenium (Se)	0.01
Chemical	mg/l.	Silver (Ag)	0.05
Alkyl benzene			
sulfonate (ABS)	0.5	Fluoride (F) at air	Desirable range, mg/l.
Arsenic (As)	0.01	temp., °F	
Chloride (Cl)	250.0	From 50–53.7	From 0.9–1.7
Copper (Cu)	1.0	To 79.3–90.5	To 0.6–0.8
Carbon chloroform			
extract (CCE)	0.2	Radioactivity	Beta concentration,
Cyanide (CN)	0.01		$\mu\mu$cur/lit:
Iron (Fe)	0.3		1000
Manganese (Mn)	0.05		
Nitrate (NO_3)	45.0	Bacteriological	Coliform organisms
Phenols	0.001		limited[a]
Sulfate (SO_4)	250.0		
Total dissolved solids	500.0		
Zinc (Zn)	5.0		

[a] See the USPHS standards for details.

VII. General Methods of Removing Impurities

Tables 2.8 to 2.10 classify the methods of removing the ionic, nonionic, and gaseous impurities, respectively; these processes are described in greater detail in Chapters 3, 4, and 5. Some of the methods are still in use as alternatives to demineralization in certain applications, such as makeup for boilers of medium pressure (Chapter 3). Others are treatments given before demineralization, either for reducing the ion exchange load on the resins, such as the lime pretreatment for the reduction of alkalinity (Chapter 3), or for removing impurities that would foul the resins, such as pretreatment for the removal of color, turbidity, and organic matter (Chapter 4).

Table 2.8
METHODS OF REMOVING IONIC IMPURITIES

Impurities	Methods
Cations	
1. Calcium and magnesium	a. Cold, warm, or hot lime-soda process: precipitation, settling, and filtration
	b. Ion exchange
2. Sodium, potassium, and ammonium	a. Hydrogen cation exchange, if bicarbonate present exceeds total hardness
	b. Demineralization
3. Iron and manganese	a. Oxidation (aeration) and precipitation, settling (if high amounts present), and filtration (chlorine and alkali may be needed)
	b. Filtration through manganese zeolite
	c. Ion exchange
Anions	
4. Alkalinity	a. Lime process as in 1a, but without soda ash
	b. Hydrogen cation exchange
	c. Chloride anion exchange salt-splitting (dealkalization)
5. Sulfate, chloride, nitrate, and phosphate	Demineralization
6. Silica	a. Absorption by ferric hydroxide precipitated by adding ferric sulphate; settling and filtration follow
	b. Absorption by magnesium hydroxide, formed when lime or dolomitic lime is added; settling and filtration follow; adding activated magnesia with the lime in warm or hot process is helpful
	c. Hydroxide anion exchange salt splitting (desilicization)
	d. Demineralization
7. Organic matter and color[a]	See Table 2.9; see also footnote to Table 2.1.

[a] Ionic dissolved organic matter and color are treated by the same methods as the nonionic types.

Table 2.9
METHODS OF REMOVING NONIONIC IMPURITIES

Impurities	Methods
1. Turbidity and suspended matter	a. Filtration alone for small amounts of turbidity, adding coagulant directly ahead of filters if clearer effluent desired
	b. Coagulation, settling, and filtration for larger amounts of turbidity; prechlorination usually beneficial; alkali addition, if needed for optimal pH value; coagulant aid often improves the floc

Table 2.9 (*continued*)

Impurities	Methods
2. Color	Same as 1 b, but addition of clay or other weighting agents, to densify floc, if water has low amounts of suspended matter
3. Organic matter	a. Same as 1b
	b. Addition of oxidizing agents, such as chlorine or permanganate
	c. Absorption by powdered or granular activated carbon
	d. Absorption by anion exchangers
4. Colloidal silica	a. Same as 1b
	b. Recirculation of boiler blowoff through demineralizer
5. Plankton and bacteria	a. Same as 1b
	b. Superchlorination
6. Oil	a. Same as 1b
	b. Addition of preformed alum floc and filtration
7. Corrosion products in condensate	a. Filtration with cellulose filter aid
	b. Cation exchanger
	c. Ammoniated cation exchanger for heater drains
	d. Combined filtration and ion exchange with mixed-bed demineralizer

Table 2.10

METHODS OF REMOVING GASEOUS IMPURITIES

Impurities	Methods
1. Carbon dioxide	a. Aeration: open aerator
	b. Aeration: degasifier (decarbonator) or forced-draft aerator
	c. Vacuum deaerator
	d. Heater deaerator for boiler feed
2. Hydrogen sulfide	a. Aeration as in 1a or 1b
	b. Chlorination
	c. Aeration plus chlorination
3. Ammonia	a. Hydrogen cation exchange, if the ammonia is present as ionic NH_4^+
4. Methane	Aeration as in 1a or 1b
5. Oxygen	a. Vacuum deaerator
	b. Heater deaerator for boiler feed
	c. Addition of sodium sulfite or hydrazine
	d. Anion exchanger regenerated with sodium sulfite, hydrosulfite, and hydroxide
6. Excess residual chlorine	a. Dechlorination by addition of reducing agents such as sodium sulfite or sulfurous acid
	b. Absorption by powdered or granular activated carbon
	c. Filtration through granular calcium sulfite

GENERAL REFERENCES

T. R. Camp, "Water and Its Impurities." Reinhold, New York, 1963.

P. Hamer, J. Jackson and E. F. Thurston, "Industrial Water Treatment Practice." Butterworths, in Association With Imperial Chem. Ind. Ltd., London, 1961.

F. C. Nachod, ed. "Ion Exchange Theory and Application." Academic Press, New York, 1949.

E. Nordell, "Water Treatment For Industrial and Other Uses," 2nd ed. Reinhold, New York, 1961.

S. T. Powell, "Water Conditioning For Industry," 1st ed. McGraw-Hill, New York, 1954.

W. J. Ryan, "Water Treatment and Purification," 2nd ed. McGraw-Hill, New York, 1946.

3

Removal of the Major Ionic
Dissolved Impurities in Water

The old methods of removing ionic impurities, which are discussed in this chapter, have certain limitations. They can remove only some of the cations or anions, whereas demineralizers can remove all of them. Nevertheless, they continue in use, because they are economical: the chemicals added are less expensive than the acid and caustic soda regenerants used for demineralization, and their doses are smaller. Therefore, in many demineralizing projects the old methods are included as pretreatment, and the combination often results in the lowest total operating cost. The pretreatment plant relieves the demineralizer of a considerable burden and allows it to act as a finisher and refiner in the production of high-quality effluent. The old methods are also useful for removing certain ionic impurities, such as iron and manganese, that may foul the ion exchange resins of the demineralizers. Finally, they may suffice for certain applications, such as treating makeup for medium-pressure boilers. Therefore, an evaluation of them with respect to demineralization must be made before a method is selected. It is thus important to understand the earlier processes, and for this reason they are discussed in the following pages.

The methods of removing the ionic dissolved impurities are described in this chapter in the same sequence as in Tables 2.1 and 2.8, except for dissolved organic matter and color, which are included with other organic types in Chapter 4.

I. Removal of Calcium and Magnesium: Water-Softening

The hardness of water is due mainly* to the presence of calcium and

---

* Iron, manganese, and acidity should also be included in hardness but since the amounts of these constituents in most raw waters are small they are neglected in hardness considerations.

magnesium cations, and these cations themselves are referred to as "the hardness." In most natural waters the calcium exceeds the magnesium (it is generally about double the magnesium). Hardness in water is responsible for two of the harmful effects discussed in the last chapter: the formation of deposits and the destruction of soap and other chemicals. The removal of hardness for the purpose of avoiding these difficulties is termed "water-softening."

The two general methods of softening water are precipitation with lime and soda ash (lime–soda process) and ion exchange (sodium cation and hydrogen cation cycles).

A. Cold Lime–Soda Process

The process of softening water at ambient temperatures by adding chemicals, such as lime and soda ash, was developed commercially about one hundred years ago in Great Britain. The use of lime for reducing so-called temporary hardness is attributed to Clark (1), who received a patent for a lime softening process in 1841. Then Porter (1a) in 1876 supplemented the lime with soda ash, to reduce the so-called permanent hardness. The combined cold lime–soda method has often been called the Clark–Porter process.

The term "temporary" refers to the carbonate or, preferably, the bicarbonate hardness. It expresses the transitory character of this hardness when the water is heated. The calcium bicarbonate, for example, decomposes to calcium carbonate, which being fairly insoluble, precipitates and falls out. The term "permanent"* refers to the noncarbonate hardness, the calcium and magnesium sulfates and chlorides. These remain soluble on being heated (without concentration by evaporation) and therefore do not precipitate and fall out.

From the raw-water analysis the amounts of temporary and permanent hardness can be readily calculated as follows.

Let H be the total hardness (Ca + Mg) as $CaCO_3$ and A be the alkalinity as $CaCO_3$, which consists of bicarbonate anion alone in most natural waters.

When $H > A$:

The temporary, or bicarbonate, hardness equals A.

The permanent, or noncarbonate, hardness equals $H - A$.

When $H = A$:

The bicarbonate hardness equals H or A.

The noncarbonate hardness is zero.

---

* Nitrates are also included in permanent hardness but the amounts usually present in natural waters are negligible.

When $H < A$:

The bicarbonate hardness equals H.

The noncarbonate hardness is zero.

Sodium bicarbonate is present, equal to $A - H$.

1. CHEMICAL REACTIONS

The lime reacts with the bicarbonate hardness to precipitate calcium carbonate and magnesium hydroxide. The soda ash reacts with the noncarbonate hardness to form the same fairly insoluble products. These precipitates are allowed to settle out, and the settled water is usually further clarified by filtration.

The chemical reactions appearing in many sections of this book are written in molecular form, as if the constituents were undissociated salts rather than the ions actually present. This type of equation is still in common use in the water-treatment field and depicts the reactions in a more comprehensive and simpler form than does the ionic type. In the chapter sections on ion exchange, however, equations in ionic form are included as supplements.

The molecular equations for the addition of lime are as follows.

$$Ca(HCO_3)_2 + Ca(OH)_2 \rightarrow 2\,CaCO_3 \downarrow + 2\,H_2O \tag{1}$$
$$Mg(HCO_3)_2 + 2\,Ca(OH)_2 \rightarrow 2\,CaCO_3 \downarrow + Mg(OH)_2 \downarrow + 2\,H_2O \tag{2}$$

Note that the magnesium bicarbonate in Eq. 2 requires twice as much lime as the calcium bicarbonate in Eq. 1. Note also that the bicarbonate hardness is shown to be removed without the formation of other dissolved compounds on the right-hand side of the equations. Lime treatment, therefore, reduces the total dissolved solids. In this way it differs from the soda ash and sodium cation exchange reactions.

Any free carbon dioxide present must also be removed by adding enough lime to raise the pH value to the optimum required for the process. The removal of the carbon dioxide by lime may be written as follows:

$$CO_2 + Ca(OH)_2 \rightarrow CaCO_3 \downarrow + H_2O \tag{3}$$

If the amount of free carbon dioxide present is high, it can be partly removed by aeration (Chapter 5, Section IV) before the lime treatment, which saves on the cost of the lime.

The reactions between soda ash and the noncarbonate sulfate hardness are as follows:

$$CaSO_4 + Na_2CO_3 \rightarrow CaCO_3 \downarrow + Na_2SO_4 \tag{4}$$
$$MgSO_4 + Na_2CO_3 + Ca(OH)_2 \rightarrow CaCO_3 \downarrow + Mg(OH)_2 \downarrow + Na_2SO_4 \tag{5}$$

Equations similar to Eqs. 4 and 5 may be written for the chloride hardness.

Note that sodium sulfate appears on the right-hand side of these equations in amounts equivalent to the calcium and magnesium sulfates originally present. The total dissolved solids, then, are not decreased by soda ash, as was the case in the reactions with lime, Eqs. 1 and 2.

If sodium bicarbonate is present, it too must be converted to the carbonate form by lime. This is necessary, to ensure a high enough pH value for maximal precipitation of the calcium carbonate and magnesium hydroxide. Therefore enough lime to react with most of the sodium bicarbonate must be added:

$$2\,NaHCO_3 + Ca(OH)_2 \rightarrow CaCO_3\downarrow + Na_2CO_3 + 2\,H_2O \qquad (6)$$

Thus the sodium bicarbonate is converted to sodium carbonate. If the amount of this resulting carbonate cannot be tolerated, it can be decreased by adding gypsum with the lime, as follows:

$$2\,NaHCO_3 + Ca(OH)_2 + CaSO_4 \rightarrow 2\,CaCO_3\downarrow + Na_2SO_4 + 2\,H_2O \qquad (7)$$

2. CHEMICALS USED

The lime generally used is hydrated lime or calcium hydroxide, rather than quicklime or calcium oxide. If the latter is available locally at lower cost, it is usually slaked or hydrated with water at high concentrations before being added in a dilute slurry to the water. However, some success has been recently reported with the use of pulverized quicklime without slaking (1b).

The calcium carbonate and magnesium hydroxide precipitates are often so finely divided that they settle too slowly. Therefore, in cold-process plants coagulants such as alum or iron sulfates are added, which coagulate the precipitates into larger masses that settle more readily. The coagulants are also needed to help remove appreciable amounts of suspended and organic matter originally present in the raw water. If the organic matter is high in amount, preoxidation by chlorine may be needed, because organics often inhibit precipitation.

The addition of the coagulants and other chemicals alters the water analysis and must therefore be taken into account in technical calculations. Table 3.1 gives the changes in the analysis caused by adding 1 ppm of the various coagulants, chlorine, and other chemicals.

3. RESIDUAL DISSOLVED HARDNESS IN EFFLUENTS

The lime–soda simplified equations (1 to 5) appear to indicate complete precipitation of the hardness; actually, the reactions do not go to completion, and some residual hardness is always left in solution. The residuals can be decreased by doses of lime and soda ash in excess of those stoichiometrically required. The excess increases the amounts of dissolved carbonate and hydroxide anions in the softened water, providing a common ion effect that depresses the solubilities of calcium carbonate and magnesium hydroxide.

Table 3.1

CHANGES IN WATER ANALYSIS (IN PPM) CAUSED BY THE ADDITION OF 1 PPM COAGULANTS. CHLORINE, HYDRATED LIME, OR SULFURIC ACID

Chemical	Formula	Reduc. alkalin. as $CaCO_3$	Incr. alkalin. as $CaCO_3$	Reduc. in CO_2 as CO_2	Incr. in CO_2 as CO_2	Incr. in SO_4 as $CaCO_3$	Incr. in Cl as $CaCO_3$	Incr. in hardness as $CaCO_3$
Aluminum sulfate (filter alum)	$Al_2(SO_4)_3 \cdot 14H_2O$	0.45			0.40	0.45		
Ferrous sulfate (copperas)	$FeSO_4 \cdot 7H_2O$	0.36			0.31	0.36		
Ferric sulfate (ferrisul)	$Fe_2(SO_4)_3 \cdot 2H_2O$	0.75			0.66	0.75		
Chlorine	Cl	1.40			1.30		1.4	
Hydrated lime (93% pure)	$Ca(OH)_2$		1.26	1.11				
Sulfuric acid (93% pure)	H_2SO_4	0.95			0.84	0.95		1.26

Figure 3.1 shows the residual dissolved calcium cation for various amounts of dissolved carbonate anion in water softened in both the cold and the hot processes. Figure 3.2 gives the same data for cold-process residual magnesium

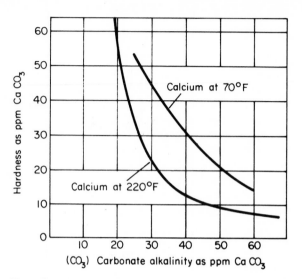

Fig. 3.1. Residual dissolved Ca versus CO_3. The cold process (solids contact process, Section IA9) is here compared with the hot process.

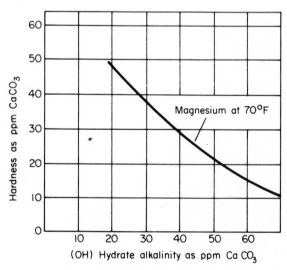

Fig. 3.2. Residual dissolved Mg versus OH in cold process (solids-contact process, Section IA9).

and hydroxide. The two diagrams assist in the selection of the dosages of excess lime and soda ash needed for the desired residual hardness and in the prediction of the analysis of the softened water. The rules of thumb that follow may also be helpful in predictions of analysis.

4. PREDICTION OF WATER ANALYSIS: LIME ALONE

(a) First the dose of alum or ferrous sulfate coagulant is assumed to be about 23 ppm, and so the raw-water analysis is modified by the effect of this coagulant, with the use of Table 3.1. If the raw water is high in turbidity or color, the dose may have to be increased to 34 or even 51 ppm (2 to 3 gr/gal). If excessive organic matter or color also is present, about 5 to 10 ppm chlorine may have to be added and, of course, the effect of this included in the modified analysis.

(b) The modified analysis, thus calculated, will be characterized in one of two ways: the alkalinity A may exceed the calcium C, that is, $A > C$, or the calcium may exceed the alkalinity, $C > A$.

(c) If $A > C$, the predicted analysis of the softened water will be calculated from the modified analysis as follows:

Cations (ppm as $CaCO_3$):   Anions (ppm as $CaCO_3$):

Na = unchanged HCO_3 = 0
Mg = reduced to 80 ppm or, if CO_3 = 35
      influent Mg is less than   OH   = 0 to 10
      80 ppm, reduced 10% SO_4 = unchanged
Ca = total anions minus   Cl   = unchanged
      (Na + Mg)

Total cations (TC) = sum of that   Total anions (TA) = sum of that
                 above   above
Free CO_2 = 0   TA must equal TC

(d) If $C > A$ (after coagulant), the predicted analysis will be, calculated from the modified analysis, as follows:

Cations (ppm as $CaCO_3$):   Anions (ppm as $CaCO_3$):

Ca = 35 HCO_3 = 0
Mg = reduced to 80 ppm or, if CO_3 = TC minus (SO_4 + Cl)
      influent Mg is less than   OH   = 0 to 10
      80 ppm, reduced 10% SO_4 = unchanged
Na = unchanged   Cl   = unchanged

TC   = sum of that above   TA = sum of that above
Free CO_2 = 0   TA must equal TC

5. PREDICTION OF WATER ANALYSIS: LIME AND SODA ASH

In pretreatments before demineralization soda ash is rarely used, because it merely converts the noncarbonate hardness to sodium sulfate or chloride (Eqs. 4 and 5), so that, the demineralizer has all the work of reducing the sulfates and chlorides. In some cases, however, in addition to feeding the demineralizer, the pretreated water is used for other purposes that may require a lower hardness than is obtainable with lime alone, and soda ash is then added to reduce the noncarbonate hardness.

Soda ash is usually more than twice as costly as lime. Therefore, all possible reduction in bicarbonate hardness by means of lime should first be planned, and then, if the total hardness of the predicted lime-softened effluent is not as low as desired, soda ash can be added, to reduce a part of the noncarbonate hardness. Equations 4 and 5 show that one part of soda ash reacts with one part of noncarbonate hardness, so the required dose of soda ash is equal to the desired reduction of noncarbonate hardness, when both are expressed in parts per million as $CaCO_3$.

The calculation of the lime–soda effluent from the modified analysis (after coagulant) is as follows:

Cations (ppm as $CaCO_3$):

$Ca = 35$
$Mg = $ use Fig. 3.2
$Na = $ increased by dose of soda
     ash (ppm as $CaCO_3$)

TC   = sum of that above
Free $CO_2 = 0$

Anions (ppm as $CaCO_3$):

SO_4 = unchanged
Cl = unchanged
$HCO_3 = 0$
CO_3 = 35
OH = 0 to 10

TA = sum of that above
TA must equal TC

6. CALCULATION OF DOSAGE OF LIME AND SODA ASH

With respect to the modified analysis (after coagulant and chlorine) the dose of hydrated lime is calculated as follows:

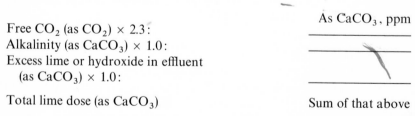

As $CaCO_3$, ppm

Free CO_2 (as CO_2) × 2.3:
Alkalinity (as $CaCO_3$) × 1.0:
Excess lime or hydroxide in effluent
   (as $CaCO_3$) × 1.0:

Total lime dose (as $CaCO_3$)   Sum of that above

Since hydrated lime is usually 93 % pure, then:

$$\text{Pounds of 93\% Ca(OH)}_2 \text{ per 1000 gal} = \frac{\text{ppm lime (as } CaCO_3)}{150}$$

The dose of soda ash in ppm as $CaCO_3$ is equal to the reduction in the noncarbonate hardness. Since soda ash is usually 98 % pure, then:

$$\text{Pounds of 98 \% } Na_2CO_3 \text{ per 1000 gal} = \frac{\text{ppm soda ash (as } CaCO_3)}{110}$$

7. CALCULATION OF BICARBONATE, CARBONATE, AND HYDROXIDE ANIONS IN LIME SOFTENED WATER

In normal waters the alkalinity is usually equal to the bicarbonate anion present. Carbonate and phosphate anions may be found occasionally in some waters but in negligible amounts.

In lime-softened waters carbonate and, often, hydroxide are present. Usually the bicarbonate is assumed to be zero when there is hydroxide. The assumption is not strictly valid, but the error is insignificant.

The bicarbonate, carbonate, and hydroxide anions in lime-softened water are not determined directly but are calculated from the alkalinities given by titrations with methyl orange (alkalinity M) and phenolphthalein (alkalinity P).

The M alkalinity is determined from the titration of a measured volume of a water sample containing a few drops of the dye indicator, methyl orange, amounts of a certain strength of acid being successively added until the color of the sample changes from yellow to pink. The color change takes place at a pH value of about 4.3.

The P alkalinity is determined by a similar titration. When a few drops of phenolphthalein are added, the sample turns red; acid is added, until the red color has disappeared and the sample become colorless. The color change takes place at a pH value of about 8.3.

The bicarbonate, carbonate, and hydroxide anions are then calculated from the M and P alkalinities so determined, according to Table 3.2.

Table 3.2

CALCULATION OF BICARBONATE, CARBONATE, AND HYDROXIDE ANIONS
FROM M AND P ALKALINITIES (ALL EXPRESSED IN PPM AS $CaCO_3$)

Alkalinity	HCO_3	CO_3	OH
$P = 0$	M	0	0
$P = M$	0	0	M
$P = M/2$	0	$2P$	0
$P > M/2$	0	$2(M - P)$	$2P - M$
$P < M/2$	$M - 2P$	$2P$	0

[a] P phenolphthalein alkalinity, M methyl orange alkalinity.

The table is based on the following equations:

If $M > 2P$, then: If $2P > M$, then:

$$M = H_2CO_3 + CO_3 \qquad M = CO_3 + OH$$

$$P = CO_3/2 \qquad\qquad P = CO_3/2 + OH$$

8. THE pH VALUE OF LIME SOFTENED WATER

The pH value of lime-softened water is usually more than 10, and it can be calculated from the M and P alkalinities by consulting Fig. 3.3.

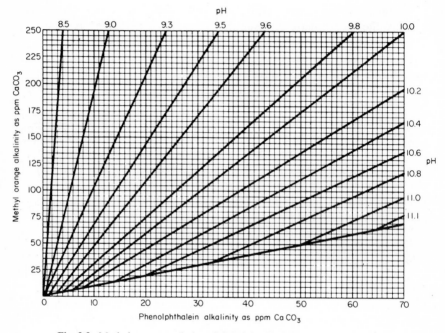

Fig. 3.3. Methyl orange and phenolphthalein alkalinities versus pH values.

9. SUSPENDED-SOLIDS CONTACT

The equipment used in cold lime treatment must provide, first, for feeding and rapid mixing of the chemicals with the water and, second, for slow mixing as an aid in forming the precipitates. The precipitates must then be separated from the water by settling. The settled effluent is usually filtered for final clarification.

Originally the conventional equipment consisted of separate basins or compartments for an initial rapid, or "flash," mix, a second, slow mix (for the reaction), and a settling (or for partial clarification). The total nominal detention time, or "residence" time, for the three steps usually amounted to more than four hours. This long time was needed, because the precipitates usually were finely divided and settled very slowly. The precipitates were small in size because the designers of the old, conventional, plain sedimentation type of equipment aimed at settling out the precipitates as early as possible in the clarification zone of the plant.

Chemists next began to experiment with stimulating the formation of better precipitates by making a contact between new precipitates and previously formed precipitates. The latter precipitates thus acted as catalytic solids-phase contact reagents. In the earliest experiments pumps recycled some of the settled precipitates, or sludge, back to the mixing chambers. This improved the chemical results but imparted objectionable tastes and odors to the settled water, because the recirculated sludge contained decomposing organic matter.

The problem was resolved by suspending the fresh undecomposed precipitates by means of an agitator before allowing them to settle out as a sludge. Spaulding, Chief Chemist of the City of Springfield, Illinois, which had a municipal cold-process lime–soda softener, demonstrated the benefits from such an arrangement. He showed that a solids contact unit in only about one hour's detention produced an effluent of less hardness with a smaller lime dose than did the conventional mixing tank and plain settling basin, which provided eight hours' detention (2).

The work resulted in the Spaulding Precipitator. Other competitive designs of suspended-solids contact units were developed all with the same purpose of combining the mixing, reaction, and partial clarification in one compact tank. In most designs, baffles separated a mixing and reaction zone from a clarification zone; the mechanical agitation in the first zone was thus prevented by the baffles from disturbing the settling in the second zone. The major four suspended-solids contact designs now being used for treatment before demineralization are described in Chapter 4, Section IIG, which discusses coagulation, because the same equipment is used for that purpose.

The solids contact units enable the cold-process lime–soda softening plants to reduce the residual hardness to 68 to 85 ppm (4 to 5 gr/gal) as $CaCO_3$ with reasonable extra amounts of lime and soda ash. The turbidity of the settled water is about 5 to 10 ppm. Silica also can be reduced to 2 or 3 ppm; silica removal is discussed in Section VI.

10. Prevention of After-Reactions

At low ambient temperatures in winter the chemical reactions are not completed in the settling tank and continue as so-called after-reactions between the excess lime and the residual hardness in the settled water. They result in the formation of "after-precipitates," which deposit on the walls of storage tanks, piping, filter beds, and ion exchange beds, when the effluent has left the settling tank. The solids contact design reduces the after-reactions to a minimum and produces very stable water, although at cold temperatures some instability may continue.

Two measures may be taken to eliminate the after-reactions: adding acid reagents, which neutralize the excess lime and reduce the pH value from more than 10.0 to less than 8.5 or 9.0, and adding polyphosphates, which inhibit the after-precipitation without reducing the pH value.

The acid reagents may be sulfuric acid, for the smaller plants, or carbonic acid, for the larger ones. The latter practice, called recarbonation, may be carried out by feeding carbon dioxide gas from bottled gas tanks, but it is usually conducted more economically with flue gas, containing the free carbon dioxide. Submerged burners are now available, which burn natural gas under water and disperse in the settled effluent the carbon dioxide formed.

In industrial plants polyphosphate inhibitors are preferred, because the feeder is an inexpensive and simple unit and the amount of polyphosphates required is only a few parts per million. The operating cost is therefore quite low. Excessive doses must be avoided, however, because they may inhibit the ion exchange reactions in the demineralization that follows.

B. Hot Lime–Soda Process

The commercial application of the hot lime–soda process began in the United States about 1900 (3). The water is preheated with steam before the chemicals are added. The heat accelerates the reactions and produces softer effluents. For this reason hot-process units have been used widely for softening the makeup for boilers of medium pressure.

Hot-process lime–soda softeners reduce the residual hardness to about 17 to 25 ppm (1.0 to 1.5 gr/gal) as $CaCO_3$ with little excess of chemicals. They also reduce the dissolved oxygen, and they reduce the silica to less than 1 ppm (as SiO_2) with proper silica-absorbing reagents. Moreover, the softened water is quite stable, so that after-reactions are avoided.

Hot-process plants can treat surface waters of moderate turbidity, because the precipitates have coagulating powers. For waters of greater turbidity coagulants such as sodium aluminate or ferric sulfate may be added with the lime and soda ash. Polyelectrolyte coagulant aids instead of coagulants have sometimes been found helpful in producing clearer settled water. (See Chapter 4, Section IID for a discussion of coagulant aids.) For waters of very great turbidity, such as the Mississippi River, the hot process has been preceded by the cold process to remove most of the turbidity in the raw water; this avoids dissolving of the silica from the siliceous turbidity of the raw water in the hot-process plant owing to the combination of high pH values and high temperatures, when very turbid raw waters are treated directly.

The chemical reactions are the same as in the lime–soda cold process, and the relation between the dissolved residual calcium cation and carbonate anion is as given in Fig. 3.1.

The steps in predicting the effluent analysis, however, differ from those for the cold process, as follows.

(a) Modify the raw-water analysis by multiplying the amounts of all constituents by 0.85, which represents the dilution effect of the steam used in the preheating.

(b) Calculate the final effluent analysis from the modified analysis as follows.

Cations (ppm as $CaCO_3$):

Anions (ppm as $CaCO_3$):

Ca = use Fig. 3.1
Mg = 10 ppm
Na = increase by dose of soda
         ash (ppm as $CaCO_3$)

TC   = sum. of that above
Free CO_2 = 0

SO_4 = unchanged
Cl   = unchanged
HCO_3 = 0
CO_3 = use Fig. 3.1
OH   = 0 to 10
TA = sum of that above
TA must equal TC

1. EQUIPMENT DESIGNS

Two designs of settling tanks have been developed: a downflow tank with sludge recirculation (Fig. 3.4) and an upflow tank with solids contact "sludge blanket" (Fig. 3.5).

The downflow type is often favored when the flow rate is to vary widely, because the blanket of sludge in the upflow type expands with increasing flow and can be carried over into the outlet, unless the level of the top of the suspended sludge is carefully controlled. However, the upflow design has been reported to produce clearer settled water than downflow in some cases.

In both types the cold water enters through a float-controlled valve that is responsive to water-level changes in the settling tank. The influent is then heated by a direct-contact spray heater. Lime and soda ash are added in slurry form to the preheated water. The uncondensable gases, liberated by the heating, escape through a vent condenser. The direct-contact type of vent condenser called "gas concentrator" has largely superseded the tubular type previously used.

In the downflow type a conical uptake near the bottom separates the precipitates by virtue of the change in direction of the water as it turns up

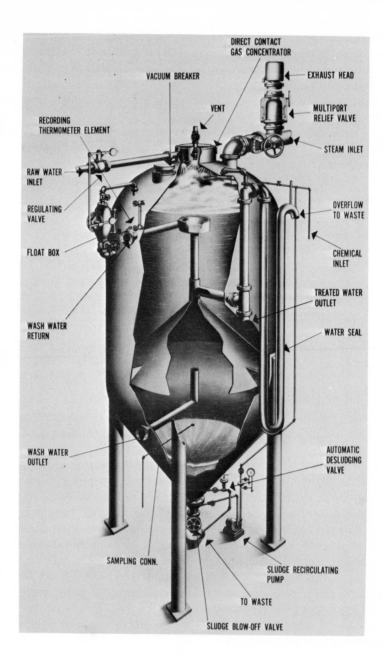

Fig. 3.4. Downflow design of hot-process settling tank.

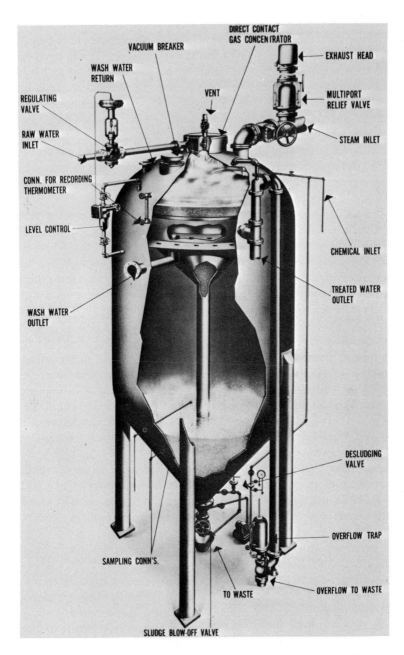

Fig. 3.5. Upflow sludge-blanket design for hot-process settling tank.

into the uptake. In the upflow type the reactions take place in the upper cone, from which a downcomer conducts the water into the lower cone. The water then rises upward through the sludge blanket or precipitates, kept suspended by the high velocity water rising from the lower cone. The sludge blanket depth is controlled by continuous sludge blowoff, so that the top of the sludge is kept well below the upper outlet collector. The settled water is finally clarified by being passed through pressure filters consisting of beds of anthracite granules. In both types the settling tank is made large enough to provide a nominal sixty-minute detention period.

The chemicals are fed, usually in wet slurry form, from chemical tanks through proportionating devices. A typical wet lime feed is illustrated in Chapter 4, Fig. 4.16. Dry feeds are used for large plants only (see Chapter 4, Fig. 4.17).

It is possible to include an internal atomizing deaerator, which receives the settled water and deaerates it, reducing the dissolved oxygen to about 0.005 ml/lit. This often saves a separate external deaerator. Further, for washing the filters without overloading of the settling tank separate compartments may be included which will store the filtered water that feeds the wash pump and will receive the dirty filter-wash effluent. The dirty wash water is gradually returned to the settling tank for clarification and is thus recovered.

2. REDUCING RESIDUAL HARDNESS WITH HOT PHOSPHATE OR HOT ZEOLITE

The residual hardness of 17 to 25 ppm (1 to 1.5 gr/gal) in the effluent of hot lime–soda plants can be reduced to nearly zero by a second-stage treatment with hot phosphate. Trisodium phosphate is added to the second settling tank, which follows the primary lime-treatment tank. The water that settles in the second tank flows to the filters. In the past a number of these plants were installed for high-pressure boiler plants, which required nearly zero-hardness feedwater.

Later (about 1949), when it was found that modern cation exchange resins in the sodium cycle could withstand the preheated-water temperatures of 220 to 300°F (varying with steam pressure), the hot lime–zeolite combination was developed. Excellent results were reported (4–6). Figure 3.6 is a flow diagram of a hot lime–zeolite plant.

The hot lime–zeolite design provided several operating improvements, as follows.

(a) Both the soda ash and the phosphate could be omitted. Since they are expensive chemicals compared with the sodium chloride used in regenerating the hot zeolite, a considerable saving in operating cost resulted.

(b) By omitting the soda ash and allowing the residual calcium to increase the carbonate alkalinity could be reduced, from the usual 50 ppm to 25 ppm. This cut in half the amount of free carbon dioxide in the boiler steam and

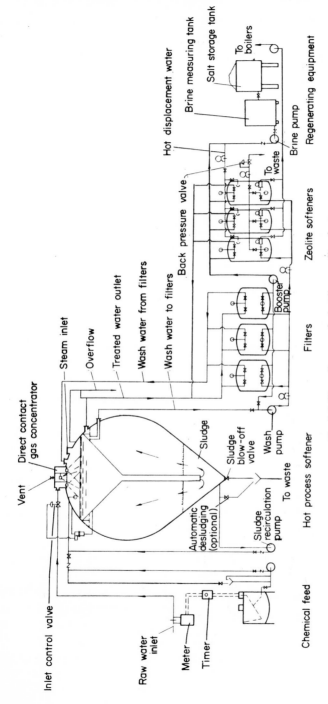

Fig. 3.6. Flow diagram of a hot lime-zeolite plant.

reduced the potential danger of corroding the piping that returns the condensate to the boiler (return lines). Figure 3.7 compares graphically the chemical results of the cold and the hot lime–soda and the hot lime–zeolite processes.

Hot lime–zeolite plants have been installed for treating makeup for boilers of 1000 psi pressure and higher. A large plant at Whiting, Indiana, uses hot lime–zeolite for a boiler plant of 1500 psi pressure (7).

3. COMBINATION OF HOT AND WARM PROCESSES AND DEMINERALIZERS

Since the anion exchange resin in demineralizers cannot withstand water temperatures exceeding about 140°F, the hot process is rarely used for treatment before demineralization, but it is possible to cool the hot-process effluent to 140°F. by heat exchangers and then to pass it through a demineralizer. This was done at River Rouge, Michigan (8). A hot-process plant had been in operation for low-pressure boilers. Later, when an old evaporator used for high-pressure boilers was replaced with a demineralizer, preclarification was needed, so that river water could be used. The hot-process plant provided the pretreatment and its effluent after cooling was passed through the demineralizer. The hot-process plant effluent (uncooled) continued to serve the low-pressure boilers.

Another solution of the temperature problem was to use a warm process instead of a hot process (9). In one instance an existing split-stream hydrogen–

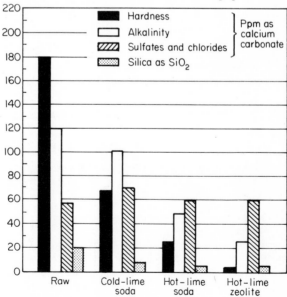

Fig. 3.7. Comparison of effects of cold lime-soda, hot lime-soda, and hot lime-zeolite processes [reproduced from *Power*, December, 1958 (6a)].

sodium cation exchange plant (Section II) was converted to an all-sodium cation exchange plant that was preceded by a warm-process lime plant, in order that a different type of river water might be used; previously a barium-containing well water of higher solids content had been used with the split-stream exchange plant. The warm-process pretreatment also reduced the silica. The plant operated at 140°F by thermostatic control of the amount of steam added for preheating of the water. Limiting the temperature avoided damaging the rubber lining of the existing hydrogen zeolite units, and it also permitted the installation of equipment for the demineralization of product processing water since, again, it avoided damaging the resin and the rubber lining in the anion unit. Other such combinations of warm-process lime plants and demineralizer plants have been installed elsewhere.

C. Sodium Cation Exchange (Sodium Zeolite)

As indicated in Chapter 1, the sodium zeolite water-softening process was the first commercial application of ion exchange. It has continued in success-ful use for the conversion of hard water to soft water in households and indus-try. No chemicals are added to the water and no precipitates are formed, and completely softened water (approaching zero hardness) is produced, even when the raw waters vary in hardness.

1. CHEMICAL REACTIONS

The zeolite converts the calcium and magnesium salts in the hard water to sodium salts, which are "soft," not soap-consuming, and not scale-forming. The calcium and magnesium ions in the water are taken up by the zeolite in exchange for sodium ions relinquished from the zeolite.

The chemical reaction of softening, written in ionic form, is

$$Na_2^+Z + \begin{Bmatrix} Ca^{2+} \\ Mg^{2+} \end{Bmatrix} \rightarrow \begin{Bmatrix} Ca^{2+} \\ Mg^{2+} \end{Bmatrix} Z + 2\,Na^+ \tag{8}$$

where Z represents the anionic part of the exchanger. If the softening reaction is written in the simplified molecular form (as if the salts were undissociated) it is

$$\begin{matrix} Ca \\ Mg \end{matrix} \Big\} \begin{cases} (HCO_3)_2 \\ SO_4 \\ Cl_2 \end{cases} + Na_2Z \rightarrow \begin{matrix} Ca \\ Mg \end{matrix} \Big\} Z + \begin{cases} 2\,NaHCO_3 \\ Na_2SO_4 \\ 2\,NaCl \end{cases} \tag{9}$$

Hard water will continue to be softened automatically, as it passes down-ward through a bed of the zeolite, until the latter can no longer produce zero hardness effluent; the zeolite is then considered "exhausted." The amount of water softened depends on the hardness of the water and the zeolite bed's capacity.

The zeolite is then regenerated with common salt (sodium chloride) brine according to the following reactions, written in ionic and in molecular forms:

$$2\,Na^+ + \left.\begin{matrix} Ca^{2+} \\ Mg^{2+} \end{matrix}\right\}Z \rightarrow \left\{\begin{matrix} Ca^{2+} \\ Mg^{2+} \end{matrix}\right. + Na_2^+Z \tag{10}$$

$$\left.\begin{matrix} Ca \\ Mg \end{matrix}\right\}Z + 2\,NaCl \rightarrow Na_2Z + \left.\begin{matrix} Ca \\ Mg \end{matrix}\right\}Cl_2 \tag{11}$$

These regeneration reactions are simply the reverse of the exhaustion reactions, Eqs. 8 and 9. The exchanger normally gives up sodium in exchange for calcium or magnesium, as in the exhaustion phase of the cycle, more easily than it does the reverse, but if an excess of sodium* in the brine and a considerable strength of brine (5 to 10%) is used for regeneration, the reverse regeneration reaction is facilitated and the sodium cations re-enter the zeolite in exchange for the calcium and magnesium cations previously removed. The latter are then discarded or eluted into the waste brine leaving the zeolite bed. The zeolite does not dissolve and can be used for years if properly handled.

2. Major Zeolite Materials

The properties and capacities of the three major exchangers in use today are briefly given in Table 3.3.

Table 3.3
PROPERTIES OF THE THREE MAJOR SODIUM ZEOLITES

Properties and limitations	Greensand	Carbonaceous material	Styrene resins
Capacity,[a] kgr/ft^3	2.8	7.0	26
Color	green	black	tan
Mesh size	16–50	16–50	10–50
Effective size, mm	0.34	0.5	0.4 to 0.6
Maximal pH	8.5	9.3	11.0
Minimal pH	6.2	none	none
Minimal silica, ppm	5.0	none	none
Maximal temp., °F	135	140	250
Shipping weight, lb/ft^3	90 to 92	30 to 32	50 to 55

[a] Based on use of 0.45 lb of salt per kilograin of hardness removed. More or less salt increases or decreases this capacity.

* "Excess of sodium" means that the total amount of sodium in the brine exceeds the total amount of equivalent calcium and magnesium in the exhausted zeolite.

Greensand is siliceous and therefore should not be used when an increase of silica in the water (dissolved from the greensand by low-silica raw waters) is not desired. It has the least capacity of the three exchangers and is used mainly for softening waters of low hardness.

The carbonaceous material is nonsiliceous. It is used for softening waters of moderate hardness. It is, however, sensitive to attack by chlorine, and the influent should be free from residual chlorine.

The styrene resins have the highest capacities and are the most stable of the three materials. They are, therefore, the most frequently used of all the three exchangers.

3. OPERATION OF THE SOFTENER

There are four steps in the operation of the softener, as follows.

Backwash. During the downward flowing of raw water in the softening process the zeolite bed has removed suspended matter from the water. Backwashing, an upward flow, expands the bed and releases the dirt, so that the dirt can be discharged to waste. This cleans and loosens the bed and classifies it (separates the large granules from the small), bringing the small granules to the top which aids in proper distribution of the brine through the bed.

Brine Injection and Displacement. The brine regenerant is injected into the water space above the bed and flows downward through the bed. It is followed by water, at a low rate of flow, which displaces the brine downward and slowly rinses the bed.

Fast Rinse. Water at a higher rate of flow flushes and rinses the adhering brine from the bed, eluting the calcium and magnesium ions to waste.

Service Run. Raw water is then again passed downward through the bed for the next softening or service run.

4. SOFTENER EQUIPMENT

The complete zeolite softener consists of a pressure-steel shell with internal distributors, zeolite and supporting material, external piping, nest of individual valves or a single control valve, meter, and regeneration equipment. Regeneration can be made fully automatic.

Figure 3.8 shows a modern zeolite softener with an automatic, Hydromatic, single control valve.

II. Removal of Calcium, Magnesium, Sodium, and Potassium: Hydrogen Cation Exchange

Hydrogen zeolite, or hydrogen cation exchange, as Chapter 1 relates, was the second ion exchange process developed. Its chief purpose was to reduce the alkalinity besides the hardness.

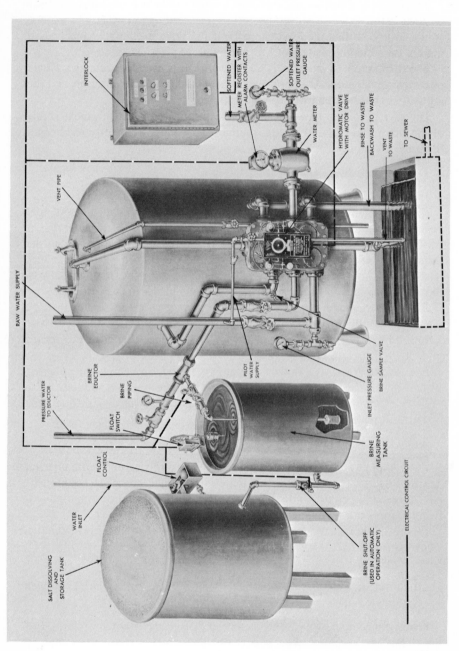

Fig. 28. Zeolite softener with automatic Hydromatic single-standard control.

The chemical reactions involved are similar to those in sodium cation exchange, except that hydrogen is exchanged instead of sodium, and sulfuric or hydrochloric acid is the regenerant instead of sodium chloride brine.

The following equations show the exhaustion phase in ionic and molecular forms, respectively:

$$\left.\begin{array}{c} Ca^{2+} \\ Mg^{2+} \\ 2\,Na^+ \\ 2\,K^+ \end{array}\right\} + H_2^+Z \rightarrow \left.\begin{array}{c} Ca^{2+} \\ Mg^{2+} \\ 2\,Na^+ \\ 2\,K^+ \end{array}\right\} Z + 2H^+ \tag{12}$$

$$\left.\begin{array}{c} Ca \\ Mg \\ Na_2 \\ K_2 \end{array}\right\} \left\{\begin{array}{c} (HCO_3)_2 \\ SO_4 \\ Cl_2 \end{array}\right\} + H_2Z \rightarrow \left.\begin{array}{c} Ca \\ Mg \\ Na_2 \\ K_2 \end{array}\right\} Z + H_2SO_4 \left\{\begin{array}{c} 2\,H_2CO_3 \\ \\ 2\,HCl \end{array}\right\} \tag{13}$$

The next equations show the regeneration phase in ionic and molecular forms, respectively, where sulfuric acid is the regenerant. An equation similar to Eq. 15 may be written for hydrochloric acid regenerant.

$$\left.\begin{array}{c} Ca^{2+} \\ Mg^{2+} \\ 2\,Na^+ \\ 2\,K^+ \end{array}\right\} Z + H_2^+ \rightarrow H_2^+Z + \left.\begin{array}{c} Ca^{2+} \\ Mg^{2+} \\ 2\,Na^+ \\ 2\,K^+ \end{array}\right\} \tag{14}$$

$$\left.\begin{array}{c} Ca \\ Mg \\ Na_2 \\ K_2 \end{array}\right\} Z + H_2SO_4 \rightarrow H_2Z + \left.\begin{array}{c} Ca \\ Mg \\ Na_2 \\ K_2 \end{array}\right\} \left\{SO_4 \right. \tag{15}$$

The destruction of the alkalinity is accomplished, as shown in Eq. 13, by the conversion of the bicarbonates to carbonic acid. This acid decomposes to free carbon dioxide:

$$H_2CO_3 \rightarrow CO_2 + H_2O \tag{16}$$

The free carbon dioxide, being gaseous, is removed by a degasifier, or decarbonator (Chapter 5, Section IV). Destruction of the bicarbonate alkalinity is often called "dealkalizing" (see Section IV).

The other mineral acids shown on the right-hand side of Eq. 13 render the effluent of the hydrogen zeolite acid. These mineral sulfuric and hydrochloric acidities must be neutralized before the effluent can be used. The neutralization is accomplished either by adding an alkali after the decarbonation or by using a split-stream hydrogen–sodium zeolite system, shown in Fig. 3.9.

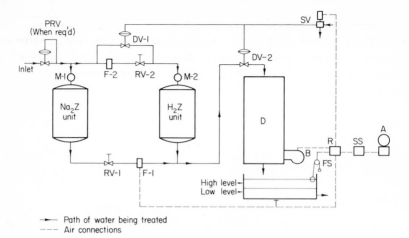

Fig. 3.9. Blended split-stream hydrogen and sodium cation exchanger: PRV, pressure-regulating valve; SV, solenoid valve; DV, diaphragm valve; M, meter; F, rate-of-flow indicator; RV, rate-setting valve; D, degasifier or decarbonator; T, storage tank (two-hour minimum for storage below low level); FS, float switch; B, blower; R, relays; SS, selector switch; A, alarm bell.

The neutralization of the free mineral acidity (FMA) in the hydrogen zeolite effluent is accomplished by the sodium bicarbonate in the sodium zeolite effluent as follows:

$$\left.\begin{array}{c} H_2SO_4 \\ 2\,HCl \end{array}\right\} + 2\,NaHCO_3 \rightarrow \left\{\begin{array}{c} Na_2SO_4 \\ 2\,NaCl \end{array}\right. + 2\,H_2CO_3 \qquad (17)$$

The carbonic acid formed by this neutralization joins the carbonic acid formed in the hydrogen zeolite effluents in Eq. 13, and both are removed together by the decarbonator. That is why the decarbonator must be large enough to handle the combined blended stream and not the hydrogen zeolite stream alone.

Equation 17, the neutralization reaction, shows that sodium sulfate and chloride are formed in amounts equivalent to those of sulfates and chlorides in the raw water. The hydrogen zeolite does not, therefore, remove sulfates and chlorides but only destroys the alkalinity and removes all the calcium and magnesium, so the effluent is of zero hardness. Although sodium is removed, Eq. 12, some sodium is returned to the water in the neutralization reaction, Eq. 17.

The removal of sodium then, is only partially accomplished by the hydrogen zeolite to the extent that bicarbonate anions are available for associating with the sodium. In other words, if the alkalinity of the raw water exceeds its hardness, such that there is an excess of bicarbonate anions available for associating with the sodium cation, then the water is said to contain sodium bicarbonate, which is removable according to Eq. 13. For the complete removal of sodium cation associated with the sulfates and chlorides as well as the bicarbonates the only method available is demineralization, which is cation exchange followed by anion exchange, in which the acids in the hydrogen zeolite effluent are absorbed by the anion exchangers.

Sodium, potassium and ammonium are similar cations and are therefore considered together. Potassium is not always present, and generally sodium predominates. The amount of ammonium cation is usually negligible and rarely determined.

Hydrogen cation exchange as the first step of demineralization is discussed in greater detail in Chapter 6.

III. Removal of Iron and Manganese

As Tables 2.5–2.7 indicate, the tolerance for iron and manganese in most applications is low, from 0.005 to 0.3 ppm. Higher amounts than these cause bad tastes and objectionable stains, streaks, and spots on many products. They also stimulate the growth of microorganisms, such as Crenothrix, which can clog pipelines. The iron stain is yellowish to reddish-brown; the manganese stain is purplish black. Iron and manganese can also foul ion exchange resins.

Manganese is not always present with the iron. The iron usually predominates. Manganese is the more objectionable and the more difficult to remove. Both are removable in similar processes and are therefore discussed together. The three major methods of iron and manganese removal, as outlined in Table 2.8 are (a) oxidation and precipitation, addition of chemicals and settling in some cases, and filtration, (b) filtration through manganese zeolite, and (c) ion exchange.

A. *Oxidation and Precipitation, Settling (in Some Cases), and Filtration*

Dissolved iron and manganese in most well-water supplies are present in ferrous (Fe^{2+}) and manganous (Mn^{2+}) forms, because most well waters are free from dissolved oxygen. Free carbon dioxide and bicarbonate anions are usually present, and the iron and manganese are then considered to be present as bicarbonates. In water that is freshly pumped from a well the dissolved iron and manganese are not visible: the water remains colorless until it dissolves oxygen from the air. Then it turns milky and finally yellowish to blackish, as the iron and manganese become oxidized to the insoluble ferric (Fe^{3+}) and manganic (Mn^{3+}) forms. The same oxidation of the metals that occurs in nature, as when iron turns to rust, occurs in the aeration of the water, applied for their removal.

The oxidation reaction in which ferrous bicarbonate is the assumed form of the iron can be written as:

$$4\,Fe(HCO_3)_2 + O_2 + 2\,H_2O \longrightarrow 4\,Fe(OH)_3 \downarrow + 8\,CO_2 \qquad (18)$$

The ferrous bicarbonate is oxidized to the insoluble ferric hydroxide, which precipitates. A similar equation may be written for manganese. About 1 ppm dissolved oxygen, will oxidize about 7 ppm ferrous iron and manganous manganese, expressed as the ions; thus, very small amounts of air absorbed by the water, can oxidize large amounts of the dissolved metals.

The speed of the oxidation varies with the pH value of the oxidized water and also with the composition of the well water. The optimum pH values for most rapid oxidations of iron are 7.0 to 9.0 and, of manganese, 9.0 to 10.5. It is the higher optimal pH value for manganese that makes its removal more difficult than that of iron. The pH value varies with the ratio of free carbon dioxide to alkalinity, as shown in Fig. 3.10. Therefore, if the pH value

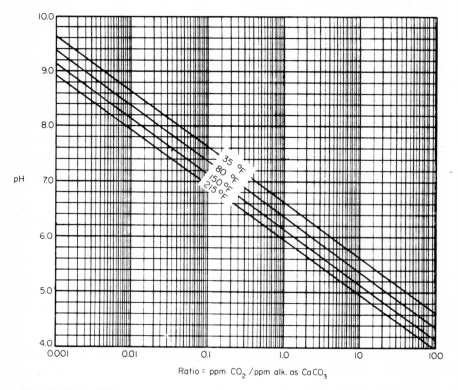

Fig. 3.10. Value of pH versus ratio of free carbon dioxide to alkalinity at various temperatures.

in the raw well water is much below the optimal range, it must be raised. This is accomplished in either of two ways: by decreasing the free carbon dioxide by means of either open or forced-draft aeration or by adding an alkali (preferably lime). Lime raises the pH value by decreasing the carbon dioxide and at the same time increasing the alkalinity. The first method (aeration) saves lime but requires repumping. The second method (lime without aeration) is justified only when the amount of free carbon dioxide present is fairly low; it is used with pressure aeration, discussed below.

The precipitation of the ferric and manganic hydroxides takes place most rapidly in those well waters that contain large amounts of total solids and, particularly, much hardness and alkalinity; such iron-bearing well waters are prevalent among mid-west supplies. On the other hand, when a well water is low in total solids, hardness, and alkalinity, the oxidation and precipitation proceed much more slowly. If appreciable amounts of organic matter and color are present, they too may inhibit the precipitation; in such case the addition of oxidizing reagents (chlorine or potassium permanganate), coagulants, and lime may be required. Settling tanks may also be needed after the aeration.

The speed of the oxidation and precipitation determines the design of the iron-removal plant, because it dictates the detention periods that should be provided for the various steps of the removal process. It is sometimes difficult to predict the speed of reaction from the well-water analysis alone, and for large plants some pilot-plant testing at the site may be advisable (10).

Surface waters are usually saturated with dissolved oxygen, and therefore the iron and manganese in them are the insoluble metal hydroxides.

If organic matter is present, the metals may be in the form of chelated metallic complexes. They are removed by the same coagulation methods used for eliminating suspended matter (Chapter 4, Section II).

Iron in acid mine-water drainage is present as the sulfate. Its removal requires the addition of lime, which neutralizes the acidity and raises the pH value before precipitation of the ferric hydroxide can take place.

1. Aeration Equipment

For the introduction of oxygen into water three types of aerator are used: the pressure aerator, the open aerator, and the forced-draft aerator.

a. Pressure Aerator

The pressure aerator is used for those well waters which respond to oxidation and precipitation most rapidly. Compressed air is injected into the water in a small, closed saturator vessel mounted on the discharge pipe of the well pump.

The bubbles of air mix with the water in the saturator, increasing the amount of dissolved oxygen in the water. The aeration is accomplished under pressure. If the pH value must be raised, a lime slurry is pumped into the water at the same time, and chlorine also may be similarly introduced (see Fig. 3.11).

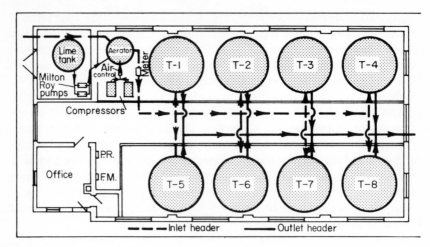

Fig. 3.11. Iron-removal plant in Jamaica, New York. T-1 to T-8 are filters. (Reproduced from Applebaum (*10*).)

Thus a single pumping of the well water through pressurized water treating equipment to service suffices, and repumping of the water is avoided. However, the amount of air introduced must be controlled if supersaturation is to be avoided, because free air bubbles are liberated when the water pressure is released at faucets. This makes the water milky until the air bubbles escape.

Pressure aeration does not decrease the free carbon dioxide in the water and therefore should be used only for well waters that do not contain large amounts of it; otherwise, the cost of the lime for neutralizing the carbon dioxide would be too high, and the hardness would be increased excessively by the calcium in the lime added.

b. Open Aerator

In the open aerator the water trickles downward over trays of coke, wood slats, or other fill, in a vertical wooden, steel, or concrete tower. The sides of the tower have openings to the atmosphere, so that air enters and is dissolved in the water trickling down. The water is broken up by the fill in the tower into thin streams or films, which facilitate the release of the dissolved carbon dioxide from the water to the atmosphere. Thus the free carbon dioxide is reduced at the same time that the dissolved oxygen is increased.

Other forms of open aerators have been used, such as spray nozzles over basins or a series of steps of stone or concrete. Any device that will break up the water into droplets or thin films will remove some carbon dioxide. The towers described in this and the next section are preferred, however, because they remove the carbon dioxide most completely.

The carbon dioxide is determined by titration, alkali being added from a burette to a sample containing a dye indicator, until the sample changes color. Iron also consumes alkali and, therefore, in tests of an aerator effluent containing appreciable amounts of iron allowance should be made for this alkali consumption in determining the carbon dioxide.

c. Forced-Draft Aerator

The sides of the tower of a forced-draft aerator are closed, and air is blown in at low pressure at the bottom, to flow upward, countercurrent to the trickling water. In other respects the design is similar to the open aerator. The controlled flow of air, however, makes the forced-draft aerator more efficient in removing carbon dioxide than the open aerator, which relies on windage or other natural air currents to introduce the air and to sweep out the gases released.

The designs of both the open and the forced-draft aerators are more fully described in Chapter 5, in which the removal of gaseous impurities is discussed.

2. SETTLING TANKS

If the oxidation and precipitation of the metal hydroxides can take place rapidly enough, and if the amounts of iron and manganese present are not too high (under about 1 to 5 ppm), the aerated water can be passed directly to the filters without first settling (presettling). In such case pressure aeration followed by pressure filtration makes for the simplest and most inexpensive plants. Jamaica, New York, has a successful, large, municipal iron-removal plant of this type (Fig. 3.11).

Settling tanks provide the long detention period required by well waters that respond slowly to the oxidation and precipitation of the iron. They also partially reduce the load on the filters by making some of the iron settle out. Settling before filtering is usually recommended for well waters containing large amounts of iron and manganese (exceeding about 5 to 10 ppm). The addition of lime for precipitating some of the bicarbonate hardness, even when complete lime softening is not required, often helps the iron hydroxide precipitates to settle out. The calcium carbonate and magnesium hydroxide precipitates add body and weight to the iron hydroxide precipitates; the latter, formed alone from only a few parts per million iron, are often fragile and light and so are easily carried out in the effluent of the settling tank. Other weighting agents that have been found helpful are clay, powdered limestone, and fly ash. The addition of chlorine and a little copper sulfate (acting as catalyst) has also been of aid in accelerating the oxidation and in obtaining a more complete removal of the iron and manganese in settling tanks.

When cold lime treatment is used for the complete removal of bicarbonate hardness, the iron and manganese are also removed, because the pH value is high and usually enough aeration takes place in the settling tank. However, if the amount of free carbon dioxide in the raw water is high enough, a separate aerator, preceding the settling tank, may be justified by the saving in lime.

Settling tanks may be of the old, plain, settling type or, preferably, of the suspended-solids contact type, discussed in Chapter 4, Section IIG2.

3. FILTERS (CONTACT ROUGHING AND FINAL)

If the amount of iron is not excessively high (5 to 10 ppm), it is possible to avoid the use of settling tanks and instead use contact roughing filters before the final filters. Contact filters have coarser particles of filtering material than those in the final filters and have therefore more space between the particles for the storage of the iron removed resulting in a slower buildup of head loss (Chapter 4, Section I). The beds in contact filters have been made of various materials, such as pyrolusite, coke, lava, and calcite, but they usually consist of gravel or coarse sand. Flow rates of 5 to 10 gal/min/ft^2 may be used.

The final filters may be of the pressure or the gravity type used in cold lime treatment or in the removal of suspended matter. The flow rates may be from 3 to 5 gal/min/ft^2. The designs are described in Chapter 4, Section I.

B. *Filtration through Manganese Zeolite*

Manganese zeolite is produced by treating greensand with manganous sulfate, then with potassium permanganate, so that films of manganic oxides are formed on the greensand granules. As the water is passed through the zeolite bed, the films give up some of their oxygen to oxidize the iron and manganese and at the same time filter out the hydroxides formed. After some period of use it is necessary to regenerate the zeolite with potassium permanganate.

Since permanganate is expensive, manganese zeolite is usually limited to treating waters containing small amounts of iron and manganese (less than about 1 to 2 ppm). The process is more suited to manganese than to iron removal. In some plants it has been found best to remove the iron by other more economical means first and then allow the manganese to be removed by the manganese zeolite.

A method of continuous, rather than intermittent, regeneration with permanganate has been developed (*11*). The permanganate is fed continuously to the influent, so that only intermittent backwashing is required.

C. Sodium and Hydrogen Cation Exchange

Both sodium and hydrogen cation exchangers will remove dissolved ferrous iron and manganous manganese by ion exchange in the same way that they remove other cations.

Care must be taken, however, to prevent any air from coming into contact with the water before the ion exchange takes place, because the air tends to oxidize the metals to their insoluble hydroxide form, so that they precipitate on the exchanger granules and foul them. Well water must therefore be pumped directly through pressure ion exchange units and not be passed through any storage tanks on the way, where it could absorb oxygen from the atmosphere. Even a leaky pipe joint on the suction side of the well pump can suck in enough oxygen to foul the exchanger with precipitated iron.

The regenerant solutions for the ion exchangers also can bring enough dissolved oxygen into the bed to oxidize and precipitate the ferrous iron being eluted from the exchanger and so cause fouling during the elution. To prevent this, reducing agents such as sodium sulfite have been added with the brine in the regeneration of sodium cation exchangers, to react with any dissolved oxygen that might enter. Occasionally also a cleaning treatment of the exchanger with stronger reducing agents, such as sodium hydrosulfite, may be advisable.

Iron and manganese may foul the hydrogen cation exchangers of demineralizers unless similar precautions are followed. It is therefore conservative practice to pretreat the water by removing the iron and manganese before demineralizing it, if the amounts of metals are appreciable and the demineralizer plants are large enough. Since a pretreatment plant will often be needed to provide iron-free water for drinking, and industrial processing, it can economically be made a little larger to provide water to the demineralizer in addition and thus prevent fouling of the resins at the same time.

IV. Removal of Alkalinity

As indicated in Table 2.8, there are three processes available for removing alkalinity: lime softening, hydrogen cation exchange, and chloride anion exchange salt-splitting.

A. Lime Softening and Hydrogen Cation Exchange

The removal of alkalinity by lime softening and by hydrogen cation exchange were discussed in Sections I and II in connection with removal of cations. At the same time that the two processes remove the cations they reduce the alkalinity, as indicated in Eqs. 1, 2, and 13. Cold lime treatment, therefore, often precedes demineralization, relieving the expensive anion exchangers, which constitute the second parts of demineralizers, of the burden of reducing the alkalinity.

The removal of alkalinity by hydrogen cation exchangers may also be a profitable pretreatment before mixed bed demineralization in some cases, as discussed in Chapter 6, Section XI, system 8.

B. Chloride Anion Exchange (Dealkalization)

Strongly basic anion exchangers (discussed in Chapter 6, Section VI) are the second stage of demineralization, absorbing the acids from the effluent of the hydrogen cation exchanger, which is the first stage. The same anion exchangers can split salts (exchange anions) as well as absorb acids, and this property led to the development of the chloride anion exchange process for dealkalizing makeup for low-pressure boilers.

In the past many of the boiler plants in institutions, hotels, and small industrial factories employed sodium zeolite units for softening the makeup and preventing scale deposits. However, the sodium zeolite did not remove alkalinity. Sodium bicarbonate, left in the softened water, decomposed in the boiler to caustic soda and free carbon dioxide gas. This gas was present in the boiler steam and, when the steam condensed, the gas dissolved in the condensate, lowering its pH value and causing return-line corrosion.

Some boiler plants then installed hydrogen cation exchangers to work with the existing sodium zeolite units in a split-stream blending system for removing the alkalinity. However, the hydrogen exchangers required acid for regeneration, and handling acid was arduous in a small plant. Therefore, boiler plants welcomed the development of the chloride anion exchangers (12, 12a), which were to follow the existing sodium zeolite softeners and remove the alkalinity from the softened water. Sodium chloride brine regenerates the anion exchanger, and this chloride is exchanged for the bicarbonate and sulfate anions in the softened water.

The salt-splitting chemical reaction during the exhaustion phase of the cycle is shown in the following equations:

$$NaHCO_3 + ACl \rightarrow AHCO_3 + NaCl \tag{19}$$
$$Na_2SO_4 + 2 ACl \rightarrow A_2SO_4 + 2 NaCl \tag{20}$$

where A is the cationic portion of the anion exchanger. Thus the bicarbonate alkalinity is converted to sodium chloride, as in Eq. 19. The sulfates also are converted to sodium chloride, as in Eq. 20, although that conversion is unsolicited and unavoidable.

The regeneration reaction is shown in the following equation:

$$A_2 \begin{cases} (HCO_3)_2 \\ SO_4 \end{cases} + 2 NaCl \rightarrow 2 ACl + Na_2 \begin{cases} (HCO_3)_2 \\ SO_4 \end{cases} \tag{21}$$

The use of some caustic soda with the sodium chloride regenerant produced a higher pH value in the effluent and increased the exchanger's capacity (13). Figure 3.12 shows a flow diagram of a typical sodium zeolite softener followed by a chloride anion dealkalizer.

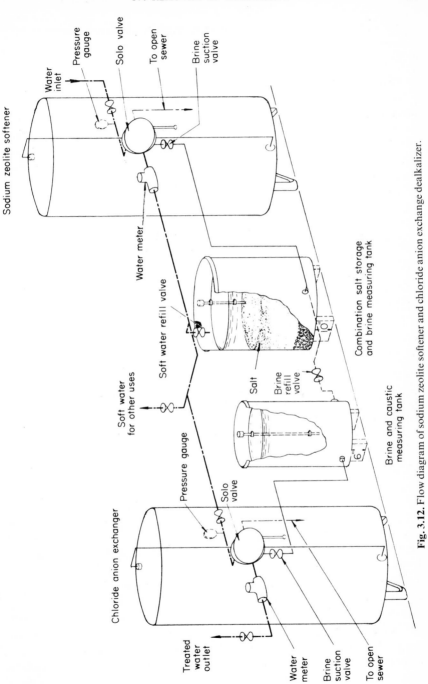

Fig. 3.12. Flow diagram of sodium zeolite softener and chloride anion exchange dealkalizer.

V. Removal of Sulfate, Chloride, Nitrate, and Phosphate

Nitrate and phosphate anions are usually present in negligible amounts. Sulfates can be precipitated as barium sulfate by adding barium carbonate instead of soda ash in the lime–soda process. A few plants of this type have been installed in the past for boiler-feed purposes, but the poisonous character of barium has discouraged its application.

Sulfates can be exchanged for chlorides or hydroxides by anion exchange salt-splitting. Likewise chlorides can be exchanged for hydroxides. However, the complete removal of sulfates and chlorides without the formation of other compounds in their place can be accomplished only by demineralization.

VI. Removal of Silica

The reduction of silica is required chiefly for boiler-feed purposes. The amount of residual silica in the water produced by the various methods for its removal usually determines which method to select. The limits on the silica residual (tolerances) in feedwater vary with boiler pressures.

A. Tolerances

The silica limits in boiler feedwater have steadily been lowered over the years, as boiler pressures have mounted. Today, with once-through drumless boilers of supercritical pressure (over 3206 psia), silica in feedwater must be kept below 0.010 ppm (10 ppb), as shown in Table 2.6. It must be limited also in the feed of drum-type boilers, which have subcritical lower pressures. Silica causes siliceous deposits not only in the boilers but, mainly, in the steam turbines. These deposits on turbine blades are glassy and hard; they are difficult to remove and cause both significant losses in efficiency and costly outages for cleaning.

Silica is present in the steam in volatile form. The amount contained is a function of the boiler pressure and the silica concentration in the boiler water. The ratio of steam silica to boiler-water silica is called the "distribution ratio." Figure 3.13 gives this ratio for drum-type boilers of pressures ranging from 500 to 3000 psig and for various pH values in the boiler water. At supercritical pressures in drumless boilers this ratio reaches 100 %.

As the steam expands in passing through the turbine, a lower pressure and temperature are reached, at which the volatile silica condenses, forming the glassy, solid deposit on the blades. The only successful method of preventing the deposits is to limit the amount of silica in the steam to extremely low levels, under 0.02 ppm. Such levels in the steam in turn require low levels in the boiler water, as dictated by the distribution ratio.

With drum type boilers the amount of silica in the boiler water can be controlled by boiler blowoff, which limits the number of concentrations of

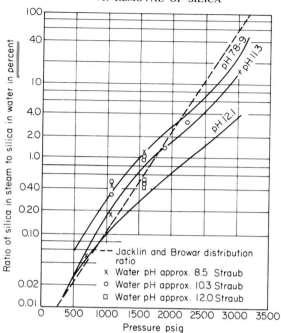

Fig. 3.13. Distribution ratio of steam silica to boiler-water silica for drum boilers at 500 to 3000 psig and various pH values.

the silica entering with the feedwater, but as the pressure increases, boiler blowoff becomes more costly, and therefore the amount of blowoff must be kept reasonably low (at less than 5% of the feedwater).

Table 3.4

TOLERANCES OF SILICA IN FEEDWATER VERSUS BOILER PRESSURES FOR
DRUM-TYPE BOILERS PRODUCING STEAM CONTAINING LESS THAN
0.02 PPM SiO_2

Boiler pressure, psig	SiO_2 in concentrated boiler water, ppm	SiO_2 in feedwater, based on 5% blowoff (20 concentrations),[a] ppm
600	35 to 50	1.7 to 2.5
800	15 to 20	0.8 to 1.0
1000	5 to 8	0.3 to 0.4
1500	2 to 3	0.1 to 0.15
2000	0.8 to 1.2	0.04 to 0.06
2500	0.2 to 0.4	0.02 to 0.04
3000	0.1 to 0.2	0.005 to 0.01

[a] 20 concentrations means that the boiler water is twenty times as concentrated in analysis as the feed water.

Table 3.4 gives the silica tolerances in the feed water for drum-type boilers of various pressures, based on 20 concentrations, which corresponds to about 5% blowoff. The table shows that for boiler pressures of less than 600 psi the silica should be less than 2.5 ppm; this can often be obtained by means of cold lime treatment. When the pressure reaches 800 to 1000 psi (medium boiler pressures), the silica in the feed should be limited to a range of 0.3 to 1.0 ppm; this requires the hot process, desilicization, or demineralization. When the pressures exceed 2000 psi (high boiler pressures), the silica in the feed should be limited to a range of 0.005 to 0.06 ppm; this can be obtained only by demineralization.

These limits refer to feedwater that consists of condensate plus makeup. If the condensate were entirely free from silica, the makeup could contain larger amounts of silica, because it would be diluted by the condensate. Most utility plants do not depend, however, on this dilution effect, because the condensate is seldom entirely silica-free. Therefore the silica amounts in the makeup for high-pressure boilers are kept below 0.005 to 0.06 ppm. For once-through boilers of about 3500 psi, which is the pressure commonly used today for new utility power plants, not only the makeup but also the condensate is demineralized. Chapter 10 discusses current condensate-demineralization practice.

B. Cold Process

1. Absorption by Ferric Hydroxide

One of the first methods developed (14) for cold-process silica removal was the absorption of silica by ferric hydroxide precipitates, which were formed by the addition of ferric sulfate with the lime and soda ash. Although this process can reduce the silica to about 2 or 3 ppm at an optimum pH value of 9.0, high doses of ferric sulfate are required; for example, to reduce the 8 ppm silica present in Mississippi River water down to 2 ppm, a dose of 140 ppm ferric sulfate is required. Another disadvantage of the process is the amount of sodium sulfate formed in the softened water from the ferric sulfate; to treat the Mississippi River nearly 90 ppm sodium sulfate (as $CaCO_3$) are so added. This increases excessively the total dissolved solids and the boiler blowoff required. A few plants of this type have been installed, but this process has been generally superseded by the superior methods developed later: absorption by magnesium compounds, desilicizers, and demineralizers.

2. Absorption by Magnesium Compounds

In cold lime treatment plants the ionic magnesium in the raw water is precipitated as magnesium hydroxide. The precipitate has been found to have a good capacity for absorbing silica. Another compound, magnesium oxide (MgO), present as an impurity in hydrated dolomitic lime, 62% Ca(OH)$_2$ and 32% MgO, also has been found capable of absorbing silica (*15*, *16*), although less efficiently.

Figure 3.14 shows the amount of silica removed by various doses of the two absorbents, when used in solids contact units. About 90 min of detention should be allowed, and water temperatures of over 90°F (by preheating, if necessary) should be used, for optimal results.

If the amount of ionic magnesium that can be precipitated by the lime is enough to reduce the silica to the desired limit then high-calcium hydrated lime would be the most economical; if it is not enough, then dolomitic lime should replace part or all of the high-calcium lime, as required.

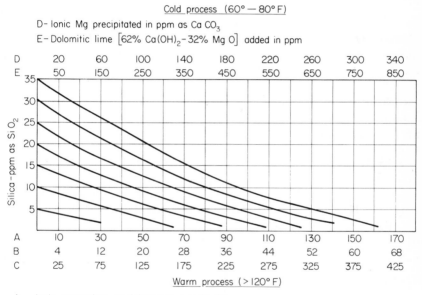

Fig. 3.14. Silica reduction in cold-process and warm-process lime treatment.

If the combination of precipitates from the ionic magnesium and from the magnesium oxide of the dolomitic lime is still not adequate to reduce the silica sufficiently, a magnesium dissolver, shown in Figure 3.15, can be used. Sludge is recirculated from the solids contact unit into the dissolver. The carbon dioxide and the bicarbonates in the raw water dissolve the ionic magnesium from the sludge. Dolomitic lime is used, so that magnesium oxide is present in the sludge and supplies enough magnesium. If the amount of carbon dioxide and bicarbonate in the raw water is not enough to dissolve

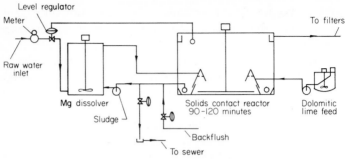

Fig. 3.15. Diagram of magnesium dissolver.

the required magnesium, additional carbon dioxide can be injected into the dissolver. The dissolver increases the ionic magnesium content of the influent and thus reduces the residual silica in the treated water.

C. Warm Process and Hot Process

Silica absorption by magnesium compounds is most efficient at the higher temperatures (*16a*). Therefore warm and hot lime treatment plants can reduce the silica more completely than can the cold-process plants and with smaller amounts of the magnesium compounds.

If the combined ionic magnesium precipitated and the magnesium oxide from the dolomitic lime are inadequate to reduce the silica sufficiently, according to the indications given in Fig. 3.14, then activated magnesia (MgO) can be added, to finish the silica removal. Activated magnesia does not absorb silica appreciably at low temperatures, but it is very effective at the warm-process (above 120°F) and the hot-process temperatures. Figure 3.14 gives the silica removal accomplished by various doses of activated magnesia at temperatures higher than 120°F.

D. Hydroxide Anion Exchange Salt-Splitting (Desilicization)

The salt-splitting or anion exchange* powers of strongly basic anion exchangers have been used in the development of the chloride anion exchange dealkalizer described in Section IVB. Another salt-splitting process was developed later (*17*), which reduced the silica in the effluents of either sodium zeolites (*17a*) or split-stream hydrogen–sodium zeolites. It has received increasing acceptance for treating makeup for medium-pressure industrial boilers. It is particularly well adapted to the removal of silica from raw waters fairly low in total solids but rather high in ratio of silica to other dissolved solids. The desilicizer may be considered an economical means of reducing this ratio for the purpose of decreasing boiler blowoff.

* As distinguished from their acid adsorptive ability when used in demineralization.

The anion resin is the Type I strong-base resin employed in demineralizers (Chapter 7, Section IIB), but when used in desilicizers it is regenerated with smaller amounts of caustic soda. This reduces the operating cost to less than that of demineralization. The chemical reaction during exhaustion is written below in ionic form and in a simplified molecular form; R represents the cationic portion of the anion exchanger.

$$R(OH)^- + (HSiO_3)^- \rightarrow RHSiO_3^- + (OH)^- \tag{22}$$

$$2\,ROH + Na_2 \begin{cases} (HSiO_3)_2 \\ SO_4 \\ Cl_2 \\ (HCO_3)_2 \end{cases} \rightarrow R_2 \begin{cases} (HSiO_3)_2 \\ SO_4 \\ Cl_2 \\ (HCO_3)_2 \end{cases} + 2\,NaOH \tag{23}$$

As the second equation indicates, sodium hydroxide is formed in an amount equivalent to the sum of all the sodium salts present. The simultaneous splitting of all these sodium salts, including the bicarbonate, sulfate, and chloride, in addition to the silica, makes the process uneconomical for waters of high solids content. That is why the desilicizer is best adapted to the treatment of waters of fairly low solids content (under 100 to 200 ppm) but of rather high silica content (exceeding 10 to 20 ppm). Many natural waters fit this description; they exist in areas where quartz predominates in the ground, such as in certain sections of the Atlantic and Pacific seaboards.

For waters of high alkalinity it may be more economical (18) to use a split-stream hydrogen–sodium zeolite plant rather than the sodium zeolite, for softening before desilicizing. The split-stream plant reduces both the alkalinity and the hardness. It thereby relieves the desilicizer of the burden of salt-splitting the alkalinity and reduces the operating cost. Further, less sodium hydroxide is formed. This may be important, because the ratio of sodium hydroxide to total solids in feedwater should not exceed about 1 to 5, if the formation of impure steam from the boiler is to be avoided. Therefore acid is often added to the effluent of the desilicizer, to convert part of the sodium hydroxide to sodium sulfate. Figure 3.16 is a flow diagram of this combination of a split-stream softener, a desilicizer, and an acid feed.

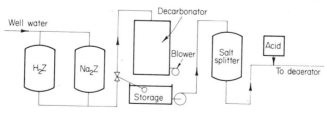

Fig. 3.16. Flow diagram of desilicizer preceded by split-stream hydrogen–sodium cation exchangers.

The regeneration reaction is the reverse of Eqs. 22 and 23. The caustic soda used is preheated to 120°F, and the regenerant effluent is reclaimed and reused for the first part of the next regeneration. This is followed by a solution of new caustic soda. Reclaiming reduces the operating cost to a minimum.

The ion exchange equipment required is similar to that of a sodium zeolite softener. It is low in cost, because the main shells, piping, and valves are not rubber-lined, as they are in demineralizers; the unlined steel is satisfactory because no acid is used as regenerant. The operating cost also is low, because smaller amounts of caustic soda regenerant are used than in demineralizers.

The reduction in boiler blowoff is accomplished by the desilicizer process because the tolerance of silica, rather than of the total solids, in the boiler water often controls the amount of the blowoff required. Table 3.5 gives the tolerances of total solids, alkalinity, and silica for various boiler pressures.

Table 3.5

SUGGESTED TOLERANCES OF TOTAL SOLIDS, ALKALINITY, AND SILICA IN BOILER WATER VERSUS BOILER PRESSURES FOR DRUM-TYPE BOILERS

Boiler pressure, psig	Total solids, ppm	Alkalinity as $CaCO_3$, ppm	Silica as SiO_2, ppm
0 to 300	3500	700	50 to 75
301 to 450	3000	600	40 to 50
451 to 600	2500	500	35 to 45
601 to 750	2000	400	25 to 35
751 to 900	1500	300	8 to 20
901 to 1000	1250	250	5 to 10
1001 to 1500	1000	200	2 to 5
1501 to 2000	750	150	0.8 to 3
2001 and over	500	100	0.1 to 1.2

[a] The first three columns are from standards issued by the American Boiler Manufacturers Association (19). The last column has been calculated from data given in Table 3.4 above 600 psig.

If, for instance, the boiler pressure were 600 psi and the effluent of a sodium zeolite softener contained a total solids of 100 ppm and silica of 10 ppm, then the allowable number of concentrations for keeping the boiler water within the tolerance limits indicated in Table 3.5, without a desilicizer, would be calculated as follows:

ALLOWABLE NUMBER OF CONCENTRATIONS WITHOUT DESILICIZER

Constituents	Makeup, ppm	Boiler water, ppm	Number of concentrations
Silica as SiO_2	10	40	4
Total solids	100	2500	25
Blowoff in percent of makeup:		100/(no. of concns. $-$ 1)	

In this case the silica would control the blowoff; the blowoff would be

$$100/(4 - 1) = 33.3\% \text{ of makeup}$$

If a desilicizer were installed, the silica could be reduced to 0.7 ppm, and then:

ALLOWABLE NUMBER OF CONCENTRATIONS WITH DESILICIZER

Constituents	Makeup, ppm	Boiler water, ppm	Number of concentrations
Silica	0.7	40	57
Total solids	100	2500	25

Now the total solids would control the blowoff; the blowoff would be

$$100/(25 - 1) = 4.2\% \text{ of makeup}$$

Thus the desilicizer would reduce the blowoff from 33.3 to 4.2% of the makeup.

VII. Comparison of Water Treatments

For low-pressure or medium-pressure boilers (of less than 1000 psi) the older methods of water treatment must be evaluated and compared with demineralization for boiler-feed makeup purification. Table 3.6 gives some general guidelines for different boiler pressures, raw-water alkalinities, and silicas. Table 3.7 gives an overall comparison of the various alternative treatments. The final selection will be determined by capital and operating costs, boiler blowoff required, space needed, raw-water characteristics, and skill of available personnel.

Table 3.6

GUIDELINES FOR SELECTION OF WATER-TREATMENT METHOD

Boiler pressure, psig	Raw-water alkalinity, ppm	Raw-water silica, ppm	Alternative water treatments indicated
Above 1000			(1) demineralizer
700 to 1000			(1) demineralizer (2) hot lime–zeolite (3) zeolite plus desilicizer
500 to 700		Above 8 to 15	(1) demineralizer (2) hot lime–zeolite (3) zeolite plus desilicizer
	Above 50	Below 2 to 5	(1) demineralizer (2) hot lime–zeolite (3) cold lime–zeolite
	Below 50	Below 2 to 5	(1) hot lime–zeolite (2) sodium zeolite plus dealkalizer (3) sodium zeolite
Below 500		Above 8 to 15	(1) hot lime–zeolite (2) cold lime–zeolite (3) zeolite plus desilicizer
	Above 50	Below 8 to 15	(1) hot lime–zeolite (2) hot lime–soda (3) cold lime–zeolite (4) sodium zeolite plus dealkalizer
	Below 50	Below 2 to 5	(1) sodium zeolite

Table 3.7
COMPARISON OF ALTERNATIVE WATER TREATMENTS

	Hardness in effluent as $CaCO_3$, ppm	Alkalinity reduc.[a]	Total solids reduc.	CO_2 in steam	Silica in effluent, ppm
(1) Sodium zeolite	0 to 2	None	None	High, if Alk. high	Not reduced
(2) Sodium zeolite plus acid	0 to 2	Up to 100%, if desired	None	As low as desired	Not reduced
(3) Hydrogen zeolite	0 to 2	Up to 100%, if desired	Reduced with Alk.	Same as item 2	Not reduced
(4) Cold lime–soda	34 to 85, Depending on excess soda	Reduced by degree removal of $Ca(HCO_3)_2$ and $Mg(HCO_3)_2$	Reduced with Alk.	$0.44 \times Na_2CO_3$ excess, usually low	2 to 3
(5) Cold lime–zeolite	0 to 2	Same as (4)	Same as (4)	Higher than (4)	Same as (4)
(6) Hot lime–soda	17 to 25	More than (4)	More than (4)	A little lower than (4)	0.5 to 1
(7) Hot lime–soda plus hot phosphate	0 to 2	Same as (6)	Same as (6)	Higher than (6)	Same as (6)
(8) Hot lime–zeolite	0 to 2	More than (6)	Same as (6)	Lower than (6)	Same as (6)
(9) Hot phosphate alone	0 to 2	Little	Little	Higher than (7)	Not reduced
(10) Sodium zeolite plus chloride anion	0 to 2	$M - P = 5$ to 10% of raw $M - P$ or 8 ppm	None	Low	Not reduced
(11) Sodium or hydrogen zeolite plus desilicizer plus acid	0 to 2	As much as desired	None	Low	0.2 to 1.0

Table 3.7 (*continued*)
COMPARISON OF ALTERNATIVE WATER TREATMENTS

	Hardness in effluent as $CaCO_3$, ppm	Alkalinity reduc.[a]	Total solids reduc.	CO_2 in steam	Silica in effluent, ppm
(12) Demineralization, weak-base anion	0 to 2	Nearly 100%	Nearly 100%	As low as required	Not reduced
(13) Demineralization, strong-base anion	0 to 2	Same as (12)	Same as (12)	Same as (12)	0.005 to 0.1

[a] M, methyl orange alkalinity; P, phenolphthalein alkalinity; see Section IA7.

NOTE: The influent must be clear for the ion exchange treatments but not for the lime-soda methods. The skill needed for operation is least for sodium zeolite, greater for the other ion exchange processes, and most for the lime-soda methods.

REFERENCES

1. T. Clark, British Patent (1841).
1a. J. Porter, British Patent (1876).
1b. A. A. Hirsch, Dry feed of ground quicklime without a slaker. *J. Am. Water Works Assoc.*, December 1962.
2. S. B. Applebaum, Cold lime soda softening. *Ind. Eng. Chem.* **32** (May 1940).
3. Cochrane Hot Process Softeners, Bull. 2.01, 1963.
4. S. B. Applebaum, Hot lime treatment followed by sodium zeolite. *Proc. Ann. Water Conf., Engrs. Soc. West. Penn.,* 11th Ann. Conf. p.127 (1950).
5. G. H. Gowdy and S. B. Applebaum, Conversion of a two-stage hot process water softener from hot lime soda phosphate to hot lime zeolite. *Am. Soc. Mech. Engrs. Ann. Meeting, New York, November 30–December 5, 1952.*
6. B. E. Varon and S. B. Applebaum, An application of hot lime zeolite to moderate high pressure boiler operations. *Proc. Am. Power Conf.* **19**, 660 (1957).
6a. R. H. Marks, Water treatment, *Power* (December 1958).
7. J. E. Harden and G. R. Hull, Operating experiences with a large hot lime zeolite system for 1500 psi boilers. *Proc. Am. Power Conf.* **19**, 672 (1957).
8. A. K. Sukumar and S. B. Applebaum, Demineralizer treating hot lime zeolite effluent replaces evaporators in Ford's River Rouge plant. *Proc. Am. Power Conf.* **20**, 687 (1958).
9. F. T. Stilwell and J. W. Strub, A unique treatment process—warm (140°F) lime-zeolite softening. *Proc. Ann. Water Conf. Soc. West. Penn.* (1964).
10. S. B. Applebaum, Iron and manganese removal. *Proc. Ann. Water Conf. Engrs. Soc. West. Penn., 16th Ann. Conf.* (1955).
11. S. F. Alling, Some operating experiences with continuous regeneration of manganese zeolite filters. *Proc. Intern. Water Conf. Engrs. Soc. West. Penn.,* (1962).

12. S. B. Applebaum, Experiences with salt splitter dealkalizers. *Proc. Ann. Water Conf. Engrs. Soc. West Penn., 13th Ann. Conf.* 1952.

12a. W. C. Bauman, U.S. Patent 2,559,529 (1951).

13. A. E. Kittredge, Dealkalization of boiler feedwater in small power plants. *Proc. Am. Power Conf.* **15**, 567 (1953).

14. M. D. Schwartz, Removal of silica from water for boiler feed purposes: The ferric sulphate and hydrous ferric oxide process. *J. Am. Water Works Assoc.* **30**, 551 (1938).

15. H. L. Tiger, Silica removal by an improved magnesia process. *Trans. ASME* **54**, 49 (1942).

16. P. C. Goetz and H. L. Tiger, U.S. Patent 2,428,418 (1947).

16a. V. J. Calise, J. Duff, and R. Dvorin, Chemical reactions in hot and cold treatment units. *J. Am. Water Works Assoc.* **48** (July 1955).

17. S. B. Applebaum and B. W. Dickerson, Silica removal by salt splitting without demineralizing. *Proc. Am. Power Conf.* **16**, 655 (1954).

17a. Process for removal of silica (and other anions) from soft water. Bull. Tech. Data T.D. Index 631:00, Nalco Chem. Co., Chicago, 1960.

18. S. B. Applebaum, U.S. Patent 2,807,582 (1957).

19. Am. Boiler Manufacturers Assoc., 1958 Manual.

4

Removal of Nonionic
Suspended and Colloidal Impurities

Suspended impurities are found mainly in surface-water supplies, such as rivers and lakes. These impurities are turbidity and mud from river banks or lake bottoms, color, organic matter, plankton and bacteria from trade wastes, sewage, decaying leaves, and other vegetable matter; see Table 2.1. The color is the yellowish or brownish cast in water remaining after suspended matter is removed. In some cases it is due to certain organic acids (humic and fulvic) in solution, but usually it is due to colloidal matter. Another colloid, non-reactive silica, is occasionally present. Oil and corrosion products are some-times found in surface waters, but they are mainly in condensate.

The tolerance limits for these impurities in most industrial applications and for drinking water are quite low; see Tables 2.5–2.7. Amounts exceeding these tolerances interfere with the production of high-quality industrial products. They also cause fouling of the resins used in demineralizers and therefore must be removed in pretreatment plants.

The methods of removing the impurities (classified in Table 2.9) consist of filtration alone, filtration combined with coagulation and settling, oxida-tion, and absorption by carbon or by chloride anion exchangers.

I. Removal of Turbidity by Filtration without Presettling

Filters are used alone, if the amount of turbidity in the influent is moderate (less than 20 to 50 ppm) and the filters have conventional single-material beds. Filters that have multiple-material beds (often called multi-media or multi-layer) can handle waters of somewhat greater turbidity without presettling.

Conventional filtration consists of passing the water, usually downward, through granular beds of one material, either sand or anthracite coal, held in shells or tanks. Supporting the filtering layers, gravel or very coarse anthracite is generally used. This is often called "subfill." The granules in single-material beds are hydraulically classified (by backwashing), so that they are finest at the top and coarsest at the bottom. The suspended matter is strained out of the water and held in the "voids" between the filtering granules, mostly in the top of the bed. The accumulating load of suspended matter in the bed causes an increasing loss of pressure during the filter run. When this loss reaches a predetermined limit, the filter is backwashed upward, discharging the suspended load out to the sewer. The rapidity with which the pressure loss builds up during a filter run depends on the rate of flow used per square foot of filter area, the size of the filtering granules, and the amount and kind of suspended matter removed from the water. Runs with industrial filters commonly last about 12 to 24 hr between successive backwashings. The filter flow rates for conventional single-media filters range from 2 to about 4 gal/min/ft^2 in most applications.

Filters are of two types, pressure and gravity. Pressure filters are in closed, round, steel shells and function under the pressure of the incoming water. Gravity filters are in steel, wood, or concrete containers that are open at the top and function at atmospheric pressure.

Pressure filters are the preferred type for many industrial applications, because they have shells of lower height, may not need repumping, can be operated to a greater pressure loss and therefore run longer between successive backwashings, and can operate at higher flow rates.

Gravity filters are the preferred type in large plants, because the containers may be made of concrete, be rectangular in shape, and be built with common walls between them. State boards of health usually must approve the designs of filters in a proposed plant even if part of the effluent is used for drinking water. They favor the gravity type, because it can work with only the pressure provided by the depth of water above the bed ("gravity head") and therefore help to prevent fast flows that might discharge suspended matter, bacteria, etc. into the outlet (the boards of health usually recommend a rate of 2 gal/min/ft^2). They favor the gravity design also because the open top allows easy inspection and maintenance.

Backwashing is accomplished by water flowing upward at rates that range from 10 to 20 gal/min/ft^2, depending on the water temperature. Colder water is more viscous and therefore expands the bed more than warm water. Backwashing should cause the filter bed to expand about 50%. This separates the granules and allows the dirt between them to escape to the waste outlet at the top. The water space (freeboard) above the bed must be sufficient to avoid losing the filtering material to waste during backwashing. Water for backwash is introduced under pressure either by pumps or by gravity head from elevated storage tanks.

Backwashing alone may not suffice to clean up the filter beds. The crust of dirt on top is often sticky. Even with backwash rates sufficient to expand the bed 50%, the crust may break up into such large masses that they fall to the bottom and form mudballs. To break up the crust into small pieces, so that they can be carried into the waste outlet at the top, two supplementary scouring devices have been developed, the Palmer rotary surface washer* and the subsurface washer. The first consists of two perforated radial pipe arms, supported in the center and located a few inches above the top of the bed. The arms *rotate*, propelled by the reactive force of high-velocity jets of water coming out of nozzles in the pipe; the jets sweep over and scour the whole top of the bed. The second device, the subsurface washer, is *stationary* and is located 6 to 12 in. below the top. It has four radial perforated pipe arms, and the jets scour the upper layers from below.

For a further cleaning up of beds heavily laden with adherent dirt compressed air, supplementing the backwash, has been found helpful. The air wash requires separate brass header–lateral distributors with small orifices, located above the supporting gravel so as to avoid upsetting it. In some designs supporting gravel is omitted and then fine-slotted strainers are used instead in an underdrain plate, and the shanks of the strainers are longer, and smaller orifices are inserted in the shank just under the plate. The small orifices distribute the air uniformly.

The filter beds consist of either sand or anthracite granules. Anthracite is nonsiliceous. It is favored for filtering waters that are warm, low in silica, and high in pH value, rather than sand because the latter will add silica to the water under these conditions. Anthracite is also less dense than sand and so can be backwashed at lower rates (about 20% less). However, the finest size of anthracite granules generally available (0.7 to 1.0 mm effective size†) is coarser than fine sand, which can be obtained in effective sizes of 0.45 to 0.6 mm. Therefore the sand beds often deliver the clearer effluents (*1*).

A. Pressure Filters

The shells of pressure filters are cylindrical. They are supplied with heads and made of steel suitable for the operating pressure. The standard pressure is 50 to 100 psi. The filters are made in either vertical or horizontal design. The standard industrial vertical units range in diameter from 3 to 11 ft and in straight height are 4 or 5 ft. The standard horizontal units are 8 ft in diameter and range in length (over the heads) from 10 to 25 ft. Vertical filters are preferred, because the filter beds, having vertical sides from top to bottom,

---

* A stationary surface washer above the bed consisting of a fixed header and perforated laterals may also be used in larger filters but it requires higher flow rates for scouring than the rotary type.

† Effective size is that screen size through which 90% of a sample passes in screening tests.

can be washed more uniformly than the horizontal ones with curved sides. Figure 4.1 shows a typical vertical unit.

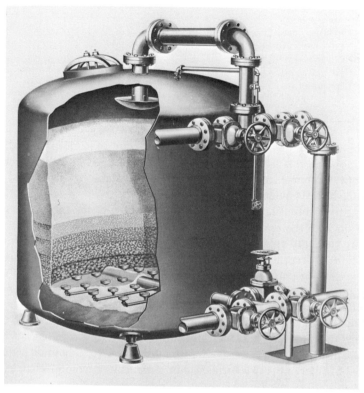

Fig. 4.1. Vertical pressure filter.

A dished baffle plate inside the top head distributes the incoming water in vertical units. The underdrain under the filter beds in the vertical units consists of either a steel, slotted diffusor plate welded in the lower head or of a steel header and lateral strainer system embedded in concrete in the lower head. The laterals are at right angles to the header, spaced on centers of 6 to 10 in.; they distribute the backwash water and collect the filtered water uniformly. The strainers are made of plastic, bronze, or stainless steel, so that they are noncorrodible. They may be furnished with lifting head tops that enlarge the internal passageways during upward flow; this facilitates backwashing. In horizontal units the upper distributor consists of a perforated pipe running the length of the unit near the top. The underdrain consists of a header–lateral strainer system similar to that used in the vertical units.

The standard filter beds of deep vertical filters (60 in. straight height), with header–lateral underdrain systems, are as in the accompanying table.

Sand	Depth, in.	Anthracite	Depth, in.
Top layer, mesh 20 to 35	26	$\frac{3}{32}$ to $\frac{3}{64}$	26
Next, mesh 6 to 10	4	$\frac{3}{16}$ to $\frac{3}{32}$	4
Next, gravel, in. $\frac{1}{4}$ to $\frac{1}{8}$	4	$\frac{9}{16}$ to $\frac{5}{16}$	4
Next, gravel, in. $\frac{1}{2}$ to $\frac{1}{4}$	4	$\frac{13}{16}$ to $\frac{9}{16}$	4
Next, gravel, in. 1 to $\frac{1}{2}$	4	$1\frac{5}{8}$ to $\frac{13}{16}$	4
Total:	42	Total:	42

In the vertical units 48 in. high the filter beds are 34 in. deep instead of the 42 in. shown in this table; the top layer is then made 18 in. deep instead of 26 in. but the coarse supporting layers remain unchanged. Horizontal filters also have beds 34 in. deep.

The gravel subfill layers support the fine-grain layers and prevent their escape through the underdrain into the outlet. Since they can, however, be upset by suddenly applied high wash rates or by free air in the wash water, an underdrain recently has been designed with an internal, flat plate and stainless-steel or plastic strainers with such fine openings are used that the gravel subfill may be omitted. This design also avoids the use of concrete for filling the lower head.

On the outside of each filter a nest of five gate valves with fittings and piping controls the filtering, backwashing, and rinsing-to-waste operations; a single control valve may be used instead of the five individual valves. A number of filter units are furnished in a battery, interconnected by pipe headers.

The backwashing and rinse-to-waste operations may be made automatic by means of pneumatic cylinder operators on the gate valves or a motor to operate the single control valve and electric program and timer devices for controlling the duration of each operating step. Loss-of-head gauges are usually included for indicating when the pressure loss has reached the limit at which the unit requires backwashing. Other auxiliaries are rate-of-flow indicators, air-relief valves, sight glasses, and pressure alum feeders. The feeders introduce a small amount of dissolved alum sulfate into the filter influent to form a mat of floc on the filter bed; this helps produce a clearer effluent, if the influent turbidity is very fine.

B. Gravity Filters

Gravity filters may be round but preferably are square or rectangular in shape. In large plants the units usually are of concrete and made in widths that range from 5 to 15 ft and lengths from 5 to 30 ft. The height is usually 10 to 12 ft, although a height of 14 ft has been used because it prolongs filter runs without necessitating resort to negative heads. The latter create a partial vacuum at the bottom of the bed, which may liberate air at low winter temperatures and cause air-binding of the bed.

The beds in gravity filters are similar to those in vertical pressure filters. Below the top of the filters a series of parallel wash troughs on about 5 ft centers collect the wash effluent evenly. The troughs are high enough above the bed (usually 2 ft) to avoid loss of filtering material in backwashing. The underdrain has been made in many designs, but an economical one is the header–lateral system similar to that used in pressure filters. The header may be made of concrete and the perforated laterals of asbestos cement (instead of steel), so that they will not corrode.

Loss-of-head and rate-of-flow gauges are frequently used. Rate-of-flow controllers on the individual outlets also are often included; they maintain constant rates of flow through each unit as the pressure loss increases during the run. Preventing suddenly varying flow rates avoids throwing suspended matter, held in the filter bed, into the effluent. Controls for automatic backwashing also can be provided. Figure 4.2 shows a typical gravity filter.

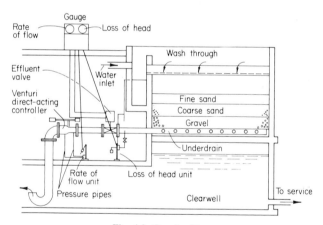

Fig. 4.2. Gravity filter.

C. Self-Washing Gravity Filter with Wash Storage

In filters designed for the storage of wash water the water is collected in a compartment mounted directly over the filter, all in one unit. The wash water flows to the filter from this compartment under a low gravity head, and the wash piping is large enough to provide an average backwash rate of 15 gal/-min/ft^2. The backwash operation, which lasts only a few minutes, takes place automatically whenever the loss of head during the filter run reaches about 5 ft.

The three major commercial designs of this type of filter are the Permutit Valveless (covered by U.S. Patent No. 2,879,891 (H. L. Beohner and D. Miller), March 31, 1959), the Cochrane Syphomatic, and the Graver Monovalve.

The first two have valveless siphons automatically primed; the third has a single, large, backwash-outlet butterfly valve that automatically opens to start the backwashing.

1. THE SYPHOMATIC FILTER

Figure 4.3 shows the Syphomatic filter with its three compartments: the backwash storage at the top, the filter in the middle, and the plenum below the underdrain plate. The strainers in the plate have fine openings, which permit omission of subfill gravel under the filtering bed.

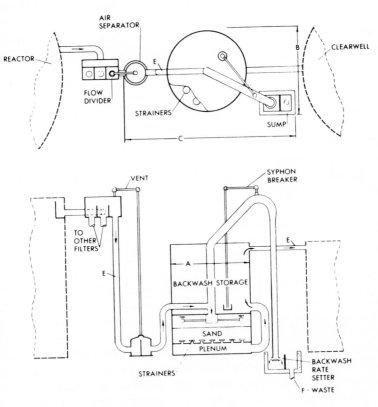

Fig. 4.3. Syphomatic filter.

Syphomatic filters range in standard sizes from 3 to 20 ft in diameter and are about 15 ft high. Flow dividers in multiunit plants distribute the flow equally to the various units. Interlocks prevent more than one filter-washing at a time. Each filter may be subdivided into two or three sections by vertical partition plates below the single wash storage; each section is then back-washed with less water, so that the wash storage may be reduced in depth.

The advantages of this general type of filter are its simplicity and low cost compared to those of conventional automatic gravity plants. The cost is reduced by the elimination of the wash pump and its piping and of the many valves, rate-of-flow controllers, and automatic controls used in conventional plants. Moreover, the effluent is discharged from the top of the filter into a clearwell alongside, rather than from the bottom of the filter into a clearwell below; this saves construction costs.

2. OPERATION OF THE SYPHOMATIC FILTER

The steps in the operation of the Syphomatic filter are illustrated in Fig. 4.4.

Filtering Run. The influent entering the top of the filter flows by gravity through the filter bed, into the plenum, up into the wash storage, and out at the top. During the filter run the wash storage is always full.

Initiation of Backwashing. The top of the siphon pipe is set about 5 ft above the top of the filter. The increasing loss of head during the run causes the water to rise in the siphon. When the level reaches the top of the loop, the siphon is primed by an external, hydraulic air evacuator (not shown), and backwashing starts automatically.

Backwashing. Water from storage flows down into the plenum and then up through the filter bed. The dirty wash water escapes through the siphon pipe to waste. This continues until the storage is empty, when a siphon breaker automatically ends the backwash step.

Refilling Storage. After the backwash filtering is automatically resumed. However, the first filtered water refills the storage, which then continually overflows into the outlet during the next filter run.

D. *Multiple-Bed (In-Depth) Filters with Coarse Granules over Fine Granules*

The filter beds in conventional single-layer filters are hydraulically classified, as previously mentioned, the finest granules being at the top and the progressively coarser ones beneath; this is so whether the layers are of sand or of anthracite. The suspended matter filtered out starts accumulating at the top of the bed, forming a "schmutzdecke" (dirt cover). This causes the pressure loss to increase during the filtering run, until the filter must be backwashed. The length of the filtering run is determined by the storage capacity of the voids in the upper, fine granule layers that hold the suspended matter.

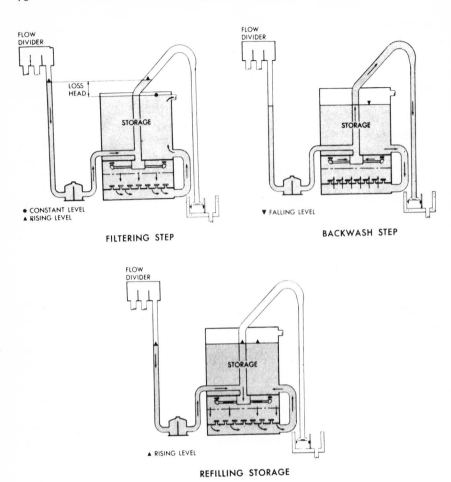

Fig. 4.4. Operation of Syphomatic filter.

It has long been recognized that coarser granules would provide more voids for storage, which would lengthen the filter runs, increase the allowable flow rates, or permit the filtering of raw waters of higher turbidity. The roughing coarse-sand filters preceding the finishing fine-sand filters described in Chapter 3, Section IIIA3, were based on this concept. However, the use of coarse granules ahead of fine ones meant separate filters, and to save the expense of the extra units the coarse layers would somehow have to be held above the fine layers. The only way that could be accomplished without mixing and overturn of the layers was to put coarser materials of *lower density* on top and finer materials of *higher density* below. Anthracite, activated carbon, and coke, are examples of low-density materials and sand, garnet, and magnetite are examples of high-density materials. An early design of a multi-layer filter was patented in 1884 (2). The inventor suggested three layers: coke over coal over sand.

The coarse, light granules at the top act as contact roughing filters, removing most of the coarse suspended matter, and the fine, heavy granules at the bottom act as finishing filters, producing the clear effluent required. Layers (20 to 21 in. deep) of anthracite granules of 0.9 to 1.0 mm effective size over layers (6 in. deep) of sand of 0.35 to 0.45 mm effective size have been successfully applied in gravity filters at Hanford (3–5). Shull (1) reported similar successful results after rebuilding a large, conventional, municipal gravity filter plant into a plant of the multiple-bed design.

Flow rates of 5 to 6 gal/min/ft^2 can be used with multiple beds and still afford reasonable lengths of filter run, even when influent turbidities of several hundred parts per million are being handled. This is because of the larger voids in the upper, coarse layers holding the suspended load. When the influent turbidity is low (less than 25 to 50 ppm), flow rates of 10 and even 20 gal/min/ft^2 are possible. The runs are, of course, shorter, the higher the rate of flow. Labor-saving automatic backwash controls become more desirable as the run shortens, but their extra cost is offset by the lower cost of the smaller high-rate filters.

The ends of runs with conventional single-layer filters are usually determined by pressure-loss buildup, but with the new high-rate multiple-bed filters they may occur when turbidity breaks through into the effluent, before the loss of head reaches a maximum. Therefore, it has been found expedient to tighten the coarse filtering layers with coagulant floc, conditioned by a polyelectrolyte coagulant aid in order to give the filter beds greater retaining power; coagulant aids are discussed in Section IID and the conditioning of the filter beds in Section IIG5. Since the penetration of suspended matter into the upper layers is greater in multiple-bed filters than in conventional single-bed filters, the name "in-depth," or "depth," has been given to this type of filtration.

To lessen the danger of early leakage or breakthrough of turbidity into the effluent a third filtering layer, below the sand, of still finer and heavier material (garnet) has been proposed (6). The depth suggested is 3 in. and the effective size 0.18 mm.

It is possible to increase further the suspended-load capacity of in-depth filters by means of lighter materials, such as carbon, above the anthracite layer. Cochrane Penetrex filters contain this type of multilayer bed. Their total void capacities are five or ten times those of the single-layer conventional filters.

Care must be taken with in-depth filters to keep the flow rates fairly constant. Sudden increases in rate may unload the bed and throw suspended matter into the effluent. Since filter runs may end because of turbidity break-through before the limit of pressure loss has been reached, it is advisable to check the effluent turbidity regularly during the run. Monitoring turbidi-meters that record effluent turbidities are now available. They can be fitted with a contactor that will ring an alarm or automatically shut off a filter when the effluent turbidity rises above the allowable limit. Small laboratory sized filters on a panel, filtering the flash mixed water may aid in regulating the best coagulant dosage to provide the clearest filtered water at all times (6).

Multiple beds may be of either the pressure or the gravity type. If high filtering flow rates are used, resulting in high pressure losses, the pressure design is usually favored. With the greater penetration of suspended matter into the upper filtering layers air scouring that supplements the backwashing may be found helpful.

E. Upflow and Split-flow Filters

A Dutch firm recently introduced an upflow filter design with the same objectives as the multiple-bed design (7): greater dirt-holding capacity, longer filter runs between backwashings, and higher flow rates. The bed is of one material, such as sand. The upward flow passes first through the gravel, then through the coarse grains, which retain part of the suspended matter, and finally through the fine grains on top, which do the "polishing."

The problem with upflow filtration, however, is expansion of the bed, par-ticularly at high filtering flow rates, which causes "channeling" or passage of unfiltered water through the bed and results in turbid effluents. To restrain expansion a grid, like a subway grating, is placed at the top of the bed, where the fine sand arches between the widely spaced bars, keeping the bed from moving appreciably.

A variation of this concept is a so-called split-flow or bi-flow filter (8). It has both downflow and upflow in the same shell. The influent is separated into two streams, one passing downward through an upper, fine, sand layer and the other upward through a lower, coarse layer. Both streams after filtration join and pass out of the filter through a header–lateral system situated at the interface of the two layers. Experience with these innovations is still limited.

II. Removal of Turbidity, Color, Organic Matter, Microorganisms, Bacteria, Colloidal Silica, and Oil, by Coagulation, Settling, and Filtration

Settling alone will remove the coarse, heavy, particles of suspended matter, as in lakes or ponds, but some suspended impurities, such as turbidity, microorganisms, and color, are very finely divided or even in colloidal form, so that they do not settle readily. Settling basins would have to be excessively large to remove these fine particles.

Coagulation, induced by adding chemicals (coagulants) to the water, agglomerates the finely divided, suspended solids into masses that settle more readily. This occurs in two ways: (a) the particles of turbidity and color have like electric charges on their surfaces, which keep them apart, because like electric charges repel one another, and the coagulant ions selected possess charges opposite to those on the suspended particles, so that they neutralize each other, permitting the particles to coalesce; (b) the coagulant reacts with the alkalinity of the water to form a gelatinous precipitate, called "floc," which enmeshes and entraps the finer of the suspended particles.

A. Major Coagulants and Their Properties

Three of the most widely used coagulants are listed in Table 4.1. Note that this table gives their names, formulas, and optimal pH ranges.

Table 4.1
THREE MAJOR COAGULANTS

Coagulant	Popular or Trade name	Chemical formula	Usual optimal pH range
Aluminum sulfate	Filter alum	$Al_2(SO_4)_3 \cdot 14H_2O$	5.5 to 7.5
Ferrous sulfate	Copperas	$FeSO_4 \cdot 7H_2O$	8.0 to 11.0
Ferric sulfate	Ferrisul or Ferrifloc or Ferriclear	$Fe_2(SO_4)_3 \cdot 2H_2O$ or $Fe_2(SO_4)_3 \cdot 3H_2O$	8.0 to 11.0; also 5.0 to 6.0 for color removal

Alum is the most commonly used, because it is the lowest in cost and the least corrosive to handle. Furthermore, the dissolved alumina remaining after improperly controlled coagulation is nearly white in color and causes less trouble than the reddish residual iron from iron coagulants. The latter are nevertheless often more effective than alum with some types of turbidity or color. A mixture of alum and iron coagulants has proved superior at certain seasons for coagulating certain water supplies.

The chemical reactions between each of these three major coagulants and calcium bicarbonate alkalinity in water, which form the hydroxide precipitates or floc, are shown in the following equations (the water of crystallization in the coagulants is omitted for simplicity).

$$Al_2(SO_4)_3 + 3\,Ca(HCO_3)_2 \longrightarrow 2\,Al(OH)_3 \downarrow + 3\,CaSO_4 + 6\,CO_2 \qquad (1)$$

$$4\,FeSO_4 + 4\,Ca(HCO_3)_2 + O_2 + 2\,H_2O \longrightarrow 4\,Fe(OH)_3 \downarrow + 4\,CaSO_4 + 8\,CO_2 \qquad (2)$$

$$Fe_2(SO_4)_3 + 3\,Ca(HCO_3)_2 \longrightarrow 2\,Fe(OH)_3 \downarrow + 3\,CaSO_4 + 6\,CO_2 \qquad (3)$$

If the alkalinity in the water is insufficient to react with the dose of coagulant, the pH value is below the optimal range. Then the alkalinity must be increased by the addition of an alkali, such as lime, soda ash, or caustic soda. Lime increases the calcium hardness, but it is the cheapest alkali and frequently makes better floc than the others. If the pH value is allowed to go below or above the optimal range, the floc formed is too small, light, and fragile and so is easily carried over in the effluent and, moreover, too much alumina and iron remain in solution in the treated water, causing undesirable side effects.

Note that in Eq. 2 the ferrous sulfate (copperas) requires oxygen to form the ferric hydroxide floc. In hot-process plants, where there is not enough dissolved oxygen in the water, ferric sulfate should be used instead of ferrous sulfate, but in warm-process plants the addition of some ferrous sulfate may help reduce the dissolved oxygen.

B. Other Coagulants

Certain ferric coagulants, not included in Table 4.1, have been found superior for coagulating difficult waters that are high in organic matter; these are ferric chloride and chlorinated copperas. Ferric chloride is often used for coagulating waste water and sewage, but it is more costly and more corrosive to handle than ferric sulfate. Chlorinated copperas is made by feeding chlorine with the copperas; the chlorine oxidizes the ferrous sulfate to the ferric form, resulting in a mixture of ferric sulfate and ferric chloride.

Sodium aluminate is an alkaline coagulant sometimes used in conjunction with common alum for supplying alkalinity and aiding coagulation. Often it is added as a coagulant in warm and hot lime–soda plants. Since it contains some caustic soda and soda ash, it reduces the dose of lime and soda ash required for the water-softening. It can often be mixed with the lime and fed in the same feeder, saving a separate coagulant feeder. For such purposes the dose of aluminate is usually limited to 5 to 10 ppm.

C. Factors Influencing Coagulation

Organic matter, if present in appreciable amounts, inhibits coagulation and narrows the optimal pH range. For the oxidation of organic matter prechlorination is desirable, because it broadens the optimal pH range and thereby makes the coagulation easier to control. Certain organics, such as phenol from coke-processing waste waters, need a stronger oxidant than chlorine, such as chlorine dioxide, for their destruction. This is made by adding chlorine to sodium chlorite solution.

The amounts and kinds of solids in the water are also factors influencing the coagulation. In general, waters high in solids coagulate more readily than waters low in solids. Calcium in water aids coagulation more than sodium; that is why it is better to add lime than soda ash, if an alkali is needed. Color is more difficult to coagulate than turbidity. Waters that are fairly low in turbidity and high in color make a lighter floc, less easily settled. In such cases it is necessary to make an artificial turbidity by adding both weighting agents and coagulant aids (see the next two subsections).

Low water temperatures inhibit coagulation. Preheating or using condenser cooling water, which is warmer than river water, is helpful in winter. Preheating, however, must be thermostatically controlled to avoid temperature variations (exceeding about $2°F/hr$), which might cause thermal upsets in the settling tanks.

The dose of coagulant must be sufficient to coagulate the turbidity and color present. Obviously, the greater their amounts, the more floc needed for enmeshing them. Further, fine turbidity and color require more floc than coarse. An alum dose of 1 to 2 gr/gal (17 to 34 ppm) usually will coagulate several hundred parts per million fine and medium-sized suspended matter. For turbidities of 500 to 1000 ppm the dose may need to be 3 to 5 gr/gal. Turbidities in the thousands of parts per million, as are found during spring freshets in the case of some large rivers, such as the Missouri and Mississippi, are frequently settled in plain presedimentation basins before coagulation; this saves coagulant.

D. Coagulant Aids

A family of polyelectrolytes (composed of long-chain molecules) has been developed and found powerful in aiding in the coagulation of difficult waters. Table 4.2 lists the major coagulant aids available at present. Some of them are cationic, others are anionic, and others are nonionic. They therefore possess different properties, and each must be tried experimentally for its effectiveness in a given water. They are expensive, but the dosage is very small (dosage is given in the third column of Table 4.2). Note that less than 1 ppm suffices in some instances.

The mechanism of their action is the formation of links or bridges between the finely divided floc particles; this enlarges them and makes them heavier. The effect is pronounced and often quite startling. Soon after the right coagulant aid is fed into a solids contact settling tank, the suspended sludge blanket or slurry shrinks, the top of the blanket drops, and the supernatant water above the blanket clears rapidly. Coagulant aids are therefore especially helpful in cold waters and in waters high in color and low in turbidity.

The order in which the coagulant, alkali, and coagulant aid are added is often important in obtaining the best floc. Frequently the best order is the coagulant first, the alkali next, and the coagulant aid last. This allows the floc to begin forming before the aid conditions the floc. Sufficient time must

Table 4.2[a]

COAGULANT AIDS[b]

Manufacturer	Product	Max. concn. recommd. by mfr., ppm	Manufacturer	Product	Max. concn. recommd. by mfr., ppm
Allyn Chemical Company	Claron	1.5	Garratt-Callhan	Coagulant Aid 70	⩽2
	Claron No. 207	2		Coagulant Aid 72	⩽2
American Cyan- amid Co.	Superfloc 16	1	General Mills, Inc.	SuperCol Guar Gum	⩽10
	Magnifloc 990	1			
	Superfloc 20	1	Hercules Powder Co.	Carboxymethyl- cellulose	1
	Magnifloc 971-N	1			
	Superfloc 84	1		Reten A-1	1
	Magnifloc 985-N	1		Reten A-5	1
Betz Laboratories, Inc.	Poly-Floc 4D	25	Frank Herzl Corp.	Perfectamyl A5114/2	⩽10
The Burtonite Co.	Burtonite No. 78	5	Illinois Water Treatment Com- pany	Illco IFA 313	10
Calgon Corpora- tion	Coagulant Aids No. 2	1			
	No. 7	0.75	Ionac Chemical Co.	Ionac Wisprofloc 20	5
	No. 11	4			
	No. 18	15		Ionac Wisprofloc- 75	5
	No. 801	6			
	No. 952	3	Kelco Company	Kelgin W	2
	No. 961	5		Kelcosol	2
	Coagulant Aid 233	⩽1	Key Chemicals, Inc.	Key-Floc-W	25
	Coagulant Aid 243	⩽1			
	Coagulant Aid 253	⩽1	Metalene Chemical Co.	Metalene Coagu- lant P-6	5
Commercial Chem- ical Products, Inc.	Coagulant Aid- Speedifloc No. 1	10	Nalco Chemical Co.	Nalcolyte No. 110	5
Dearborn Chem- ical Co.	Aquafloc 422	1		Nalco 671	1
The Dow Chem- ical Company	Separan NP10 Potable Water Grade	1	Narvon Mines Ltd.	Sink-Floc Z-3 and AZ-3	10
	Purifloc N17	1		Sink-Floc Z-4 and AZ-4	10
	Separan AP 30	1	National Starch and Chemical Corp.	Floc Aid 1038	5
	Purifloc A22	1		Flock Aid 1063	5
Drew Chemical Corp.	Drewfloc No. 3 (formerly Alchem Coagu-Aid No. 261)	3	North American Mogul Products Co.	Mogul CO-982	1.5
				Mogul CO-980	2
				Modul CO-983	1
	Drewfloc 21	5	O'Brien Indus- tries, Inc.	O'B-Floc	10
	Alchem Coagu- Aid 252	5	Stein, Hall and Co., Inc.	Hallmark 81	1
	Alchem Coagu- Aid 265	1		MRL-19	1
				MRL-13	1
	Drewfloc 265	1:8 alum		MRL-14	1
	Drewfloc 1	0.5:10 lime[c]		MRL-22A	1
Electric Chemical Co.	Ecco suspension Catalyzer No. 146	3.5	W. E. Zimmie, Inc.	Jaguar	0.5
				Zimmite	1

[a] Taken from *J. Am. Water Works Assoc.*, February, 1967.
[b] Approved by the United States Public Health Service (USPHS) for potable-water treatment without adverse physiologic effec⟨ The USPHS does not endorse these products for their effectiveness but only for the health aspects of their use.
[c] One part Drewfloc to 8 parts alum, when used simply as an aid in alum coagulation, and 0.5 ppm Drewfloc to 10 ppm lime, whe⟨ used in connection with lime softening.

be allowed between the addition of the three reagents; a time interval of some seconds and even minutes may be necessary. In one case of a very cold surface water containing large amounts of colloidal silt a large mixing chamber was required, so that the initial, fine floc would have time to form before the polyelectrolyte was added.

E. Weighting Agents

Waters that are low in turbidity and high in color form light, fragile flocs. They more readily coagulate if a weighting agent is added. Examples of such agents are bentonite clays of volcanic origin, powdered limestone, and fly ash (a power-plant byproduct). Adding these weighting agents may be said to provide synthetic turbidity to waters of low turbidity, so that the floc has a nucleus on which to form. The floc then becomes denser and settles more readily.

Some chemical firms that market polyelectrolyte coagulant aids have available, in addition, several mixtures of electrolyte and clay, which take care of waters of different turbidities (Calgon Corporation products, Table 4.2).

F. Tests for Coagulation

From the foregoing it is apparent that coagulation is an art rather than a science and that it takes considerable experimenting to determine the effect of prechlorination, the optimal pH range, the most suitable coagulant, the dose of coagulant, the proper coagulant aid or weighting agent, if any is to be used, the order of adding the reagents, and the necessary time intervals between their addition. The test work is best done at the site of the plant with samples freshly drawn, because specimens sent to a distant laboratory are liable to change their coagulating characteristics in transit. The tests are run in beakers or jars and are therefore called "jar tests." An example of a jar-test log sheet is shown in Table 4.3.

The jars have motor-driven paddle agitators, as shown in Fig. 4.5. This figure contrasts the effects of adding the coagulant aid Separan in 1 ppm and 2 ppm doses and also shows the benefit of adding the alum before the aid; see Table 4.3. The time of the first appearance of the floc and the size of the floc particles are noted; Table 4.4 is a rough description of relative floc sizes. The rate of settling of the floc in a 600 ml beaker is then observed. Table 4.5 classifies the various rates according to the times required to settle the top 4 in. depth of floc. These settling-rate tests help in selecting the "rise rates" (rate of flow per square foot of top area) which determine the areas of settling tanks; Table 4.6 gives the rise rates for the round Reactor (see Section IIG2).

If the effect of suspended-solids contact with previously formed precipitates is to be tested, a large volume of raw water should first be treated and the precipitates be collected after settling. The precipitates can then be added in various doses in jar tests together with the other reagents, to determine their benefit.

The jar test is a valuable indicator of optimal conditions and dosages of chemicals to add in the large plant. But it has certain shortcomings: the

Table 4.3
JAR-TEST LOG SHEET

Raw-water characteristics

Source: Charles River	Color:	200 ppm	Total hardness:	75 ppm
Temperature: 65°F	pH:	7.1	Ca hardness:	50 ppm
Turbidity: 75 units	CO_2:	2.0 ppm	Alkalinity:	40 ppm
	Odor:	none	Total solids:	160 ppm

Mixing: 10 min at 100 rpm   Flocculation: 15 min at 25 rpm

	Sample 1	Sample 2	Sample 3	Sample 4
Chemicals added, ppm				
(1) alum	40	40	40	40
(2) lime	—	—	—	—
(3) Separan	2	—	2	1
Sequence	3–1	—	1–3	1–3
pH	6.5	6.4	6.5	6.5
Floc	Fine and slow forming	Pinpoint	Dense and rapid forming	Dense
Settling rate	Poor	Poor	Excel.	Excel.
Supernatant				
turbidity	39	28	6	18
color	150	100	50	75
Conclusions	Failure	Failure	Very good	Very good

Table 4.4		**Table 4.5**	
ESTIMATE OF FLOC SIZE		FLOC SETTLING RATES	

Size, in.	Description	Time for settling the top 4 in. depth of floc (min.)	Description
Very fine	Pinpoint		
$\frac{1}{64}$	Fine	Less than 2	Excellent
$\frac{1}{32}$	Small	2 to 4	Good
$\frac{1}{32}$ to $\frac{3}{64}$	Fair	5 to 7	Fair
$\frac{3}{64}$ to $\frac{3}{32}$	Good	More than 7	Poor
$\frac{1}{8}$ or more	Large		

evaluation is subjective varying with the operator; the water in the jar is quiescent and this does not duplicate conditions in the large plant where the water is moving; it often does not indicate the minimal dose of coagulant to provide the clearest filtered water. The jar test must therefore be supplemented by experiments in the large plant itself.

Another laboratory technique of evaluating coagulation has been developed which measures the electrophoretic mobility or the so-called Zeta potential of the particles in the water after adding the coagulant. Research work by Mattson, Black and his associates, Riddick, Bean and others has

Fig. 4.5. Jar test (see Table 4.3).

Table 4.6
RISE RATES PER SQUARE FOOT OF TOP AREA OF REACTOR

	Rate, gal/min/ft^2
Lime softening of well water	
Ca hardness > Mg hardness	1.7
Ca hardness < Mg hardness	1.5
Lime softening of river waters	1.5
Coagulating of river waters	
turbidity < 3000 ppm	1.3
turbidity > 3000 ppm	1.1
Coagulating, if color and	
algae high	1.1

been valuable in perfecting this method. Shull (*6a*) has recently summarized this work and described his own contributions towards more successful use of the technique in a municipal plant. But the new technique is not a cure-all for control of coagulation and the jar test must still be used followed by testing in the large plant itself.

G. Equipment for Coagulation and Settling

Two general types of equipment are available: the conventional type with flocculation and settling in separate tanks or compartments, and the suspended-solids contact type with flocculation and settling in one tank.

1. CONVENTIONAL EQUIPMENT

Figure 4.6 shows the arrangement of a flash mixer, flocculator, and settler in separate compartments. The water first enters the flash mixer, where it is

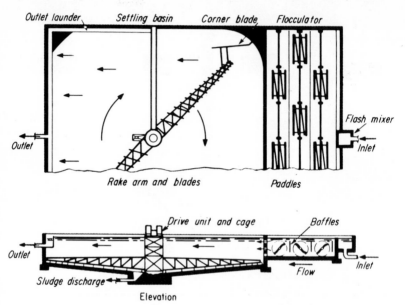

Fig. 4.6. Conventional flash mixer, flocculator, and settler, in separate compartments [reproduced from *Power*, December, 1958 (6b)].

mixed with the chemicals by means of a high-speed agitator. Usually several minutes of detention are needed in the chamber. The mixed water then enters the flocculator chamber, where slowly rotating paddles provide more gentle agitation, stimulating the growth of the floc, which enmeshes the turbidity, color, and other suspended matter. About 20 to 60 minutes of retention are allowed in the flocculator.

The flocculated water then is distributed uniformly to the horizontal-flow settling-basin compartment, where the floc and precipitates settle out. A slowly rotating sludge scraper rakes the settled sludge to the center for discharge to waste. The settled, clarified water flows to the outlet launder or flume at the top, from which it passes to the filters (not shown).

The settling basin for the horizontal flow may be a square or rectangular chamber, as shown in Fig. 4.6, or it may be a round, vertical tank for radial, inclined flow from the bottom of a central cylindrical downcomer to a peripheral launder. In the latter case the flocculator may be in a separate chamber or be inserted in the downcomer. The detention time for the settling varies from 2 to 6 hr. The speed of flow should be kept at less than 1 to 2 ft/min for a good separation and settling of the precipitates and floc.

2. SUSPENDED-SOLIDS CONTACT EQUIPMENT

In Chapter 3, Section IA9, the suspended-solids contact unit is discussed. The same design is widely applied in pretreatment plants (treatment before demineralization) for the coagulation, and clarification (by settling) of surface waters.

The following four major commercial designs (in alphabetical order) are illustrated in Figs. 4.7 to 4.11: the Infilco Accelator, the round Permutit Precipitator, the Graver Reactivator, and the Cochrane Reactor (both round and rectangular). Figure 4.12 shows the path of flow in the round Reactor, and Fig. 4.13 shows the Reactor sludge-blowoff and backflush arrangement.

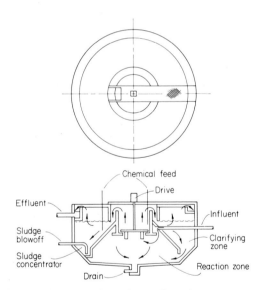

Fig. 4.7. The Infilco Accelator. The elevated propellor agitator operates at fairly high speeds and acts also as a low-head pump to move the slurry from the reaction zone to the clarifying zone. Excess slurry is recirculated back to the reaction zone. Sludge settling in the reaction zone is prevented by the eddy currents from the agitator. A sludge concentrator occupies a portion of the peripheral volume at the bottom of the clarifying zone. The water rises from the top of the suspended slurry upward to the top outlet launder. Radial outlet flumes are often used.

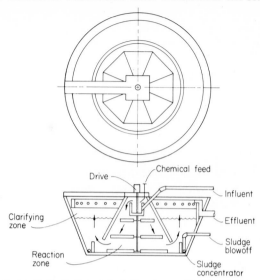

Fig. 4.8. The Permutit Precipitator. Agitation is provided by the slowly rotating paddles sweeping over the whole bottom, preventing the sludge from settling in the reaction zone. The outer tank wall and inner baffles are both conical, so that the upflow speed decreases gradually. A sludge concentrator is located all around the periphery of the clarifying zone. A rectangular Precipitator is available in addition to the round one shown.

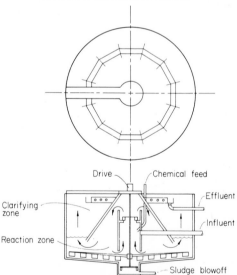

Fig. 4.9. The Graver Reactivator. Agitation is provided by an elevated propellor in a central mixing zone. Sludge is not recirculated from the clarifying zone back to the reaction zone. Instead of being collected in a peripheral sludge concentrator the sludge settles out at the bottom of the reaction zone and is scraped by a slowly rotating rake to the central sludge outlet. The sludge level in the clarifying zone is usually kept low to reduce sludge carryover. Radial effluent launders collect the upward-flowing settled water.

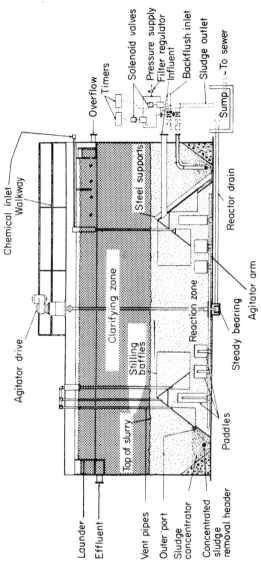

Fig. 4.10. The Cochrane Round Reactor. Agitation is provided by slowly rotating paddles, sweeping over the whole bottom and preventing sludge settling in the reaction zone. Flow from the reaction to the clarifying zone is up through the large central port and then radially to the peripheral launder. The radial flow decreases in velocity (see Fig. 4.12). The sludge concentrator is at the bottom, all around the reaction zone. Sludge is blown off in proportion to the influent flow after backflushing the orifices in the sludge collector (see Fig. 4.13). The entire top area of the Reactor is available for clarification, because the baffles do not go up into the top of the clarifying zone. The usual range of flow rates, expressed in gallons per square foot of top area, is as given in Table 4.6 (see Section IIF). Round Reactors may be made of concrete or be equipped with all-steel side and bottom or with steel side sealed in a groove in a concrete bottom. The Reactor in concrete may also be square and have the same vertical-shaft agitator; in such case the corners are filled with sloping concrete, forming a polygon bottom, within which the agitator operates.

The contact unit has two zones: the reaction zone, where the slurry of previously formed precipitates is agitated and mixed with the chemicals and water, and the clarifying zone, where the treated water separates from the floc slurry and emerges clear. The two zones in most designs are kept apart by baffles, which prevent the turbulence of the agitation in the reaction zone from disturbing the settling in the clarifying zone. Uniform distribution of the influent and uniform collection of the effluent must be effected, to avoid short-circuiting or channeling, or passage of the water through the tank in currents or streams without proper contact with the precipitates. The agitator in the reaction zone should have a variable-speed geared motor drive for changing the speed to suit seasonal changes in water temperature and

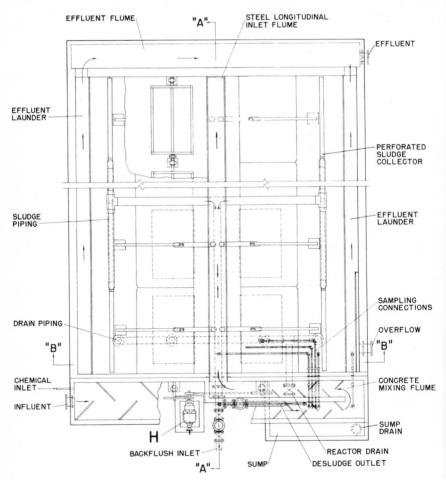

Fig. 4.11. The Cochrane Rectangular Reactor (plan view).

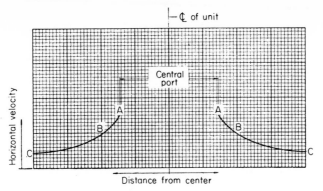

Curve of horizontal velocity of flow from central port to launder

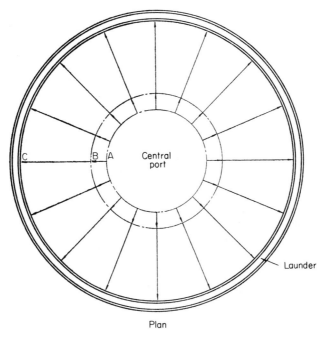

Plan

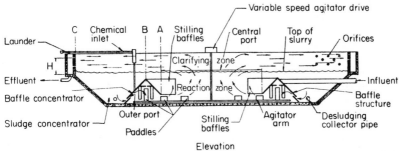

Elevation

Fig. 4.12. Round Reactor, path of flow, and curve of horizontal velocities. The velocities are calculated by dividing the flow by the vertical cross-sectional areas at various distances from the center, such as *A*, *B*, and *C*. The depth *H* of these areas is indicated in the elevation.

composition. The agitation preferably should be greatest at the start and less as the flow proceeds into the clarifying zone; this minimizes dispersion of the floc and stimulates its growth. The speed of flow should decrease from inlet to outlet of the clarifying zone; in this way the finest floc particles settle out. A large sludge concentrator should be provided, where the settled sludge can concentrate, to permit sludge blowoff with a minimum of water wastage.

The advantages of the suspended-solids contact design are as follows: the slurry of old precipitates, when suspended and mixed with the water and chemicals, provides nuclei on which the new precipitates may plate out and grow; the chemical reactions are fast and the precipitates settle out rapidly, so that the required retention time is reduced to 1 hr; small chemical doses are needed; and the settled water is quite clear, the usual effluent turbidity being 5 ppm.

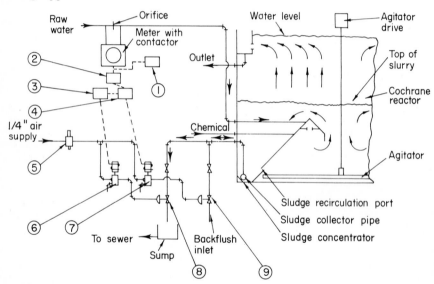

Fig. 4.13. Cochrane Reactor blowoff and backflush arrangement: 1, Timer (chemical feed); 2, counter; 3, timer (desludging); 4, timer (backflush); 5, filter regulator; 6, solenoid $\frac{1}{4}$ in. three- or four-way valve (desludging); 7, solenoid $\frac{1}{4}$ in. three- or four-way valve (backflush); 8, desludging valve; 9, backflush valve. Each time a measured quantity of raw water passing through the meter makes a contact, causing the chemical feeding system to deliver a measured volume of chemical to the softener; at the same time the counter advances one step. When a desired number of meter contacts have been counted, an impulse is given to the backflush timer, which operates the solenoid valve, causing the backflush valve to open, allowing admittance of flush water and clearing out the perforations in the sludge-collecting pipe. Upon completion of the backflush, determined by setting of the backflush timer (usually a few seconds), the solenoid valve is de-energized, allowing the backflush valve to close. At the same time the desludging timer receives an impulse from the backflush timer, energizing the desludging solenoid valve and opening the desludging valve. The desludging valve remains open for period of time set on the desludging timer.

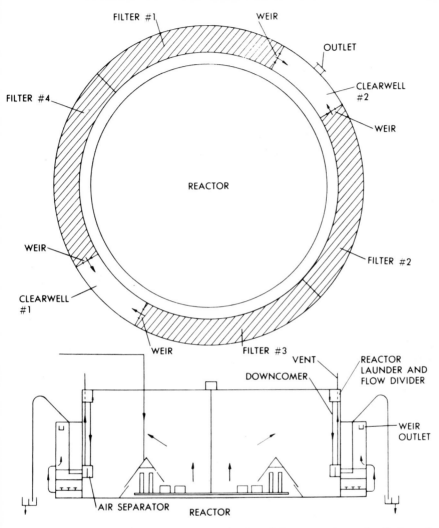

Fig. 4.14. Combination design based on the Round Reactor and annular Syphomatic filters.

Various names reflecting these advantages have been given to this general design: rapid-flow, rapid-rate, high-rate, upflow, slurry-type, sludge-blanket, etc., but the more descriptive name, suspended solids contact, is generally favored today.

3. COMBINED REACTOR AND SYPHOMATIC FILTER

The usual clarification plants have in the past been so designed that the settling tank and gravity filters were separate, and piping or flumes conveyed

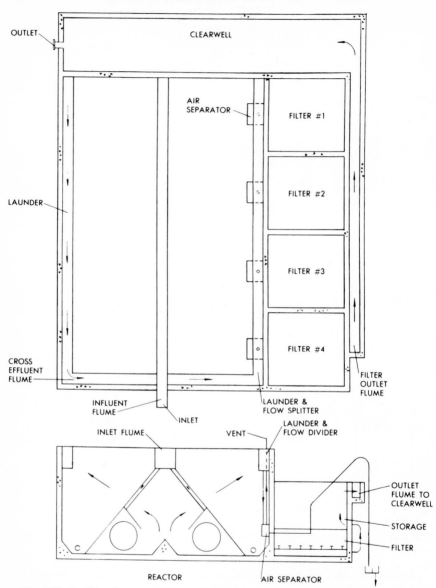

Fig. 4.15. Combination design based on the Rectangular Reactor and square Syphomatic filters.

the settled water to the filters, but recently a type was developed (9) that in design is a round Reactor surrounded by annular Syphomatic filters (Section IC1, 2); see Fig. 4.14. It presents a number of advantages: it saves walls and floor space and reduces foundation work, it incorporates the clearwell within the structure, it eliminates interconnecting piping, and it saves the expensive building for the filter. A similar combination design of a rectangular Reactor and Syphomatic filters along the side is shown in Fig. 4.15.

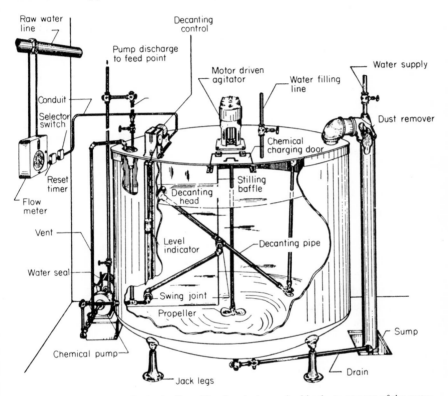

Fig. 4.16. Wet chemical feeder for lime. The chemicals required in the treatment of the water must be added in the right amount and in proportion to the flow of raw water for best results. Chemical feeds must, therefore, be accurate and dependable. The chemicals are fed either in solution or in suspension. The latter requires an agitator, to keep the chemicals in homogeneous strength whether the tank is full or nearly empty. The chemical tanks must be properly protected against corrosive attack of chemicals. The decanting control is connected to a timer and meter contactor. When a predetermined volume of water passes through the meter, the contactor closes, establishing a circuit to the timer and dec. control. The control then operates for a period of time determined by the timer setting. The control stops operating and the timer resets before the next meter contact is delivered. The interval between contacts is usually 30 sec at the maximal flow rate through the meter. After the decanter has been in operation for a period of time, such as 12 to 24 hr, as desired, the drawoff decanting head of the decanting pipe will have dropped down to the point where there is only a small amount of chemical left in the tank. This point is quickly determined by noting the position of the level indicator, which travels alongside the calibrated scale on the outside of the tank. It is then necessary to prepare a new chemical charge. However, it is first necessary to raise the decanting pipe to a predetermined upper position.

4. CHEMICAL FEEDERS

Feeders are of two general types, "wet" and "dry," for wet and dry chemicals. Figure 4.16 shows a common wet feed, as used for lime, supplied with a decanting pipe; the caption describes its operation.

Dry feeds are used when the plants are large and the amounts of chemicals to be fed between successive rechargings of a wet feeder tank would be too large. The dry feeder may be designed for either volumetric or gravimetric measurements of the feed. The volumetric type controls the amount of chemical by volume, whereas the gravimetric type actually weighs the amounts fed. Both types of feeder usually are supplied with extension hoppers leading to an upper chemical-storage floor, from which the chemical is charged into the feeder periodically. Figure 4.17 shows a typical dry-feed installation, and the inserts show gravimetric and volumetric feeders.

5. "IN-LINE" COAGULATION BEFORE IN-DEPTH (MULTIPLE-BED) FILTERS

In the past, especially in municipal clarification plants, it was considered good practice to use filters for finishing ("polishing") only; they were conventional single-bed filters. The real workhorses for the removal of the bulk of suspended matter were the coagulation and settling tanks. They reduced the turbidity to about 5 ppm, and the filters polished the water free from this residual turbidity.

For producing acceptable drinking water this practice used to be considered the most conservative one, because the filters would more reliably prevent leakage of bacteria into the effluent when they were used for polishing only. Furthermore they involved less operating labor, because they ran longer between successive backwashings (filter runs in municipal practice are commonly two or more days long). However, backwashing is not a costly operation, even when filter runs are much shorter and, besides, chlorination is more reliable than filtration for producing sterile water anyway.

In industrial pretreatment plants, where water is treated before being demineralized, this policy of using filters for polishing is being reappraised. The general technological trend of doing "more with less" (mentioned in the preface) has recently led designers to make the filters take over part or all of the work formerly assigned to the settling tank. With the development of the in-depth, multilayer, filter (Section ID), this trend is advancing rapidly.

Instead of presettling for reducing the turbidity to 5 ppm the in-depth filters alone can handle raw-water turbidities of several hundred parts per million with reasonable lengths of filter run. For greater raw-water turbidities the settling tanks can at least be smaller, to allow the settled water to contain somewhat more than 5 ppm turbidity.

Gravimetric Dry Feeder

Volumetric Dry Feeder

Fig. 4.17. Dry chemical feeder: inserts show volumetric and gravimetric feeders. (Courtesy of Wallace & Tiernan, Inc.)

In raw waters of moderate turbidity but containing color or other colloidal matter a fine floc has greater capacity for adsorbing these colloids than fully formed, large floc, since its particles have much greater surface areas for adsorption. To keep the floc fine, the coagulant is added to the water in a small contact tank (15 to 20 min of retention time), and the addition of coagulant aid is delayed until just before the in-depth filtration. The three major commercial systems of this type are the Neptune Micro-Floc (3–6), the Graver Mono-Floc, and the Cochrane Sorb-Floc. Figure 4.18 is a flow diagram of a Sorb-Floc plant.

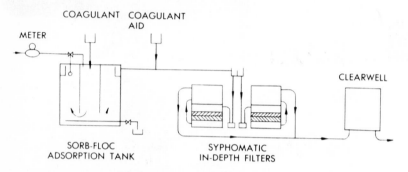

Fig. 4.18. Flow diagram of Sorb-Floc plant with Syphomatic in-depth filters.

For some waters even the small contact tank may be omitted. The coagulant is put directly into the raw-water pipe a sufficient distance upstream of the in-depth filters for sufficient contact time in the inlet pipeline itself. Then the coagulant aid is added right at the filter inlet, to condition the fine floc so that the upper, coarse layers in the filters can properly retain it. This practice has been named "in-line coagulation."

III. Removal of Organic Matter

Organic matter is a major foulant of the strong-base anion resin used in demineralizers. Many of the organics are high-molecular-weight materials, such as humic acid, which is derived from decomposing vegetable matter. They diffuse in and out of the gel structure of the ion exchanger, but so slowly that they become irreversibly bound, and regeneration does not elute them. The internal exchange sites are thus gradually blocked off and the resin becomes "fouled"; the exchange capacity of the resin and effluent purity then decrease appreciably. Anion exchange resins of great porosity and with large pores have been developed (Chapter 6, Section IXF3) to alleviate this difficulty. Cleaning of the resins may also be effected by means of warm brine and caustic soda, which extract the organics from the resin beads (Chapter 6, Section IXF2), but maximal removal of the organics before demineralization obviously is a prime requisite since it reduces the frequency of the cleaning treatments. In the following paragraphs several types of organic-removal pretreatment are discussed.

A. Prechlorination

Chlorination is the first important step in pretreatment, because chlorine destroys many of the organics by oxidation. A residual chlorine of more than 0.5 ppm should be maintained in the chlorinated water, so that the "chlorine demand" of the water is certain to have been satisfied. The destruction of microorganisms and oxidation of organic matter is often more rapid at low pH values; therefore prechlorination of raw water has sometimes been carried out in a raw-water contact tank located ahead of the coagulation or lime softening tanks, where the pH value may be higher than in the raw water. The organic matter left after prechlorination is then still further reduced by the coagulation that follows.

B. Powdered Activated Carbon

Powdered activated carbon is used in most municipal clarification plants for reducing objectionable tastes and odors due to microorganisms and organic matter. It is used in industrial suspended-solids contact units in pretreatment plants before demineralization for the absorption of organics (*10*). The carbon is added at the inlet with the coagulant and is kept suspended and mixed with the floc in the reaction zone of the solids contact unit. The carbon turns the floc black and so provides the secondary advantage of keeping out sunlight and thereby discouraging algae and slime growths on the solids contact unit and filter walls. It also keeps the settled sludge "sweet," that is, it prevents its decomposition, which may cause objectionable tastes and odors. Finally, it acts as a dechlorinator, reducing excessive residuals of chlorine, which may damage the exchange resin of the demineralizer.

One of the companies marketing powdered carbon suggests that in some cases the carbon should be added first and the chlorine next (*11*). This sequence is claimed to save some chlorine and also to avoid the development of objectionable tastes due to chlorophenol, which results from the chlorination of certain organic compounds.

C. Granular Carbon Beds

The usual form of carbon for organic absorption in demineralizer pretreatment plants is granular rather than powdered. The carbon granules constitute a filter bed, generally in pressure units, which follow sand filters. The area of the carbon filter shells and the depth of the carbon beds depend on the amount and kind of organic matter present. Carbon beds are usually 2 to 5 ft deep and function at 1.0 to 1.5 gal/min per cubic foot of carbon. Large amounts of organics require more time in the carbon bed for complete absorption, and the beds should then be 5 to 10 ft deep (*12*).

The limitation of carbon filter beds is their short life; they become fouled and lose their absorptive capacity very rapidly. Smith and Reppin (*13*) recently described their experience with carbon for absorbing organics from Jersey City water to protect a demineralizer. The demineralized effluent at first was very pure (0.2 to 0.4 μmho conductivity), but as the carbon became fouled, the conductivity rose to 0.8 to 1.4 μmhos, and the demineralizer capacity dropped nearly 50%. The carbon was then steam-washed. This helped for a while, and steam washings were carried out regularly after every five filter runs, but the returns from this program soon diminished, and the carbon bed was finally replaced. The same experience was reported at other plants (*14*). Carbon beds usually must be replaced one or more times each year.

Rejuvenating a carbon bed by continuously removing small parts of it, one at a time, to a kiln, where the organic contents are burned off, and then returning it to the filter is a good solution of the problem. This system has been employed in the decolorizing of brown sugar juice (Chapter 14) and also in a large plant for the treating of waste water so that it can be reused (*15*). This continuous rejuvenation of carbon may be the system of the future for waste-water conversion when our water-shortage problem becomes more acute; it has not yet, however, been applied in carbon pretreatment plants preceding demineralizers.

D. Ion Exchange Organic Scavengers (Traps)

Organic scavengers, or "traps," are exchange units containing strong-base anion resin regenerated with sodium chloride brine. The organics absorbed by the resin appear to be eluted satisfactorily by the salt regeneration. Considerable success has been reported with this process abroad, and it is being introduced in the United States; tests were recently described (*16*).

A macroreticular resin, Amberlite IRA-904 has been suggested for this purpose (*17*). Its capacity is about 30 g of organics (expressed as potassium permanganate consumed) absorbed per liter of resin; a Japanese installation of this type showed an average capacity of 25 g/lit during the first year.

The usual salt regenerant level is about 10 lb per cubic foot of resin, but 1 lb of caustic soda mixed with 7 or 8 lb of salt per cubic foot of resin produces a still better elution. The regenerant solutions should be heated to 120 to 140°F for optimal results.

The maximal flow rates recommended for the scavenger unit are 3 gal/min per cubic foot of resin for less than 5 ppm organics (expressed as permanganate consumed), 2 gal/min for 5 to 20 ppm, and 1 gal/min for more than 20 ppm. During the passage of the water through this chloride form of strong-base anion resin the bicarbonates and sulfates are exchanged for chloride, as in the dealkalizer described in Chapter 3, Section IVB; the effluent composition will reflect this exchange.

The operating cost and first cost of the organic traps must be compared with the cost of periodic defouling of the resin with brine and caustic soda (mentioned at the beginning of this section). The life of Amberlite IRA-904 or another resin used for this purpose will have to be determined after some years of actual operating experience before the merits of the process can be properly evaluated.

IV. Removal of Colloidal Silica

Colloidal silica, found occasionally in natural waters, has caused problems in some demineralizer operations, because this type of silica is not removed by ion exchange. It is nonionic and is often called "nonreactive silica."

An early experience with this problem was reported from a large utility demineralizer in New York (*18*). The station had ten boilers (1400 to 1710 psi pressure) producing more than 6,000,000 lb of steam per hour. Part of the steam was extracted from the turbine and used for central-heating purposes in the city. The makeup therefore was high, 40% of the total feed. The boiler blowoff was 6 to 8%, to keep the total dissolved solids under 300 ppm and the silica under 25 to 40 ppm in the concentrated boiler water. Even this silica level caused turbine fouling, which required costly turbine outages for cleaning every four or six weeks. Therefore the station converted an existing split-stream hydrogen–sodium cation exchange plant to a (cation plus mixed-bed) demineralizer in order to reduce the silica together with the other dissolved solids present in the New York municipal supply. The silica in the city water had been 6.2 ppm, and the silica in the demineralized water (according to the usual silicomolybdate colorimetric test) appeared to be 0.02 ppm, as expected. This should have meant that the previous 25 to 40 ppm in the boiler water was reduced to 0.3 ppm and the previous 6 to 8% boiler blowoff to 1%. However, the actual boiler operation showed that the "silica in the boiler water was reduced to below 2 ppm, but at the expense of a continued 4% blowdown. Thus, the boilers are saying that they are actually receiving approximately 0.08 ppm silica in feedwater, which means 0.24 ppm in the deionized makeup" (*18*).

The station then embarked on a gravimetric testing procedure to establish the true values of total silica (soluble plus colloidal) in the demineralized makeup. They found that the average total silica was 0.3 ppm higher than the reactive soluble silica (determined by the molybdate test). The demineralizers removed all of the soluble silica but only about 85% of the colloidal silica. Consequently, the demineralizers stopped the turbine fouling, but the boiler blowoff was much higher than anticipated, because all the colloidal silica had not been removed.

Another history was that of a New England paper company that had a pretreatment clarifying plant and a demineralizer. A coagulant, alkali, and a coagulant aid were used for the coagulation. The coagulant aid added was activated silica sol, made by neutralizing some of the alkali in sodium silicate and then diluting the solution to prevent formation of silica gel. Normally the use of activated silica sol as a coagulant aid does not cause any colloidal silica to be added to the coagulated water but, owing to some fault in the neutralizing procedure, silica in the boiler water suddenly increased to very high values. The demineralizer removed the soluble silica, but not the colloidal silica, which was converted to the reactive, soluble form in the boiler by virtue of the high temperature and pH value there. In the end a polyelectrolyte coagulant aid was adopted, and no further colloidal silica problems was experienced.

The conversion of nonreactive to reactive silica in the boiler itself led to a new method of determining total silica. Into a small laboratory platinum bomb alkali was put with the water sample being tested. The bomb was kept at 30 psig pressure and 190°C temperature for 24 hr. The total silica in the sample was then determined by the molybdate method. Another method of testing for colloidal silica was recently reported (19). A sample of water is filtered through a very fine "Millipore" paper filter. Colloidal silica is retained on the filter and is then dissolved by hydrofluoric acid. The soluble silica thus formed is determined by the usual colorimetric molybdate test.

Normally the coagulation process, when properly controlled, will coagulate colloidal silica by means of the floc formed, so that settling tanks and filters will remove it satisfactorily. However, if the coagulation is not monitored carefully or if the raw-water turbidity is suddenly increased because of a storm, and the turbidity becomes colloidal, nonreactive silica may slip through the clarification plant and the demineralizer.

An experience of this sort was reported (20) at a utility station with supercritical once-through boilers, extremely sensitive to silica. In this case Lake Erie was the raw water. The clarification pretreatment plant used lime softening. Ordinarily no trouble with colloidal silica had been experienced, but after a severe storm the silica in the boiler water suddenly climbed to over 100 ppb. This called for emergency action in the middle of the night. Fortunately, the supervising staff had had previous experience with a similar trouble at another plant, where it had been found that a special clay coagulant aid had solved the problem. A supply of this clay was quickly obtained and fed to the clarification plant. This helped to coagulate the colloidal silica properly, and the silica in the boiler water soon descended to normal values again.

An interesting solution of the colloidal silica problem was recently reported from a utility station in Puerto Rico (21). The makeup was treated by a demineralizer. The influent to the demineralizer came from a municipal coagulation and filter plant, which treated a surface supply. During heavy rainfall the surface water became highly turbid, the municipal clarification plant was overloaded, and about 3 ppm colloidal silica slipped through into the city water and also slipped through the demineralizer into the boilers. When this first occurred, it was necessary to reduce the boiler pressure (from 1600 to 1300 psi) and increase the boiler blowoff (to 10%), to avoid fouling of the turbine. Increasing the boiler blowoff led to a vicious cycle, because more makeup, with its high colloidal silica, was needed to replace the water blown off, the increased makeup increased the silica in the boiler, and the increased silica required still more blowoff.

The solution of this problem (21) consisted of reclaiming part of the boiler blowoff water (instead of wasting it) and mixing it with the city-water influent to the demineralizer. The blowoff water had a total dissolved solids of only 18 ppm, of which the silica was 2 ppm; this was superior to the city water, which had a total dissolved solids of more than 150 ppm and dissolved silica of 22 ppm. Therefore, the boiler blowoff was less costly to demineralize than the city water, which it partly replaced.

The blowoff water had to be cooled through heat exchangers before entering the demineralizer, because the high temperature would damage the anion resin. Reclaiming part of the boiler blowoff water reduced the total silica in the effluent by 25%, saved the heat and water in the excessive boiler blowoff previously wasted, and reduced the city-water makeup requirement.

At another station of the same utility a similar procedure is being followed. The effluent from a demineralizer treating water for boiler makeup is mixed with precooled boiler blowoff in a storage tank, and the mixture is pumped through two other demineralizers. The second demineralizers serve the dual purpose of reducing the colloidal silica and of polishing the effluent of the first demineralizer. Figure 4.19 is a flow diagram of this arrangement.

Powdered-resin filters used on the main feedwater stream of a utility station have been reported to reduce colloidal silica that slipped through a makeup demineralizer treating city water (22).

It has recently been proposed that a macroreticular strong-base anion resin (Rohm and Haas Amberlite XE-238) be used in a separate unit after demineralization for scavenging colloidal silica that may have leaked through (23). This is recommended for the production of "ultrapure" water, which is required in the manufacture of semiconductors.

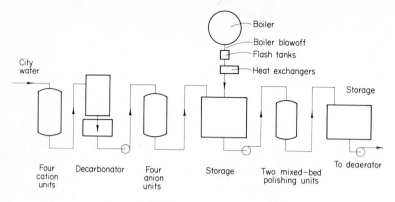

Fig. 4.19. Colloidal silica removal plant.

Nevertheless, a good coagulation procedure, with the use of modern coagulant aids, properly applied and monitored and followed by well-designed filters, still appears to be the most reliable method of removing, not only colloidal silica, but also other colloids, from surface supplies. Its success has been proved by the absence of problems with the many existing demineralizers that receive water from coagulation clarification plants.

V. Removal of Oil from Surface Waters and Condensates

Oil spills from refineries situated in drainage areas above surface-water sources have occasionally contaminated river waters. Leakage from oil pipelines also is a potential danger. A vast network of oil pipelines now extends into all parts of the continent, and the chance of large spills is greatest at river crossings during floods.

Oil may be coagulated with other suspended matter. However it tends to float, and in solids contact units it therefore causes light floc particles to be carried over. To avoid this, weighting agents should be added to increase the density of the floc. The heavy precipitates from lime softening are also helpful in absorbing oil. Where oil is present in substantial amounts, the solids contact units should be designed for lower flow rates (in gallons per minute per square foot of tank area).

Oil has also been found in the condensates of exhaust steam from lubricated reciprocating engines. The oil in the condensate is often emulsified, and the condensate is then milky in appearance. It may be absorbed from the condensate by diatomaceous earth filters, but the siliceous composition of diatomite presents the danger of silica pickup, if the condensate is hot and has a high pH value. Therefore, nonsiliceous anthracite filter beds with preformed floc added have found greater acceptance. The floc (about 2.5% in slurry strength) is prepared by mixing 2 parts of alum sulfate with 1 part of alkali (soda ash or caustic soda) at an optimal pH value of 6 to 7, so that a good aluminum hydroxide precipitate is formed. It is kept suspended in a tank by an agitator and is injected into the filter at the start of the filter run, making a mat on the top of the filter bed; about 0.2 lb of alum sulfate per square foot of filter area will make such a mat. In addition, a small amount of the floc introduced continuously during the filter run, will keep the mat freshened with new absorptive precipitate; about 0.5 ppm alum sulfate is added for each part per million oil. The filter works best at low concentrations of oil (less than 25 ppm), although as much as 50 ppm has been removed at times. The preformed floc easily breaks up the oil emulsions, and the filter reduces the oil to low amounts (less than 0.2 ppm). If the condensate has high pH values (over 9.0), iron sulfate is substituted for the alum in the preparation of the preformed floc.

The filter rates may be 3 to 5 gal/min/ft^2, and the filter runs last about 24 hr to a 10 psi pressure-loss buildup, if the amount of oil is less than 25 ppm. For the best quality of effluent a deep penetration of the oily floc, into the lower layers of the anthracite bed, should be avoided by limiting the length of the run and the loss of pressure (23a). Rotary surface washers or motor-driven rake agitators have sometimes supplemented the water backwash in cleaning of the beds.

VI. Removal of Corrosion Products from Condensates

Iron and copper oxides may be present in condensates owing to corrosion of steel or brass piping and other parts. When these corrosion products appear in the feedwater of industrial and utility high-pressure boilers, they cause boiler-tube failures (24); therefore, either the corrosion should be prevented or the corrosion products removed.

Corrosion inhibitors, such as neutralizing or filming amines, can be added to the boiler feedwater or the steam. The amines are volatile in the boiler steam. The neutralizing amine reacts with carbonic acid to raise the pH value of the condensate. The filming amine performs no neutralization but tends to make a continuous film on the internal surface of the condensate piping and so makes a protective coating. However, amines are not universally successful, and therefore the removal of the corrosion products by filtration has been recommended (24).

The filters may be of a mechanical type, in which a cellulose filter aid lies on a septum in a pressure filter. However, the cellulose can tolerate water temperatures of only about 150°F (24), and the septum may get clogged and require periodic chemical cleaning. Therefore a granular filter bed, made of cation exchange resin (in a pressure unit like a hot zeolite softener) has become the more popular type of filter, since the resin can stand 300°F water temperature. Being an ion exchanger, it also is able to remove dissolved iron, copper, calcium, and magnesium (total iron can be reduced to less than 20 ppb). It is regenerated with sodium chloride mixed with sodium sulfite. The regenerations are infrequent (once or twice a week). The flow rates may be 20 to 30 gal/min/ft^2, so the units are small in size. One of the earliest of such combinations of ion exchange and filtration was used with success in a paper mill (25). Further data on this system are given in Chapter 10, Section X, other methods of treatment of condensate are also discussed in that chapter.

REFERENCES

1. K. E. Shull, Experiences with multiple-bed filters. *J. Am. Water Works Assoc.* (March, 1965).
2. J. W. Hyatt, U.S. Patent 293,745 (1884).
3. W. R. Conley and R. W. Pitman, Test program for filter evaluation at Hanford. *J. Am. Water Works Assoc.* **52**, 205 (1960).
4. W. R. Conley and R. W. Pitman, Innovations in water clarification. *J. Am. Water Works Assoc.* **52**, 1319 (1960).
5. W. R. Conley, Experiences with anthracite sand filters. *J. Am. Water Works Assoc.* **53**, 1473 (1961).
6. W. R. Conley, Integration of the clarification process. *J. Am. Water Works Assoc.* (October 1965).
6a. K. E. Shull, Filtrability techniques for improving water clarification. *J. Am. Water Works Assoc.* (September 1967).
6b. R. H. Marks, Water treatment, *Power* (December 1958).
7. P. Smit, Upflow filters. *J. Am. Water Works Assoc.* (June 1963).
8. K. J. Ives, Progress in filtration. *J. Am. Water Works Assoc.* (September 1964).
9. S. B. Applebaum, U.S. Patent 3,214,021 (1965).
10. R. I. Smith and H. D. Reppin, Four years of operating experience with a 3200 GPM demineralizer, *Proc. Am. Power Conf.* **23** (1961). S. B. Applebaum, Discussion of same. *Ibid*, **23** (1961).
11. Taste and odor control. Co. Bull. West Virginia Pulp and Paper Co., 1955.
12. M. E. Flentje and D. G. Hager, Removal of organic contaminants by granular carbon filtration. *J. Am. Water Works Assoc.* (November 1965).
13. R. I. Smith and H. D. Reppin, A combination arrangement for high flow condensate polishing and make-up demineralization at Hudson Generating Station. *Proc. Am. Power Conf.* **28** (1966).
14. H. C. Farmer and S. B. Applebaum, Two bed primary system solves mixed bed demineralizer problems. *Proc. Am. Power Conf.* **21** (1959).
15. W. Priday, H. E. Moyer and R. L. Culp, The most complete waste water treatment plant in the world. *Am. City* (September 1964).
16. S. B. Applebaum and G. J. Crits, Organic trap to prevent organic fouling of anion resin in demineralizers. *Proc. Intern. Water Conf. Engrs. Soc. West Penn.* (1966).
17. Preliminary data on the use of IRA904 as an organic scavenger. Tech. Bull. Rohm and Haas Co., 1966.
18. I. B. Dick, Demineralization by mixed bed treatment at waterside station of Consolidated Edison Co. of New York, Inc. *Proc. Am. Power Conf.* **18**, 651 (1956).

19. J. L. Dwyer, A new technique for colloidal silica analysis. *Ind. Water Eng.* (February 1965).
20. H. J. Vyhnalek and C. D. Banks, Water treatment experiences during start-up and initial operation of the Avon supercritical unit. *Proc. Ann. Water Conf. Engrs. Soc. West Penn. 21st Ann. Conf.* **21**, 133 (1960).
21. D. Pagan and P. G. Schmidt, Control of nonreactive silica in the boiler feedwater of a high pressure utility boiler. *Proc. Intern. Water Conf. Engrs. Soc. West. Penn.* (1964).
22. J. S. Grant and R. P. Crouse, The history of Powdex condensate polishing equipment at Bay Shore Station, Toledo Edison Co. *Proc. Am. Power Conf.* **28** (1966).
23. R. Kunin, New developments in the production of high quality water for industrial use. *Natl. Assoc. Corrosion Engs.* at Drexel Inst. Technol., *Philadelphia Sect. Meeting*, September 1966.
23a. V. J. Calise, Removing oil from water by flocculation and filtration. *Power Eng.* April (1954).
24. V. P. Murphy, Reduction of metal-oxide levels in boiler feed-water. *TAPPI* **49**, No. 7, 69A (1966).
25. Y. T. Allen and S. B. Applebaum, New regenerable process upgrades condensate for boiler feed. *Power* (March 1964).

5

Removal of Gaseous Impurities

The major gases dissolved in water (Table 2.1) are carbon dioxide, hydrogen sulfide, ammonia, oxygen, and chlorine. Their removal before demineralization either protects the demineralizers or supplements their work. Nitrogen is also present in water, since the atmosphere is 78% nitrogen and 21% oxygen, and rain dissolves both gases from the air; but since nitrogen is inert and harmless, its removal is of no technical interest. Chlorine is not present in natural waters, but it is introduced in pretreatment plants for the oxidation of organic matter and for sterilization. Residuals of excess free (uncombined) chlorine are usually left in the chlorinated water to assure rapid and complete sterilization and oxidation (See Chapter 4, Section IIIA). When these residuals exceed several tenths of a part per million, they are harmful to most ion exchange resins, and consequently they must be removed by a pretreatment process called dechlorination.

The methods of removing the major gases (Table 2.10) involve the following processes: aeration (open and forced-draft), cold-water (vacuum) deaeration, hot-water (heater) deaeration, oxidation by chemicals, hydrogen cation exchange, reduction by chemicals, anion exchange (with regeneration by reducing agents), and absorption. Aeration is used to remove gases other than dissolved oxygen. In fact, the oxygen content usually increases during aeration. In open aeration, the water is broken up into films or drops which are subjected to the action of the air introduced by the wind or air currents, entering the open sides of the aerator. In forced draft aeration, the sides are closed and air is introduced by a blower, resulting in more complete gas removal (See Chapter 3, Section IIIA1). In cold water (vacuum) deaeration, no air is blown in, but the water is subjected to a vacuum at which it boils, allowing dissolved oxygen as well as the other gases to be removed. This reduces corrosion and protects the anion resins of demineralizers. Hot water (heater) deaeration also removes dissolved oxygen as well as the other gases (and more completely than cold water deaeration) but it operates at above atmospheric pressure and at temperatures exceeding 212°F. Since anion resin cannot stand such high temperatures, hot water deaeration is only used after the demineralizers. Oxidation by adding oxidant chemicals will remove certain gases (see Table 2.10) and is discussed below. Due to the high cost of these chemicals they are used only when the amount of gas to be removed is small. Hydrogen cation exchange is used to remove ammonia gas if present as ionized ammonium. Chlorine is removable by adding chemicals such as reducing agents but again the cost of these chemicals limits their use to removing only small amounts of chlorine. Anion exchange resins have been used to remove dissolved oxygen where no deaerator is available. But their operating cost is also relatively high. Chlorine is also removable by absorption on powdered or granular carbon. The limitations of carbon are discussed below.

I. Laws of Gas Behavior

Gases consist of molecules in continuous movement, and the size of the molecules is small compared to the spaces between them. Furthermore, gases tend to expand indefinitely unless confined. In these respects gases differ from liquids. The movement of gas molecules increases in velocity with higher temperatures. When gas is confined, a pressure is created by the frequency and velocity with which its molecules impinge on the container walls.

An understanding of the mechanism of gas removal requires a familiarity with some well-known laws developed by a number of scientists.

Boyle's Law. The pressure of a gas is inversely proportional to the volume when the amount of the gas and its temperature are kept constant.

Charles' Law. The pressure of a gas is directly proportional to the amount of the gas, when the temperature and volume are kept constant. For example, if the gas in a cylinder is allowed to escape until the pressure drops to half, then the quantity of gas left is also one half of the original amount.

Dalton's Law. The total pressure exerted by a mixture of several gases is equal to the sum of the partial pressures of the individual gases. Each gas acts separately and independently of the other gases. The space between the molecules is so great that the various gases do not interfere with each other. Then, according to Charles' law, the partial pressure of each gas is determined by the amount of that gas in the mixture. Thus, if a mixture of gases consists of three quarters oxygen and one quarter carbon dioxide in a confined space under a total pressure of 100 psia, the partial pressure of the oxygen is 75 psia and that of the carbon dioxide is 25 psia.

Henry's Law. The solubility of a gas in water is directly proportional to the partial pressure of that gas in contact with the water.

II. Other Factors in Gas Solubility

The solubility of gases decreases as the temperature of their solvent increases. When water reaches its saturation temperature (boiling point corresponding to its pressure), all uncombined gases are theoretically insoluble in it and may then be removed.

Gases are in the uncombined form to the extent that they are not ionized and do not chemically react and combine with ions in a solvent. Oxygen in solution is always in the uncombined form, but other gases, such as carbon dioxide, hydrogen sulfide, and ammonia, partially react with ions in the solvent. In the case of the latter gases, therefore, to increase the amount of their "free" molecules and so effect their more complete removal a change in pH value may be necessary (see Sections V, A and V, C).

III. Application of the Laws and Other Factors

From the foregoing it is evident that the solubility of a gas may be decreased, so as to effect its more complete removal from water, in several ways: by lowering its partial pressure by inserting another gas in the mixture in contact with the water, as in aeration (the air enters and dilutes the other gases in the mixture); by decreasing the total pressure, as in cold-water deaeration (the water boils at a given vacuum pressure, and the water vapor formed acts as a diluent of the other gases, decreasing their partial pressures); and by lowering the partial pressure by heating the water to the boiling point corresponding to the pressure of the steam introduced, as in hot-water deaeration (steam dilutes the gases in the spaces in contact with the water, and the gases then liberated are vented away).

IV. Removal of Carbon Dioxide

Rainwater and most surface supplies contain small amounts of carbon dioxide (less than about 5 ppm), but underground waters, such as wells, usually contain appreciable amounts, ranging from five to several hundred parts per million. Decaying organic matter is the main source of the carbon dioxide in well waters.

Only part of the carbon dioxide dissolved in ground water remains in the uncombined "free" form. Some of it combines with carbonates in the soil, such as limestone (calcium carbonate). The carbon dioxide reacts with the carbonate to produce bicarbonate alkalinity. The carbon dioxide thus combined is said to be "half bound." Only a small amount of this half-bound carbon dioxide can be released *by aeration or by deaeration*. The amount of carbon dioxide in the water in excess of that required to form the bicarbonates is in the uncombined "free" form and can be removed *by aeration or by cold or hot deaeration*. This uncombined "free" carbon dioxide depresses the pH value of the water and thereby increases its corrosiveness. The relation between free carbon dioxide, bicarbonate alkalinity, and pH value is given in Fig. 3.10.

In the first stage of demineralization (the hydrogen cation exchange) the bicarbonates are converted to carbonic acid (Chapter 3, Eq. 13). The carbonic acid decomposes to gaseous carbon dioxide and water (Chapter 3, Eq. 16). The gaseous carbon dioxide thus formed is removable mechanically *by aeration or by cold deaeration*. It is usually profitable in large plants to remove it by these mechanical means before the second stage of demineralization (the anion exchange), because the latter is then relieved of the burden and there is not the cost of removing the gas chemically.

Aerators for removing free carbon dioxide between cation and anion exchange are called "degasifiers," "degassers," or "decarbonators". They are less costly to install than cold deaerators (cold-water vacuum deaerators, or, simply, vacuum deaerators). However, the latter remove dissolved oxygen in addition to carbon dioxide and are therefore frequently preferred for decreasing the corrosiveness of the water due to its oxygen content. For example, if a deaerating heater (hot-water deaerator, for boiler feed, Section VI) that follows a demineralizer is located some distance away, the steel piping connecting the two may be subject to corrosion, particularly at warm-water temperatures. This piping is often rubber-lined for protection against corrosion, but a vacuum deaerator, installed between the cation and anion exchange units, lessens the need for the expensive rubber lining, if the pH of the demineralized water is over 8.5 to 9.0. Another advantage of the vacuum deaerator is the greater protection it provides against oxidative attack of the expensive anion exchange resin. A longer life of some types of anion exchange resin has been reported (*1*) when a vacuum deaerator was installed rather than a decarbonator. Furthermore, in decarbonators, as explained below, air is blown in to accomplish the aeration, and in dusty locations the air (despite air filters on the suction side of the blower) will contain dirt that may contaminate the water and then foul the anion exchange resin. For all these reasons vacuum deaerators are gaining acceptance for the removal of both the carbon dioxide and the dissolved oxygen just before anion exchange. However, wood decarbonators are much less expensive and are still being used with many makeup demineralizers for the removal of carbon dioxide alone.

A. Aerators (Decarbonators)

When decarbonators are used for aerating the acid effluents of a hydrogen cation exchange unit (first stage of the demineralizer), they must be made of acid-proof material. The shells of the decarbonator tower are therefore constructed of wood or rubber-lined steel. If of wood, they may be made square with plywood sides but are commonly made round with wood staves 2 or 3 in. thick, held together by steel hoops. Redwood or cypress are the usual preferred woods used.

Figure 5.1 shows a typical wooden decarbonator with internal packing of wooden slat trays, called "fill," over which the water trickles down from a stainless-steel spray pipe at the top. Air is blown in at the bottom and rises countercurrent to the downward-trickling water.

The spray pipe and the trays divide the water into droplets or thin films, exposing new surfaces to the gas phase. The trays also serve to agitate the water by splashing and thus allow the dissolved gases to leave the water readily. This agitation overcomes the tendency of the water to retain gas bubbles through surface tension and viscosity. The tray stack also provides the detention time, while the water trickles down over the trays, that is necessary for a close approach to the equilibrium solubility of the gas in the water. Because complete equilibrium would require too long a retention time and too deep a tray stack, some residual gas remains in solution in the effluent, even though at equilibrium the gas would be insoluble at the temperature and partial pressure imposed.

Ceramic Raschig rings may be used instead of wood slats for the fill. They are gaining favor because they provide more surface area and, therefore, equilibrium is reached more rapidly than with wood trays. Raschig rings thus permit a reduction in the height of the decarbonator.

The height required for the tray stack or Raschig-ring fill increases when the amount of influent carbon dioxide is greater, when the amount of effluent carbon dioxide desired is lower, and when the operating water temperature is colder. It is customary to aim at an effluent carbon dioxide of not less than about 10 ppm in small plants and about 5 ppm in large plants. The operating design water temperature selected for such effluent carbon dioxide contents is usually not lower than 50°F, even though the actual water temperature in winter may be lower than this for a short time. During the cold-water periods the effluent carbon dioxide would be only a few parts per million more than the desired 5 ppm. Usually the anion exchange resin can remove these few extra ppm chemically at less cost than it would take to build a decarbonator tall enough to remove them mechanically.

Decarbonators are designed with flow rates that range from 20 to 30 gal/min per square foot of area. The height of the Raschig-ring fill varies from 5 to 15 ft. For example, the fill would be 7 to 8 ft deep to reduce 100 ppm carbon

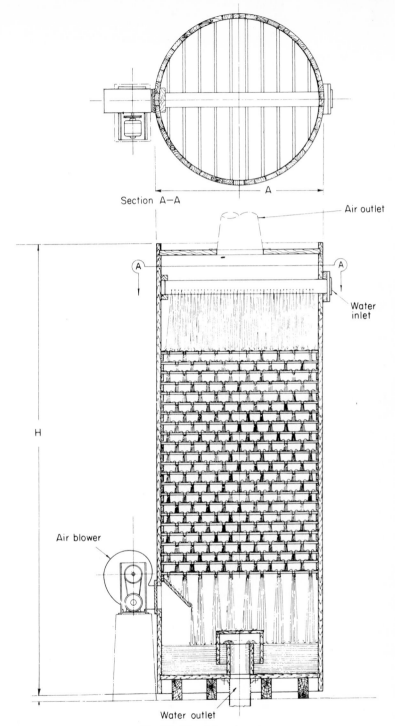

Section A—A

Air outlet

A

A

Water inlet

H

Air blower

Water outlet

Fig. 5.1. Wood decarbonator.

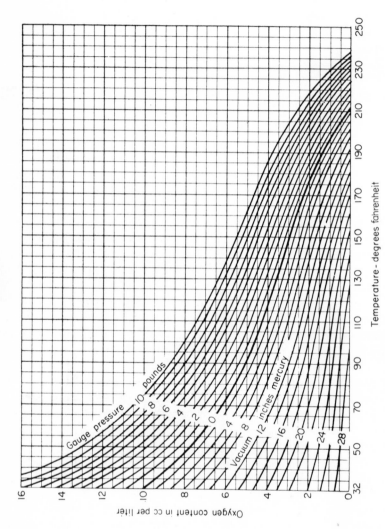

Fig. 5.2. Solubility of oxygen in water at various temperatures and pressures.

dioxide to 5 ppm at 50°F. The top spray chamber plus the bottom air-inlet chamber would add another 5 or 6 ft. Storage space for decarbonated water also should be provided below the air chamber, to hold 1 or 2 min supply of water storage on the suction side of the decarbonator pumps. The blower capacities would be 2 to 3 scfm of air for each gallon per minute of water treated at an air pressure equal to 2 to 4 in. of water, depending on the depth of the fill.

B. Cold-Water (Vacuum) Deaerators

The solubility of a gas in a liquid increases with the partial pressure of the gas and decreases with the water temperature. Figure 5.2 shows the solubility of oxygen in water at various temperatures and pressures.

In cold-water deaeration the water is brought to the boiling point without being heated by lowering its pressure with vacuum-producing equipment. For example, at 40°F water boils at an absolute pressure of 0.25 in. of mercury, which corresponds to a vacuum of 29.75 in. and at 60°F it boils at 0.52 in., or a vacuum of 29.48 in.

Water vapor is thereby formed and is mixed with the noncondensible gases. The water vapor dilutes the noncondensible gases and thus reduces their partial pressures. In this respect it has the same effect as air blown into decarbonators, which likewise dilutes and reduces the partial pressures of the other gases.

Agitation and surface exposure is accomplished by spraying the water at the top through a spray pipe or spray nozzle and making it trickle down over the Raschig-ring fill. The vacuum-producing equipment extracts the mixture of water vapor and non condensible gases from the bottom (see Figs. 5.3 and 5.4); in some designs it extracts it from the top.

The amount of noncondensible gases and water vapor withdrawn, or the evacuating rate, influences the amount of carbon dioxide and oxygen remaining (1a). The higher the evacuation rate, the lower the residuals, and also the lower the height required for the packing or fill. The higher the evacuation rate, however, the larger the vacuum pumps needed. The most economical design, therefore, must be selected after some trial calculations, in which relative first cost and operating costs are compared.

The most economical vacuum-producing equipment is the steam ejector, or steam-jet evacuator. At low water temperatures three-stage ejectors with condensers between them (called intercondensers) may be required. The condensers liquefy the water vapor, thereby reducing the load on the ejectors that follow. At high temperatures a single or a two-stage ejector usually suffices. Figure 5.3 shows a two-stage ejector system used at Oak Ridge (2) for a vacuum deaerator that follows a demineralizer and reduces corrosion in the long, unlined, steel pipes that carry the demineralized water. Figure 5.4 shows

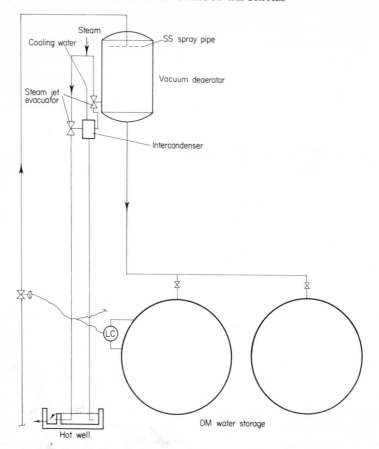

Fig. 5.3. Vacuum deaerator with two-stage ejector system.

a three-stage ejector system. As the diagrams indicate, the steam jets and condensers are supported by a tail pipe about 34 ft above a sump, into which the cooling water, gases, and condensed steam are discharged to • waste. This height is needed to seal the vacuum and allow free flow to the atmosphere.

When steam is not available, a mechanical motor-driven vacuum pump is used. Since such pumps are more expensive than steam ejectors, the evacuation rate must be kept at a minimum. A low evacuation rate results in high partial pressures, and high oxygen or carbon dioxide concentrations in the gas space of the unit. Therefore, to offset the effect of low evacuation rates, the internal fill is proportionately higher.

In large plants with mechanical vacuum pumps the use of multistage deaerators may be justified. The shell is divided into two or three stages, or

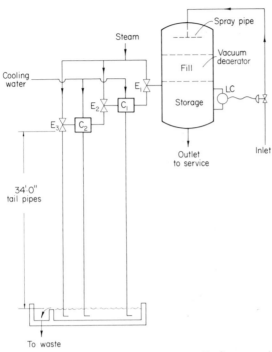

Fig. 5.4. Vacuum deaerator with three-stage ejector system: E_1, first-stage ejector; E_2, second-stage ejector; E_3, third-stage ejector; C_1, first condenser; C_2, second condenser; LC, level controller.

compartments, with sealed drains between them. The highest-pressure compartment, at the top, drains into the lower-pressure compartments below. Usually each compartment has its own vacuum pump. Multistaging reduces the overall evacuating capacity required of the pumps, because the gases are removed from the first stage at the highest partial pressure and, hence, the least volume, and only a part of the gases are withdrawn from the lowest stage, at which the greatest vacuum is required for the desired results. If only one stage were used to achieve the same results, all the gases would have to be withdrawn at the greatest vacuum and largest volume. As a rough rule of thumb, a two-stage deaerator will require only one quarter of the total pumping capacity of a single-stage deaerator, and a three-stage one will require only one ninth. Consequently, whenever a single-stage vacuum pump requires more than about 10 hp, it may be economical to use the multistage arrangement.

Since it is more difficult to remove carbon dioxide than oxygen, the main factors that influence the design of vacuum deaerators are the total amount of carbon dioxide gas to be removed and the minimal water temperature. If the water temperature goes down to 35°F for a few weeks in winter, it is usually

uneconomical to design the deaerator for an effluent carbon dioxide of 5 ppm
at that low temperature. It is, instead, customary to design for a temperature of
50°F and an effluent carbon dioxide that will rise a few parts per million, when
the water temperature drops. To illustrate the economy of using 50 instead of
35°F as the design water temperature, Table 5.1 gives the comparative
deaerator dimensions and the steam and cooling-water requirements for
deaerating 2500 gal/min of water at both temperatures.

Table 5.1

COMPARISON OF VACUUM DEAERATORS DESIGNED FOR 50 AND 35°F WATER TEMPERATURES

Flow of water treated : 2,500 gal/min
Influent CO_2 : 88 ppm
Influent O_2 : saturated

	Design water temperature	
	35°F	50°F
Effluent CO_2, ppm	5	5
		or 8 at 35°F
Effluent O_2, ppm	0.2	0.2
Size of vacuum deaerator, diam × height, ft	10 × 17	10 × 15
Total evacuation, ft³/hr	1,900,000	690,000
Steam (at 100 psi) required for steam ejectors, lb/hr	3000	1450
Cooling water for condenser, gal/min	140	75

Comparing the two designs the savings in capital and operating cost
realized by the former would be appreciable. If mechanical vacuum pumps
were used in this case instead of ejectors, the cost disparity would have been
even greater, because the deaerator itself would then have to be multistage, to
reduce the size of the vacuum pumps. Generally, the costs of vacuum pumps
rise greatly with evacuation rates, whereas the costs of ejectors rise inappreci-
ably. Multistage deaerators are therefore rarely justified if steam-jet evac-
uators can be used.

Commonly there is a separate pump for each stage of a multistage deaerator. The pumps are preferably of equal capacities, so that one spare pump
may be used for all stages, reducing the spare parts required to a minimum.
Piston vacuum pumps have suffered from lubrication problems, and therefore rotary vacuum pumps have recently come into greater use.

The diameter of the vacuum deaerator is determined by the loading rates,
which range from 30 to 50 gal/min per square foot of area. The higher the
loading rate selected, the deeper the internal fill required to give the low
oxygen content and, particularly, the low carbon dioxide content, desired

in the effluent. Moreover, the loading rate must not be so high that a flooding of the fill with water could take place. If high loading rates are needed, the Raschig rings may have to be larger than the usual 1 in. in diameter.

A height of several feet should be allowed above the top of the fill for the top spray section. Below the bottom of the fill sufficient height also should be provided for vapor drawoff, for draining of the fill when the float valve closes, and for water storage. Table 5.2 gives data on typical vacuum deaerators that have been installed for various operating conditions.

C. Combination of Decarbonator and Vacuum Deaerator

If large amounts of free carbon dioxide must be reduced to very low residuals, the use of a decarbonator before the vacuum deaerator may prove economical, particularly if mechanical motor-driven vacuum pumps are used. The decarbonator partially reduces the uncombined carbon dioxide, and the vacuum deaerator completes its reduction. Figure 5.5 shows the design of a combination of decarbonator and two-stage deaerator.

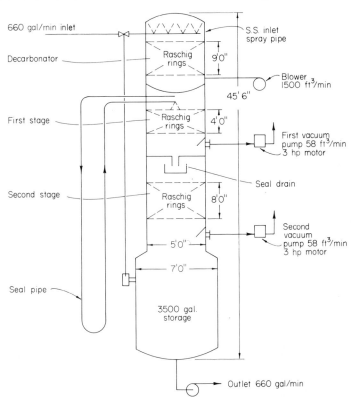

Fig. 5.5. Combination of a decarbonator and vacuum deaerator.

Table 5.2

TYPICAL VACUUM DEAERATORS

Location, state	Water flow, gal/min	No. of units	Diam., ft in.	Height, ft in.	Influent, ppm O_2	Influent, ppm CO_2	Effluent, ppm O_2	Effluent, ppm CO_2	Temp., °F	No. of deaer. stages	Evacuating equipment[a]
Wash.	60,000	20	11 0	56 6	8.5	70	0.05	2.5	70	3	3-stage steam jet: steam, 136 lb/hr
N.J.	5500	1	14 0	43 0	11	—	0.1	—	50	3	3 REC vac. pumps, ea. 5500 ft³ hr, 10 hp
N.J.	1650	1	8 0	58 0	11	—	0.1	—	50	2	3-stage steam jet
Texas	500	1	4 0	22 0	10	54	0.1	2.5	60	1	3-stage steam jet
Texas	1000	1	6 0	15 3	5	—	0.1	—	100	1	2-stage steam jet
Pa.	750	1	5 6	33 0	—	100	—	5	70	2	2-stage steam jet
Pa.	1020	1	6 0	24 3	5	—	0.1	—	80	1	REC vac. pump
Texas	200	1	3 6	20 0	—	135	—	10	75	2	2 Rot. vac. pumps, ea. 15 hp
N.J.	270	1	3 6	21 6	8	102	0.4	10	50	2	1–3 stage rot. vac. pump, 30 hp
Pa.	532	1	4 6	21 4	11	50	0.1	4	50	2	3-stage steam jet: steam, 430 lb/hr

[a] REC = reciprocatory piston.

The following are the conditions in that case:

Flow:	660 gal/min	Effluent CO_2:	5 ppm
Influent CO_2:	243 ppm	Effluent CO_2:	0.1 ppm
Influent O_2:	11.2 ppm	Storage at the bottom:	460 ft³
Design water temperature:	48°F	Raschig-ring fill height:	9 ft, 0 in.
Decarbonator diam.:	5 ft, 0 in.	Raschig-ring fill heights of the two	
Blower:	1500 scfm at 4 in.	deaerator stages:	4 ft, 0 in.
pressure		and 8 ft, 0 in.	

The two mechanical vacuum pumps were each for 58 scfm requiring only 3 hp motors.

A considerable saving in the cost of power for evacuation was, then, achieved by placing a decarbonator ahead of a vacuum deaerator.

V. Removal of Hydrogen Sulfide, Methane, and Ammonia

A. Hydrogen Sulfide

Hydrogen sulfide is found in some well waters in areas where the soil contains certain types of organic matter, decomposing under anaerobic conditions. The usual amount of sulfide is small (less than 10 ppm), although as much as 100 ppm has occasionally been encountered. The gas has a characteristic rotten-egg odor in concentrations as low as 0.5 to 0.1 ppm. Hydrogen sulfide causes corrosion of steel piping and forms sulfur and iron sulfide deposits, which will foul demineralizer resins. Therefore it should be removed by pretreatment.

Hydrogen sulfide is an example of a gas, as stated in Section II, that is not completely in the uncombined form. At high pH values the sulfide anion is mostly combined with sodium, forming sodium sulfide. Table 5.3 shows the

Table 5.3

EFFECT OF pH VALUE ON
AMOUNT OF HYDROGEN
SULFIDE IN
UNCOMBINED FORM[a]

pH	Uncombined H_2S in % of tot. sulfides
5.0	98.0
6.0	82.0
7.0	33.0
8.0	5.2
9.0	0.5

[a] From Pomeroy (3).

effect of pH value on the percentage of total sulfides in the uncombined gaseous form. Since only the gaseous form can be removed by aeration, the pH value often must be lowered before aeration is carried out. This can be accomplished by means of sulfuric acid or carbonic acid. The latter may be added to the water with the use of a trickling, forced-draft tower, into which flue gas containing carbon dioxide is passed. The tower may be mounted over the forced-draft aerator, through which air is blown for the removal of the hydrogen sulfide gas.

If the pH value is lowered sufficiently, the forced-draft aerator can then reduce the hydrogen sulfide to less than 1 ppm. This residual then can be further reduced by adding chlorine after aeration. The chlorine will oxidize the hydrogen sulfide to sulfuric acid according to the following equation:

$$H_2S + 4\,Cl_2 + 4\,H_2O \rightarrow H_2SO_4 + 8\,HCl \tag{1}$$

The acids formed in this equation are neutralized by the alkalinity in the water. About 8 ppm chlorine is required to oxidize 1 ppm hydrogen sulfide. Some residual hydrogen sulfide can be dissipated by slow oxidation in a large storage tank after aeration and before the chlorine is added. Municipal plants in Florida practice this to save chlorine (4). However, some precipitated sulfur may be formed in the storage tank, as in the next equation:

$$2\,H_2S + O_2 \rightarrow 2\,H_2O + 2\,S \tag{2}$$

If the amount of hydrogen sulfide is high (20 to 30 ppm), coagulation with ferric chloride after aeration and chlorination is advisable, to remove the milky, colloidal sulfur from the aerated water (5). The coagulation tank should provide several hours' retention and then be followed by filters for the removal of residual floc.

B. Methane

Methane has been found occasionally in some well waters. It is removable by aeration, but since it is combustible and explosive, certain precautions must be taken. It is best to situate the aerator outside a building in the open air. If the aerator is inside it must be of the forced-draft type so that the vent pipe can be conducted outside to the atmosphere, so as to avoid accumulation of the explosive methane within the building.

C. Ammonia

Ammonia is introduced into surface waters when they are polluted by trade wastes and sewage. It is corrosive to copper and brass at pH values over 9.0. It is another example of a gas that can combine with its solvent, in this case to form ammonium hydroxide. The amount of uncombined gaseous ammonia in the solvent increases with the pH value. The addition of an alkali to raise the pH value before deaeration is therefore helpful in ammonia removal.

Ammonia is very soluble in water, and therefore a very low partial pressure of ammonia in the gas space of the unit is required for its removal. Joos (6) reported on a special design of deaerator that would reduce ammonia from 5.0 to 0.01 ppm. It included an internal reboiler evaporator at the bottom, which generated enough excess steam vapor to act as a diluent of the ammonia in the gas space of the unit and so reduce its partial pressure. An extra-large vent condenser, very deep tray stack, and internal preheater were needed to condense the steam vapor. The mechanical removal of ammonia by deaeration is therefore not applied today.

Ammonia can be removed chemically by adding chlorine (7), forming monochloramine and dichloramine as intermediate products and nitrogen and hydrochloric acid as final products, according to the following equations:

$$2\,NH_3 + 2\,Cl_2 \rightarrow 2\,NH_2Cl + 2\,HCl \tag{3}$$

$$NH_2Cl + Cl_2 \rightarrow NHCl_2 + HCl \tag{4}$$

$$NH_2Cl + NHCl_2 \rightarrow N_2 + 3\,HCl \tag{5}$$

About 10 ppm chlorine will oxidize 1 ppm ammonia. A retention period of 2 hr is needed for the reactions at pH values of 7 to 9.

In hot lime–soda plants chloride of lime may be substituted for part of the lime. It will provide the chlorine for the reactions given above (Eqs. 3 to 5) and will destroy the ammonia chemically.

Ionized ammonium is removed by hydrogen cation exchange in the same way that sodium and other cations are removed. In the demineralization of condensate (Chapter 10, Section IX) the resin beds remove ammonia that was previously added to the condensate to raise its pH value, the first appearance of ammonia in the effluent determining the end of the demineralizer run.

VI. Removal of Oxygen

Dissolved oxygen in water is responsible for the corrosion of steel, particularly at high water temperatures. Its removal is therefore essential for boiler-feed purposes, to protect the feed piping and the boiler itself. The removal of oxygen at cold water temperatures has been discussed (Section IVB); its removal at high water temperatures is accomplished by hot-water deaerators, or deaerating heaters.

A. Hot-Water Deaerators (Deaerating Heaters)

In hot-water deaeration the water is heated with steam to the full saturation temperature (boiling point at the pressure involved). A low partial pressure of noncondensible gas is obtained by dilution with excess steam; the latter is then condensed, and the gas is vented out.

Figures 5.6 and 5.7 show a jet–tray type of deaerating heater. This design utilizes two internal heaters in series. The preheater, where the water is introduced, is at the top of the shell and is of the jet or spray type. The second heater is a tray stack that provides adequate spilling edge lengths and surface area for contact with the steam and for release of the gases.

The tray stack is surrounded by inner-chamber walls, which protect the steel shell of the deaerator from corrosion. The trays are made of stainless steel. The stack consists of heating trays above and air release trays below.

The steam enters the tray compartment through ports and flows downward, parallel to the water flow. It then rises to the top, where it heats the water sprayed by the preheater. Thus the purest steam is used first in the tray stack.

The water sprayed by the jets in the preheater releases most of the non-condensible gases. The preheated water passes through seals to the tray

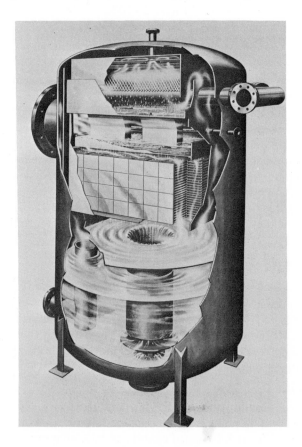

Fig. 5.6. Deaerating heater, vertical jet–tray design.

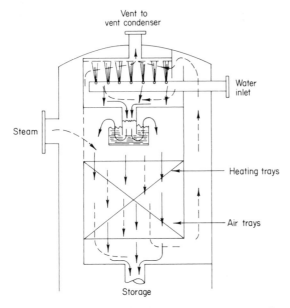

Fig. 5.7. Deaerating heater, vertical jet–tray design, elevation diagram.

compartment. The seals are barriers to the passage of gases from the preheater section, to prevent recontamination of the water in the tray stack. The
deaerated water falls to the storage space below. The stored water is blanketed
by pure inlet steam, to prevent its recontamination.

The preheater heats the water to within a few degrees of the boiling point.
Therefore very little of the steam introduced into the tray stack, where the
heating is completed, is condensed there. In fact, almost the entire volume of
uncontaminated steam is employed in "scrubbing," ensuring removal of the
final traces of oxygen. The deaerated water contains not more than 0.005 ml
of oxygen per liter of water (equivalent to less than 8 ppb). The free carbon
dioxide is reduced to zero, if the bicarbonate alkalinity is more than 5 ppm.
The final temperature of the deaerated water is at the boiling point corresponding to the steam pressure.

Two other types of deaerator are available: in one there is a flow of steam
across the tray stack, and in the other, an upflow, or counterflow, of steam
against the water. The parallel downward flow of both steam and water,
however, shown in Fig. 5.7, has the virtue of good distribution of the water
through the tray stack without disturbance by the flow of steam; damming
of the water and water hammer are thus prevented.

The gases to be vented away, from any of these types of deaerators, first
pass through an internal direct-acting vent condenser, where most of the

excess steam used and water vapor formed is condensed, and the noncondensible gases are then discharged through a vent valve to the atmosphere. The internal condenser has largely superseded the external tubular vent condenser previously used.

For the handling of large amounts of water the shell of the deaerator is made horizontal. Large storage capacities are provided by separate, horizontal tanks, over which the horizontal deaerators are mounted. Table 5.4 gives data on a number of large, utility, horizontal deaerators with separate storage tanks.

Table 5.4

TYPICAL LARGE HORIZONTAL UTILITY DEAERATORS

Location, state	Capacity, lb/hr	Storage, ft³	Deaerator Diam., ft	Deaerator Leng., ft	Storage Diam., ft	Storage Leng., ft	Design press.,[a] psig
N. Mex.	5,452,000	8080	8	34	12	82	110 and f.v.
Mass.	4,594,000	6740	10	38	$11\frac{1}{2}$	65	100 and f.v.
Ala.	3,868,000	5750	9	46	12	$64\frac{1}{3}$	120
Japan	4,650,000	4000	9	43	10	53	100 and f.v.
Mass.	2,640,000	4360	9	$31\frac{1}{2}$	11	50	150 and f.v.
Mo.	2,319,000	3500	9	$30\frac{1}{2}$	11	$41\frac{1}{2}$	150 and f.v.
Ill.	2,200,000	5800	8	37	12	$56\frac{1}{2}$	125 and f.v.
Ga.	2,268,000	7000	$7\frac{1}{2}$	$24\frac{1}{2}$	12	66	175
Pa.	2 units, each 2,565,000	1000	11	$20\frac{1}{2}$	8	$28\frac{5}{6}$	100
N.Y.	2 units, each 2,800,000	4000	8	$43\frac{2}{3}$	10	54	200

[a] Here "f.v." stands for "full vacuum."

B. Deaerating Condensers

In utility power stations the main condenser, located after the turbine, operates at a vacuum and has air-removal devices. A number of utility engineers have therefore found that they can get adequate deaeration in the condenser, if it is suitably designed, and thus omit the deaerating heater (8). Precautions must be taken, however, to prevent air from leaking in through joints and recontaminating the water after it has left the condenser. Further, when the deaerator is omitted, the drains from both the high-pressure and low-pressure extraction heaters usually are cascaded all the way back to the condenser, and this causes a considerable loss of heat. Not so much heat is lost when the deaerator is retained, because it is located between the high-pressure and low-pressure extraction heaters and receives drainage from the former, only the drains from the latter being cascaded back to the condenser.

Again, a deaerating heater provides extra storage space on the suction side of boiler-feed water pumps. A large storage capacity has been found advantageous in control of the cycle, and generally the hotwell of a condenser is not big enough. Moreover, at times of low load the usual deaerating condenser can cause "condensate refrigeration," or cooling to below the boiling point, which results in poor deaeration and high gas residuals (see Section VIC).

For these reasons the latest designs of utility power stations have reverted to the inclusion of deaerating heaters as supplements to the deaerating condensers.

C. Anion Exchangers

Dr. Sturla, of Edisonvolta, (now ENEL), Italy, has reported (9) on pilot plant tests using anion resin for removing dissolved oxygen from condensate formed at low loads (see end of Section VIB). Sturla tested three anion exchangers, Dowex SAR, Duolite S-10, and Dowex SBR-P. The results with Dowex SAR were unfavorable.

Duolite S-10 was first impregnated with copper by having cupric sulfate passed through it. Then it was regenerated with an alkaline solution of a reducing agent, sodium hydrosulfite, yielding metallic copper, which is highly susceptible to oxidation. Sturla found that the resin thus treated showed good oxygen removal, but he reported, "Unfortunately it was accompanied by substantial copper leakage; apparently there is a proportional relation between the influent oxygen concentration and copper in the treated effluent (with 2000 ppb of oxygen, 50 to 100 ppb copper; with 8000 ppb of oxygen, 500 ppb copper)."

Dowex SBR-P was preferred, because it is regenerable with reducing agents without adding any copper. It gave good results, being able to remove 5 to 6 g of oxygen per liter of resin. The regenerant was a mixture of sodium sulfite and sodium hydrosulfite. The only difficulty encountered was that the pH value of the condensate dropped from 9.0 to 4.1 during the run. To prevent this, caustic soda was mixed with the sulfites during regeneration.

Later Sturla described the start-up of the large La Spezia Units 1 and 2 (10). The large-scale anion exchange units for the removal of oxygen used Dowex SBR-P and a regenerating mixture that was 90% sodium sulfite, 5% sodium hydrosulfite (hyposulfite), and 5% caustic soda; 15 lb of the mixture was used per cubic foot of resin. The oxygen was reduced from 1500 or 2000 ppb to practically zero. If the influent oxygen was as much as 2000 to 8000 ppb, the effluent oxygen was about 70 ppb. The effluent oxygen could be brought from 70 ppb down to zero, by decreasing the flow rate 50%.

Anion exchangers were recommended for this oxygen removal because there was no deaerating heater in the cycle of Units 1 and 2, which have boiler pressures of 2550 psi, and the Italian network is subject to frequent idle periods when hydroelectric power is available. However, for the Units 3 and 4, which have supercritical-pressure boilers, deaerating heaters were installed showing the trend back to the deaerator previously mentioned.

VII. Removal of Chlorine

Chlorine is added in pretreatment plants for the oxidation of organic matter, so as to protect the demineralizer anion exchange resins from organic fouling. The amount of chlorine added must exceed the "chlorine demand" of the water, providing the driving force required to kill spores and rapidly oxidize resistant organic matter; that is, a free-chlorine residual should be present, of 0.5 to 1.0 ppm. This practice has been called "superchlorination." Unfortunately, high chlorine residuals will damage most ion exchange resins by oxidation. Therefore, dechlorination often must be carried out before demineralization. Carbon and a number of reducing agents may be used as dechlorinating chemicals.

A. Powdered or Granular Carbon

Powdered carbon may be fed to solids contact coagulation tanks, where it will mix with the suspended floc and react with the residual chlorine; however most carbon dechlorinating plants have granular carbon beds in pressure units that follow the sand or anthracite filters (Chapter 4, Sections IIIB, IIIC). The limitation of carbon beds is their short life due to fouling; the carbon beds must be replaced one or more times a year. The chemical reaction between carbon and chlorine is given in the following equation:

$$2\,Cl_2 + C + 2\,H_2O \rightarrow 4\,HCl + CO_2 \tag{6}$$

The hydrochloric acid is neutralized by the alkalinity of the water. It takes 1 lb of carbon to react with 6 lb of chlorine. Then, if the water contains 1 ppm residual chlorine, 1,000,000 gal will contain 8.3 lb of chlorine and will require 1.4 lb of carbon for its removal. The carbon in the bed will gradually be consumed in this reaction.

B. Sodium Sulfite or Bisulfite

Solutions of the reducing agents sodium sulfite or sodium bisulfite, pumped into the influent of the demineralizer, will react with the chlorine. The following equation gives the reaction with sodium sulfite:

$$Na_2SO_3 + Cl_2 + H_2O \rightarrow Na_2SO_4 + 2\,HCl \tag{7}$$

Since 1 lb of sodium sulfite reacts with 0.56 lb of chlorine, 1,000,000 gal of water containing 1 ppm residual chlorine will require 14.9 lb of sodium sulfite. The following equation gives the reaction with sodium bisulfite:

$$2\,NaHSO_3 + 2\,Cl_2 + 2\,H_2O \rightarrow Na_2SO_4 + 4\,HCl + H_2SO_4 \tag{8}$$

Since 1 lb of sodium bisulfite reacts with 0.67 lb of chlorine, 1,000,000 gal of water containing 1 ppm residual chlorine will require 12.3 lb of sodium bisulfite.

C. Sulfur Dioxide Gas

In large plants the feeding of sulfur dioxide gas is preferred for dechlorination. A sulfonator similar to a chlorinator is used for this purpose. Its successful performance ahead of a large demineralizer at Linden, New Jersey, was reported in 1962 (11). The sulfonator is set to reduce the chlorine to less than 0.1 ppm. Continuous automatic control is afforded by a residual-chlorine analyzer.

At the Linden plant chlorine is fed into a raw-water storage tank, and powdered carbon for organics adsorption is fed into a flash mixer (a first, fast mixer) ahead of two large solids contact units, which are capable of coagulating 5,000 gal/min of a badly contaminated surface supply. The carbon acts as a primary dechlorinator, and the sulfonator, therefore, acts as a secondary one. Typical results in 1962 showed that the residual chlorine was 2 to 7 ppm at the inlet of the mixing tank, 0.1 to 0.5 ppm after the solids contact units and filters, and 0 to 0.1 ppm at the inlet of the demineralizer. The effectiveness of the dechlorinator in protecting the demineralizer is shown by the fact that no cation resin replacements were made in six years of operation, during which 6,000,000,000 gal of water were treated with 5000 ft^3 of cation resin.

D. Calcium Sulfite (DeChlorit)

DeChlorit is a foreign commercial name for calcium sulfite granules made to be used as beds in pressure filters. The sulfite slowly dissolves as it reacts with the chlorine in the water passed through the filters. The dechlorinating reaction is similar to that of sodium sulfite and is shown in the following equation:

$$CaSO_3 + Cl_2 + H_2O \rightarrow CaSO_4 + 2\,HCl \tag{9}$$

DeChlorit will react in the proportion of 1 lb to 0.6 lb of chlorine. Its cost is about ten times that of sodium sulfite, but the DeChlorit filters avoid the use of a chemical feeder, and they are operated automatically. The rates of flow through the filters are high, 16 to 30 gal/min/ft^2, with bed depths of 30 to 36 in. The filters are, then, quite small, and their first cost is less than that of carbon filters, which sustain rates of only 3 to 5 gal/min/ft^2. But they have not yet been used in the U.S.

REFERENCES

1. L. J. Wirth, The expected life of anion exchangers under various conditions of de-ionizer design and operation. *Proc. Am. Power Conf.* **16**, 626 (1954).

1a. A. W. Kingsbury and E. L. Phillips, Vacuum deaerator design. *Am. Soc. Mech. Engrs. Paper* No. 60-WA-214 (1960).

2. G. W. Brush, S. B. Applebaum, and G. J. Angele, Mixed bed demineralizer operations at A. E. C. Facilities, Oak Ridge, Tennessee. *Proc. Ann Water Conf., Engrs. Soc. West. Penn., 17th, Ann. Conf.* (1956).

3. R. Pomeroy, Measuring low sulfide concentrations, *J. Am. Water Works Assoc.* **33**, 943 (1941).

4. S. W. Wells, Hydrogen sulfide problems of small water systems. *J. Am. Water Works Assoc.* (February 1954).

5. J. E. Foxworthy and H. K. Gray, Removal of hydrogen sulfide in high concentrations from water. *J. Am. Water Works Assoc.* **50**, (1958).

6. C. E. Joos, Removal of ammonia from boiler feedwater. *Power Plant Engr.* (January 1945).

7. A. E. Griffin, Removal of ammonia by chlorination. *Proc. Ann. Water Conf., Engrs. Soc. West Penn. 5th Ann. Conf.* (1944).

8. Panel discussion of power station design as related to boiler feed water degasification. *Proc. Ann. Water Conf.* 9th (1948).

9. P. Sturla, Polishing condensate and deaerating by ion exchange. *Intern. Water Conf.,* October 1962.

10. P. Sturla, Performance and value of condensate treatment, including dissolved oxygen removal, during start-up LaSpezia thermo-electric power plant. *Proc. Am. Power Conf.* **25**, (1963).

11. S. H. Newberry and E. C. Wackenhuth, Discussion of dechlorination ahead of demineralizers. *Intern. Water Conf., Engrs. Soc. West Penn.*, October 1962.

6

The Demineralization Process and Systems

The process of demineralizing water or solutions by ion exchange consists of the conversion of salts to their corresponding acids by hydrogen cation exchangers and the removal of these acids by anion exchangers. The two exchangers commonly are in series in separate columns, the water or solution passing first through one column and then through the other; in such case demineralization is a "two-step process." Figure 6.1 shows a typical two-bed plant. Usually the cation exchanger precedes the anion exchanger, but sometimes this order is reversed. The two exchangers may also be mixed together in single columns; these are called mixed beds.

I. Nature of Ion Exchange and Exchange Materials

Salts dissolved in water dissociate into positively charged (cations) and negatively charged ions (anions), which allow the solution to conduct electricity: the dissolved substances are therefore called electrolytes. The solutions are in a state of electroneutrality, which means that the number of positive charges balances the number of negative charges.

Likewise, ion exchangers contain positively charged cations and negatively charged anions in a condition of electroneutrality. But the exchangers differ from solutions in that only one of the two ionic species is mobile, i.e. exchangeable. For example, a typical sulfonic acid cation exchanger has immobile ion exchange sites consisting of the anionic radicals SO_3^- to which are attached the mobile cations, such as H^+ or Na^+, that may be exchanged in an ion exchange reaction. An anion exchanger similarly has immobile cationic sites to which are attached mobile (i.e. exchangeable) hydroxide anions.

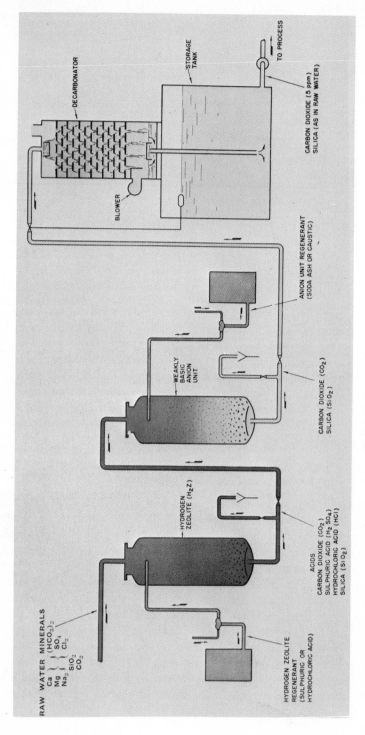

Fig. 6.1. Typical two-bed demineralizer.

When ion exchange occurs, the cations or the anions in the solution are interchanged for those in the exchanger, but both the solution and the exchanger remain in a condition of electroneutrality. In the case of cation exchanger, for example, one calcium cation, which has two positive charges (Ca^{2+}), when it leaves the water, must replace, in the exchanger, two hydrogen cations, which each have a single positive charge ($2H^+$).

Ion exchange between a solid exchanger and water containing electrolytes takes place without structural changes in the solid material; that is, the solid does not go into solution. The ions in the solution rapidly diffuse into the molecular network of the exchanger, reaching the exchange sites, where interchange of the ions occurs. The ions in the exchanger similarly diffuse out of the exchanger into the solution.

The major ion exchange materials used in demineralization are synthetic resins made by the polymerization of various organic compounds. The most frequently used compounds are styrene and divinylbenzine. The long-chained copolymer formed from these compounds contains a major proportion of styrene (80–92%) and a minor proportion of divinylbenzine (8–20%). The latter act as crosslinks to hold the long polymeric chains together.

In the manufacture of the resins (1), the styrene and divinylbenzine are mixed together, and a peroxide and a stabilizing agent are added. This mixture is then added to water and is agitated so that it disperses into suspended droplets of regulated size. Heating follows until polymerization starts, when the temperature is controlled by cooling. The droplets gradually become viscous and finally turn into spherical particles or beads and heating is continued until the polymerization is completed. The beads thus formed constitute the polystyrene matrix. To make strong acid cation exchangers from them, they are sulfonated, i.e., treated with concentrated sulfuric acid, which attaches the functional ionizable groups—SO_3H to the hydrocarbon network; from 8 to 10 of these groups are thus introduced for every 10 benzene groups in the network. To make most anion exchangers, the matrix is chloromethylated and aminated.

The resin, when dry, shrinks, so that the chains come very close together, and the bead cannot readily be penetrated by the ions, but when placed in water, it takes on water and swells, so that the chains spread apart and permit the diffusion of the ions. The degree of swelling depends on the degree of crosslinking, that is, the number of crosslinks: the greater the number of crosslinks, the less the moisture-holding capacity and the swelling. From the kinetic viewpoint, for a speedy exchange reaction it would be desirable to have as low a degree of crosslinkage as possible, but this would result in a high degree of swelling and an accompanying gelatinous structure having poor hydraulic properties. The design of a commercial ion exchange resin, therefore, involves a choice of crosslinking that represents a compromise between kinetic and hydraulic performance.

Dr. Kunin, of Rohm and Haas Company, drew the sketch on which Fig. 6.2 is based, giving his schematic representation of a hydrated strong-acid cation exchanger. As he put it, "In describing an ion exchange resin to the layman, I usually draw the analogy between the crosslinked polymer chains of an ion exchange resin and a plate of spaghetti which has cooled to the point where the individual strands have become glued or cemented together because of the soluble starches. The cementation corresponds in my analogy to crosslinkage. The polymer chains, crosslinks, water of hydration, fixed ion exchange sites, and mobile exchangeable ions are shown in this drawing."

Cation exchangers of the hydrogen type, as used for demineralization, are acidic, but the strengths of their acidities vary. Some exchangers are strongly

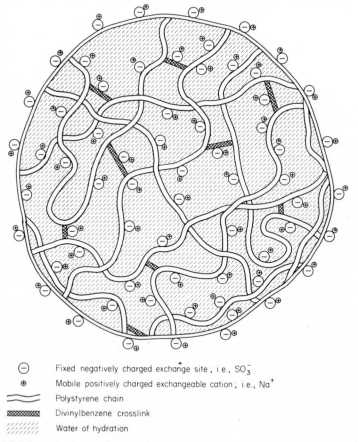

⊖   Fixed negatively charged exchange site; i.e., SO_3^-

⊕   Mobile positively charged exchangeable cation; i.e., Na^+

〰〰   Polystyrene chain

▨▨▨   Divinylbenzene crosslink

╱╱╱   Water of hydration

Fig. 6.2. Schematic picture of hydrated strong-acid cation exchanger [courtesy of Kunin (*1a*)].

acidic, containing the sulfonic acid functional group, $-SO_3H$, whereas others are weakly acidic, containing the carboxylic acid group, $-COOH$. Sulfonated coal, "Zeo–Karb," which was the first nonsiliceous cation exchanger (see Chapter 1), is mainly sulfonic, but it also contains some carboxylic groups (see Chapter 7, Section IA). The sulfonic exchangers are called strong-acid and the carboxylic ones are called weak-acid.

Similarly, there are strongly basic and weakly basic anion exchangers. Two kinds of strongly basic exchangers exist (2): Type I, with a quaternary ammonium functional group,

$$\left[\begin{array}{c} \\ \text{CH}_2-\underset{\underset{\text{CH}_3}{|}}{\overset{\overset{\text{CH}_3}{|}}{\text{N}}}-\text{CH}_3 \end{array} \right]^+ \text{OH}^- \qquad \text{Type I}$$

and Type II with a slightly modified quaternary ammonium functional group,

$$\left[\begin{array}{c} \\ \text{CH}_2-\underset{\underset{\text{CH}_3}{|}}{\overset{\overset{\text{CH}_3}{|}}{\text{N}}}-\text{CH}_2-\text{CH}_2\text{OH} \end{array} \right]^+ \text{OH}^- \qquad \text{Type II}$$

In the Type II exchanger one of the methyl groups is replaced with an ethanol group. Types I and II exchangers differ mainly in their affinities for chloride and hydroxide anions and in their chemical stabilities. Type I has somewhat less exchange capacity, but more stability, than Type II.

The weak-base anion exchangers have polyamine functional groups containing primary amine, $-NH_2$, secondary amine, $-NHR$, and tertiary amine, $-NR_2$. There are also intermediate-base anion resins, containing a mixture of both weakly and strongly basic groups.

The strength of acidity or basicity of an exchanger may be determined by titration, which measures the change in pH value while a suspension of the exchanger is neutralized through the addition of an alkali or an acid, as the case may be. In the case of a strong-acid (sulfonic) cation resin the pH value starts at about 1 and, as alkali is added, increases to 12, whereas when a weak-acid (carboxylic) cation resin is similarly neutralized, the pH value starts at about 3 and requires much more alkali to reach 12. When a strong-base anion resin is neutralized with acid, the pH value starts at about 13 and drops to under 2, whereas when a weak-base anion resin is similarly neutralized, the pH value starts at 8 and requires much more acid to reach 2.

When we say strong or weak acid cation exchangers we refer to their degree of ionization (or dissociation into ions) just as we call sulfuric or hydrochloric acids strong acids and carbonic or silicic acids weak acids. Strong acid means highly ionized rather than concentrated. For example, a low concentration of the strong acids will attack flesh whereas weak acids like boracic acid can be used even in eyes. The same is true of the strong base or weak base anion exchangers, the former resembling strong or highly ionized caustic soda and the latter being similar to weakly ionized sodium bicarbonate. Again a low concentration of caustic soda will cause damage to skin whereas sodium bicarbonate will not.

The strong-acid exchangers easily split salts, converting them to acids. By contrast, the weak-acid exchangers cannot readily do so, and they operate efficiently only with waters in the pH range above 7; however, under such conditions they remove cations equivalent to the alkalinity present, and the efficiency of their regeneration is very high. The contrast between the two exchanger types may be shown by the lengths of the arrows in the following equations, written in molecular form, where Z is the matrix of the exchanger:

Strong-acid cation exchangers:

$$Z \cdot SO_3H + NaCl \rightleftharpoons Z \cdot SO_3Na + HCl \qquad (1)$$
$$Z \cdot SO_3H + NaHCO_3 \rightleftharpoons Z \cdot SO_3Na + H_2O + CO_2 \qquad (2)$$

Weak-acid cation exchangers:

$$Z \cdot COOH + NaCl \rightleftharpoons Z \cdot COONa + HCl \qquad (3)$$
$$Z \cdot COOH + NaHCO_3 \rightleftharpoons Z \cdot COONa + CO_2 + H_2O \qquad (4)$$

All of these reactions (further discussed in the next section) are reversible as indicated by the two arrows but the comparative length of the two arrows indicate whether the reactions tend to go more to the right or more to the left. The difference between Eqs. 1 and 3 and Eqs. 2 and 4 is due to the difference in affinity for hydrogen between the two types of exchanger (see Section II for discussion of affinity). The strong-acid materials containing the highly ionized sulfonic groups have little affinity for the hydrogen ion, but the weak-acid materials containing the weakly ionized carboxylic groups have a very great affinity for it. For example, in Eq. 1 the sodium in the NaCl easily displaces the hydrogen from the exchanger and hydrochloric acid forms, whereas in Eq. 3 it displaces the hydrogen with great difficulty, if at all, and the hydrochloric acid, that forms as a reaction product, is so highly ionized that it tends to reverse the reaction. However, when water to be demineralized contains salts of weak acids, such as bicarbonates, both types of exchanger readily give up their hydrogen for the sodium of the bicarbonate (Eqs. 2 and 4). The weak carbonic acid formed as a reaction product has little regenerating potential for reversing the reaction; therefore weak-acid cation exchangers are useful for dealkalization, have high exchange capacity, and require very low acid regenerant levels, that is, the levels approach the stoichiometric amounts, without the need of any acid excess.

The weak-acid materials may be placed in units preceding those containing the strong-acid materials, or the two materials may be combined in the same unit. The saving in acid that results when waters are high in alkalinity not only reduces the operating costs but often helps to solve the problem of neutralizing the demineralizer regeneration rinse waters, as discussed in Chapter 7, Section IC.

The strong-base anion exchangers are highly ionized and can operate over the entire pH range; therefore they can remove both the highly dissociated strong acids (sulfuric and hydrochloric) and the weakly dissociated weak acids (carbonic and silicic). The weak-base anion exchangers, on the other hand, are highly ionized in the salt form only, and therefore they operate only when the pH is below 7. Being weakly ionized in the free base form, they have little, if any, salt-splitting capacity and so can remove the strong acids but not the weak acids. However, their capacity for removing the strong acids is much greater than that of the strong-base exchangers: about twice as much for the same amounts of caustic soda regenerant. Because of this, in the demineralization of waters high in sulfates and chlorides the weak-base exchangers often precede, or are combined with, strong-base anion exchangers, to save caustic soda regenerant and reduce operating cost. The three-bed demineralizer (System No. 3) described in Section XI exemplifies this practice.

The compositions, exchange capacities, and performances of the major cation and anion exchangers are discussed in detail in Chapter 7.

II. Ion Exchange Equilibria

Ion exchange in demineralization takes place with equilibrium (reversible) reactions. They may be expressed in simple form by the following two equations:

Cation exchange:

$$Z_s \cdot a^+ + b^+ \rightleftharpoons Z_s \cdot b^+ + a^+ \tag{5}$$

where Z_s is the matrix and anionic fixed site of the cation exchanger, and a^+ and b^+ are two cations.

Anion exchange:

$$A_s \cdot c^- + d^- \rightleftharpoons A_s \cdot d^- + c^- \tag{6}$$

where A_s is the matrix with cationic fixed site of the anion exchanger, and c^- and d^- are two anions.

In Eq. 5 the exchanger gives up the cation a^+ attached to its fixed site in exchange for cations b^+ in the water or solution but, as the arrows show, the reverse may take place, cations a^+ in the solution replacing cations b^+ in the exchanger, as during regeneration. The same reversibility is true of the anion exchange in Eq. 6.

The direction the reaction will take depends mainly on the affinity of the resin for the various ions in the water or solution; this is called the "selectivity" of the resin. Ion exchange equilibria are often expressed in terms of "selectivity coefficients" K. If the reaction in Eq. 5, for instance, reaches equilibrium, the value of K for cations a^+ and b^+ is calculated from the following equation:

$$K_{a^+ b^+} = \frac{(\text{concn. of } a^+ \text{ in resin}) \times (\text{concn. of } b^+ \text{ in soln.})}{(\text{concn. of } b^+ \text{ in resin}) \times (\text{concn. of } a^+ \text{ in soln.})} \tag{7}$$

This simplified equation applies to ions of equal valences; the equation is more complex in the case of ions of different valences.

The selectivity coefficient depends on many external factors, such as temperature and pressure, but mainly on the nature and valence of the ion, the type of exchanger, the degree of saturation of the ion exchange resin, and the concentration of the ions in the water or solution.

In general, at low concentrations of ions in the water or solution the divalent ions are held more tightly by a resin than are the monovalent, and the trivalent more than the divalent. Even among ions of the same valence the resins have preferences. For example, the following two series express the relative selectivities of many strong-acid cation resins with respect to the major cations:

$$Ba^{2+} > Ca^{2+} > Mg^{2+}$$
$$NH_4^+ > K^+ > Na^+ > H^+$$

Thus, at low concentrations the cation exchangers select cations of the higher valences such as calcium or magnesium, in preference to sodium. In sodium zeolite softening, for example, calcium and magnesium in the water in low concentrations (several hundred parts per million) are readily and completely exchanged for the sodium in the zeolite. This is the exhaustion phase. How then does the reverse or regeneration reaction take place? By increasing the sodium concentration in the sodium chloride brine to 5–10%, or 50,000–100,000 ppm, as NaCl, and by using an excess of sodium in the brine compared to the calcium and magnesium in the exchanger, the selectivity of the exchanger for sodium increases and, hence, the reverse reaction can readily occur. The same is true of hydrogen cation exchange and of hydroxide anion exchange in demineralization.

Strong-base anion resins Type I show the following relative selectivities for the major monovalent anions

$$NO_3^- > HSO_4^- > Cl^- > HCO_3^- > OH^-$$

III. Strong-Acid Hydrogen Cation Exchangers

The major cations in water are calcium, magnesium, sodium, and potassium. They are exchanged for hydrogen in the strong-acid cation exchanger (with sulfonic acid functional group SO_3H), as in the following equation, in ionic form:

$$\left.\begin{array}{l} Ca^{2+} \\ Mg^{2+} \\ 2\,Na^+ \\ 2\,K^+ \end{array}\right\} + Z \cdot 2(SO_3H^+) \; \rightleftharpoons \; Z \cdot 2(SO_3) \left\{\begin{array}{l} Ca^{2+} \\ Mg^{2+} \\ 2\,Na^+ \\ 2\,K^+ \end{array}\right. + 2\,H^+ \tag{8}$$

where Z is the matrix of the exchanger.

The reaction is reversible: to the right during the exhaustion phase of the exchange cycle, when the water is being treated, and to the left during the regeneration phase, when the regenerants (sulfuric or hydrochloric acid) remove (elute) from the exchanger the cations previously taken from the water and restore the exchanger to its hydrogen form.

The following equation representing the exhaustion phase, is written in molecular form (as if the salts present were undissociated) and shows the cations in combination with the major anions, the bicarbonate, sulfate, and chloride anions. The sulfonic group, SO_3H, has been deleted and replaced with hydrogen, H, for simplicity in the equation.

$$\left.\begin{array}{l} Ca \\ Mg \\ Na_2 \\ K_2 \end{array}\right\} \left\{\begin{array}{l} (HCO_3)_2 \\ SO_4 \\ Cl_2 \end{array}\right. + H_2Z \rightarrow \left\{\begin{array}{l} Ca \\ Mg \\ Na_2 \\ K_2 \end{array}\right\} Z + \left\{\begin{array}{l} 2\,H_2CO_3 \\ H_2SO_4 \\ 2\,HCl \end{array}\right\} \tag{9}$$

Thus the salts in the water are converted to their corresponding acids.

The regeneration with sulfuric acid is given in the next equation, also written in molecular form:

$$\left.\begin{array}{l} Ca \\ Mg \\ Na_2 \\ K_2 \end{array}\right\} Z + H_2SO_4 \rightarrow H_2Z + \left.\begin{array}{l} Ca \\ Mg \\ Na_2 \\ K_2 \end{array}\right\} SO_4 \tag{10}$$

Thus the cations are eluted from the exchanger as sulfates. An equation similar to Eq. 10 could be written for hydrochloric acid as regenerant; the cations then would be shown to be eluted as the more soluble chlorides.

IV. Weak-Acid Hydrogen Cation Exchangers

As discussed in Section I, the weak-acid exchangers contain carboxylic acid functional groups, COOH, and remove only that part of the total cations that is equivalent in amount to the bicarbonate alkalinity present.

The exhaustion reaction, written in molecular form, is given in the next equation, where the carboxylic acid group, COOH, has been deleted and replaced with hydrogen, H, for simplicity, and Z is the matrix of the exchanger:

$$\left. \begin{array}{c} Ca \\ Mg \\ Na_2 \end{array} \right\} (HCO_3)_2 + H_2Z \rightarrow \left\{ \begin{array}{c} Ca \\ Mg \\ Na_2 \end{array} \right\} Z + 2\,H_2CO_3 \tag{11}$$

Thus the bicarbonates in the water are converted to carbonic acid.

The regeneration reaction is similar to Eq. 10 for the strong-acid exchanger.

V. Weak-Base Anion Exchangers

The first anion exchangers developed, as indicated in Chapter 1, were weakly basic. Weak-base exchangers can remove only the highly dissociated acids (sulfuric, hydrochloric, or nitric acid) from the effluent of the first exchanger, the hydrogen exchange column; they cannot remove either the weakly dissociated carbonic acid from the alkalinity or silicic acid from the silica content in the water.

The following ionic equation expresses anion exchange with weak-base exchangers in the hydroxide form:

$$\left. \begin{array}{c} (SO_4)^{2-} \\ 2\,Cl^- \\ 2(NO_3)^- \end{array} \right\} + 2\,A_s(OH)^- \rightleftharpoons \left. \begin{array}{c} (SO_4)^{2-} \\ 2\,Cl^- \\ 2(NO_3)^- \end{array} \right\} 2\,A_s + 2(OH)^- \tag{12}$$

where A_s is the matrix and fixed cationic site of the exchanger.

Pure demineralized water, H_2O, results from the neutralization and combination of the hydrogen cations from the acids in the influent and the hydroxide anions in the effluent.

The exhaustion reaction written in molecular form may be expressed either as hydroxide anion exchange or as an acid adsorption:

$$\left. \begin{array}{c} H_2SO_4 \\ 2\,HCl \\ 2\,HNO_3 \end{array} \right\} + 2\,A_sOH \rightarrow \left\{ \begin{array}{c} SO_4 \\ Cl_2 \\ (NO_3)_2 \end{array} \right\} 2\,A_s + 2\,H_2O \tag{13}$$

$$\left. \begin{array}{c} H_2SO_4 \\ 2\,HCl \\ 2\,HNO_3 \end{array} \right\} + 2\,A_s \rightarrow 2\,A_s \left\{ \begin{array}{c} H_2SO_4 \\ 2\,HCl \\ 2\,HNO_3 \end{array} \right. \tag{14}$$

The regenerants of weak-base resins may be sodium hydroxide (caustic soda), sodium carbonate (soda ash), or ammonia. The reactions for each of these are shown below, written in molecular form:

$$2\,A_s \begin{cases} H_2SO_4 \\ 2\,HCl \\ 2\,HNO_3 \end{cases} +\; 2\,NaOH \rightarrow 2\,A_s + Na_2 \begin{cases} SO_4 \\ Cl_2 \\ (NO_3)_2 \end{cases} + 2\,H_2O \tag{15}$$

$$2\,A_s \begin{cases} H_2SO_4 \\ 2\,HCl \\ 2\,HNO_3 \end{cases} +\; Na_2CO_3 \rightarrow 2\,A_s + Na_2 \begin{cases} SO_4 \\ Cl_2 \\ (NO_3)_2 \end{cases} + H_2CO_3 \tag{16}$$

$$2\,A_s \begin{cases} H_2SO_4 \\ 2\,HCl \\ 2\,HNO_3 \end{cases} +\; 2(NH_4OH) \rightarrow 2\,A_s + (NH_4)_2 \begin{cases} SO_4 \\ Cl_2 \\ (NO_3)_2 \end{cases} + 2\,H_2O \tag{17}$$

Weak-base resins are used in many demineralizers despite their inability to remove carbonic and silicic acids. Some typical applications of weak-base anion exchange are in the demineralization of water for the following: mirror silvering, processing of ceramics, deproofing or cutting of alcohol in distilleries, plating, glass manufacture, and automobile painting.

VI. Strong-Base Anion Exchangers

The major application of demineralizing has been in the preparation of proper quality feed water for boilers, in which silica removal is important. This need required the development of a strong-base anion exchanger that could remove both the weakly dissociated and the strongly dissociated acids.

Written in ionic form, the reactions with strong-base anion exchangers are given in the following equation:

$$\left.\begin{array}{l} (SO_4)^{2-} \\ 2\,Cl^- \\ 2\,(HSiO_3)^- \\ 2\,(HCO_3)^- \end{array}\right\} + 2\,A_s \cdot (OH)^- \rightleftharpoons \left\{\begin{array}{l} (SO_4)^{2-} \\ 2\,Cl^- \\ 2\,(HSiO_3)^- \\ 2\,(HCO_3)^- \end{array}\right\} 2\,A_s + 2\,(OH)^- \tag{18}$$

Only a strongly basic alkali (caustic soda) can be used for regeneration. Expressed in molecular form, exhaustion and regeneration are as follows:

$$\left.\begin{array}{l} H_2SO_4 \\ 2\,HCl \\ 2\,H_2SiO_3 \\ 2\,H_2CO_3 \end{array}\right\} + 2\,A_s \cdot OH \rightarrow \left.\begin{array}{l} SO_4 \\ Cl_2 \\ (HSiO_3)_2 \\ (HCO_3)_2 \end{array}\right\} 2\,A_s + 2\,H_2O \tag{19}$$

$$\left.\begin{array}{l} SO_4 \\ Cl_2 \\ (HSiO_3)_2 \\ (HCO_3)_2 \end{array}\right\} 2\,A_s + 2\,NaOH \rightarrow 2\,A_sOH + Na_2 \begin{cases} SO_4 \\ Cl_2 \\ (HSiO_3)_2 \\ (HCO_3)_2 \end{cases} \tag{20}$$

VII. Exchange Techniques

Four techniques have been developed for the application of exchange operations. They are called "batch," "fixed bed," "fluidized bed," and "continuous bed."

A. Batch

The earliest technique was an intermittent process, in which the exchanger and the solution to be treated were mixed together, in a "batch," for the exhaustion and then were separated for the regeneration. Although the simplest, it has had practically no application in water treatment. It has been used in certain chemical processes, such as the production of pectin from grapefruit peel (3), the recovery of gold from cyanide solutions (4), and the removal of calcium from milk (5); viscous solutions or slurries in general afford the best field of application. The batch technique is inefficient; because of the equilibrium relationship between exchanger and solute the ions are removed only partially and, moreover, the process is cumbersome and requires too much operating labor.

B. Fixed Bed

In water treatment by means of ion exchange the downflow fixed-bed technique predominates. It is so called because the exchanger material is not moved during exhaustion and stays compact (unexpanded) as a bed or column, through which the water or solution percolates during the exhaustion phase of the cycle. The percolation allows time for the ions in the solution to make contact with the exchanger particles. The top of the column captures most of the ions during the downward flow, and the bottom receives the leftovers; therefore it is the bottom part that accomplishes the final purification and determines the purity of the effluent.

When the exchange bed no longer produces the quality of effluent desired, it is considered "exhausted." The appearance in appreciable quantity of the unwanted ions in the effluent is called the "breakthrough" of the ions, and the end of the exhaustion phase at that point is known as the "endpoint" of the service run. The flow of water or solution through the bed is then shut off, and the exchanger regenerated. Exhaustion and regeneration follow each other intermittently.

The exhaustion phase is called the service run. This is followed by the regeneration phase which includes four steps: backwashing to clean the bed, introduction of the regenerant, a slow rinse or displacement to push the regenerant slowly through the bed, and finally a fast rinse to remove the excess regenerant from the resin and elute the unwanted ions to waste.

The direction of flow during exhaustion and during introduction of the regenerant is usually downward and then the cycle is known as a "parallel downflow." In some cases the regenerant passes upflow through the bed in the reverse of the exhaustion flow; this operation is called "counterflow" (see Sections IXA2).

C. Fluidized Bed

In some special applications the direction of flow during exhaustion is upward. In such cases, unless a special blocking flow is effected or effluent collectors are located near the top of the bed (Section IXA2), the exchanger bed expands, the degree of expansion depending on the rate of flow, the viscosity, and the temperature of the solution. The bed then is no longer compact and is called "fluidized." An expanded bed allows "channeling," or passage of the solution through the enlarged spaces between the exchanger particles, and therefore provides less efficient contact. However, in certain chemical processings in which valuable suspended materials are not to be removed the fluidized-bed technique is necessary (see Chapter 14, Section IIC).

D. Continuous Technique

Instead of the fixed-bed the "continuous," or moving-bed, technique may be applied. This consists of moving in "pulses" a small exhausted portion of the bed out of the main column to another zone or vessel for regeneration and simultaneously moving regenerated portions back to the exhaustion column. Although the pulses are intermittent, they are so frequent and of such short duration that the motion has been called "continuous." Details of continuous designs are given in Chapter 13. The main advantages claimed for this technique are greater regeneration efficiency, which reduces the operating cost for regenerants and rinse water, a smaller amount of exchanger required, saving in space, and saving in capital costs. The disadvantages are the greater complexity and cost of the mechanical controls and the excessive attrition, or wear and tear, of the exchangers subjected to the frequent pulses. Its future main fields of application will be for chemical processing or the demineralization of high-solids or brackish waters, since such waters would require excessive amounts of exchanger material if fixed beds were used.

VIII. Regeneration Phase

A. In-Place and External Regenerations

Regeneration may be either "in place" or "external." In the former the regenerant solutions are brought to the exhausted columns, and the regeneration is conducted there; thus, the exchanger is regenerated "in place." External regeneration occurs in external zones or vessels, to which the exchanger is hydraulically "sluiced," or transferred, after exhaustion. The advantages of external regeneration are reduction of the danger of accidental passage of the regenerants into the product effluent, simplification of the control valves and of the internal distribution in the main columns, and rapid restoration of the exhausted main column (by means of spare regenerated exchanger from a storage vessel). External regeneration is used in utility condensate demineralizers. It is discussed in Chapter 10, Section VI.

B. *Hydrogen Cation Exchanger*

Either sulfuric acid or hydrochloric acid is used for the regeneration of hydrogen cation exchangers. The high cost of hydrochloric acid, however, limits its use to small demineralizers. As Eq. 10 showed, the sulfuric acid regeneration results in eluting the unwanted cations in the form of sulfates.

1. PREVENTING OF CALCIUM SULFATE PRECIPITATION IN RESIN

Since the solubility of calcium sulfate is low, especially in the presence of excess acid and the common sulfate anion, there is danger of its precipitation in the exchanger beds. Fouling of the exchanger would then result, and its capacity would be reduced. The quality of the effluent would suffer and result in the presence of hardness during part of the ensuing run, until the calcium sulfate precipitates have been dissolved.

To prevent this precipitation two measures are employed: progressively increasing* the concentration of the sulfuric acid solution during regeneration and decreasing the time of contact by using higher regenerant flow rates.

The first measure, progressively increasing the acid concentrations, prevents calcium sulfate precipitation by eluting most of the calcium cations during the first part of the regeneration, while the concentration of acid in the regenerant solution is low. The solubility of calcium sulfate is greatest at low concentrations, because there is less of the common sulfate anion present. A higher concentration is required in the last part of the regeneration, to provide the driving force for reversing the reaction (Eq. 8), so as to convert the exchanger as completely as possible to the hydrogen form. In this way, the high-concentration acid having passed through the bed only after most of the cations have been eluted, the precipitation of calcium sulfate is minimized.

The increase in acid concentration usually is accomplished in the following steps. If 4 lb of sulfuric acid are required to regenerate each cubic foot of exchanger, there are two steps, the first being the addition of a 2% solution, and the second, of a 4% solution; if 6 lb of acid are required, the steps are

---

* This progressive increase in acid concentration is not needed for sulfonated coal (see Chapter 7, Section IA) which can be regenerated adequately by a single dose of 2% sulfuric acid.

2, 4, and 6 %; if 8 lb are required, the steps are 2, 4, 6, and 8 %. The progression may also be made stepless. This can be done by gradually opening a concentrated-acid valve in the discharge of a centrifugal strong-acid pump or by increasing the speed of a reciprocating pump motor while keeping the dilution water flow rate constant. Some typical dilution-control systems are described in Chapter 8, Section VD.

The second measure, decreasing the time of contact between the acid and the exchanger, is necessary in addition to the progressive increase in acid strength. Fortunately, there is a time lag for equilibrium to be reached before precipitation occurs, and during this time the acid solution remains supersaturated with calcium sulfate. Therefore, if the flow of acid solution is increased sufficiently the solution leaves the exchanger bed, on the way to the sewer, before the supersaturation is relieved. As a check on whether the flow rate of the dilute acid is great enough to accomplish this result or whether precipitates have formed in the exchanger bed, samples of waste acid leaving the bed may be inspected for cloudiness, indicating the presence of precipitates, and for how much time elapses before they become cloudy.

The flow rate of dilute acid must be greater, the higher the proportion of calcium to the other cations in the water; that is, high-calcium waters call for high flow rates. Here is a rough rule of thumb:

$$\text{dilute acid (gal/min) per exchanger (ft}^3) = 2 \times Ca/(Ca + Mg + Na)$$

where the cations are all expressed as $CaCO_3$. For example, if the calcium is one half of the total cations, the flow rate of dilute acid is 1 gal/min per cubic foot of exchanger. The time of contact between acid and exchanger may be as little as 10 min with high-calcium waters, and the sizes of the acid pump and the piping must be adequate to pass the high-rate flows.

The use of hydrochloric acid avoids the calcium sulfate precipitation problem, because the chlorides eluted from the bed are all very soluble. The exchange capacity of cation exchange materials is greater with hydrochloric acid than with sulfuric acid, (see Tables 7.4 and 7.5). Therefore a smaller amount of exchange material may be used with hydrochloric acid than with sulfuric acid for equivalent total exchange capacities. Nevertheless, the former is so much more expensive than the latter that its application is limited to small demineralizers, whose low first cost outweighs the high operating costs. In other countries hydrochloric acid is used more frequently, because its cost there is closer to that of sulfuric acid.

2. RECLAIMING OF ACID

A portion of the excess acid leaving the exchanger bed during regeneration may be reclaimed and stored in a tank and then used for the first part of the next regeneration. The portion selected for reclamation should be the lowest in content of unwanted cations eluted. After the reclaimed acid is passed through the bed, new, pure acid is passed through to finish the regeneration. This reclaiming of acid reduces the amount of total acid required and, hence, the operating cost. However, the calcium sulfate precipitates in the reclaimed acid must be separated by settling before the acid can be reused; a conical bottom to the reclaimed-acid storage tank has been found useful for this purpose. It is important also that precipitates be washed from the sides of the tank. Despite these difficulties, the reclaiming of sulfuric acid has been effected (6). If hydrochloric acid is available at reasonable costs as, for example, when an acid manufacturer is near-by, then reclamation is not very troublesome and may even be justified for the larger demineralizers (7).

C. Anion Exchanger

The successful reduction of the amount of rinsing required for anion exchangers and the satisfactory elution of silica during regeneration were two problems that entailed a certain amount of research and development work.

1. RINSING PROBLEM WITH WEAK-BASE RESINS

The earliest weak-base anion exchangers were relatively unstable, losing capacity fairly rapidly (40 to 50% loss in 1 to 2 years). They also suffered from greatly increasing rinse requirement as they aged (from 50 to 300 gal per cubic foot of resin), particularly at cold-water temperatures.

The need for more rinsing was attributed to an oxidative attack by the water, which caused the formation of weak-acid groups in the exchanger (8). When resins thus degraded were regenerated with sodium alkalis, the sodium combined with the weak-acid groups. Then, when they were rinsed, the sodium hydrolyzed off the groups too slowly, and this required large amounts of water and of time for reducing the pH value enough to permit starting the next service run. Although part of the rinse water could be recovered by being recycled back to the cation unit inlet, the excessive time for rinsing still remained a serious problem.

One solution was to use the more weakly ionized ammonia instead of caustic soda for regeneration. The ammonium that had combined with the weak-acid groups hydrolyzed off more rapidly. A large demineralizer at an eastern oil refinery reported that, when caustic soda was replaced with ammonia, the rinse water needed decreased from 115,000 to 30,000 gal for 340 ft^3 of Amberlite IR-45 resin (9). The time for rinsing also was reduced from 300 to 90 min, even at cold-water temperatures and with resins more than 4 years old. Another user installed a heater for warming the water to 90°F throughout the year, so as to lessen the amount of rinse water (10).

Recently several more stable weak-base anion resins were developed that do not require excessive rinsing as they age, and the results of their use have been reported (*10*). The properties and capacities of the new resins are outlined in Chapter 7, Section IIA.

2. RECLAIMING OF RINSE WATER

Even with stable weak-base and strong-base anion exchangers rinse water is costly because it is the effluent of the cation resin. As rinsing of the regenerant out of the anion exchange bed proceeds, the dissolved-solids content of the rinse decreases sufficiently to justify its reclamation. Recycling of this anion rinse effluent back to the cation inlet received an early patent (*11*). Recycling commences when the conductivity of the rinse effluent drops to that of the raw water; see Fig. 6.3. In large demineralizer plants, the cost of the recycling pump and the piping is soon returned by the saving in water besides the saving in cation exchange resin and the acid regenerant required to produce the anion rinse water. About one half of the total anion rinse water can thus be recovered.

3. ELUTING OF SILICA FROM STRONG-BASE RESINS

Silica removal was one of the main reasons for the development of the strong-base anion exchangers, as related in Chapter 1. However, although silica was removed satisfactorily from the water during exhaustion, it proved more difficult to elute from the exchanger during regeneration. The silica therefore accumulated on the material and caused both a reduction in the exchanger capacity and more silica in the effluent.

The problem was solved by preheating the dilute caustic soda solution to about 120°F and by allowing longer time for contact with the regenerant (*11a*).

The water for diluting the caustic soda can be heated by steam or electrically. Various heating and dilution systems are described in Chapter 8, Section VD6.

To increase the time of contact, the flow rate of dilute caustic soda must be kept sufficiently low that the regenerant is introduced and displaced in not less than 60 min and, preferably, in 90 min; the total regeneration periods therefore amount to 3 or 4 hr, including backwashing, introduction of caustic soda, slow rinse or displacement, and fast rinse. By contrast, the total regeneration periods for cation exchangers are 60 to 90 min.

4. LESSENING OF RINSE WATER BY OMISSION OF SUBFILLS

The resin bed commonly is supported by a granular subfill, which prevents its escape through the underdrain. Anthracite supports anion resin, because it is nonsiliceous and therefore will not give up silica, as would gravel in the

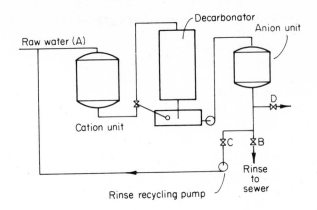

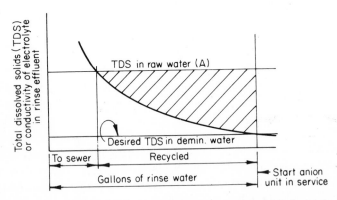

Fig. 6.3. Anion rinse recycling. When the total dissolved solids (TDS) in the rinse to sewer at B drops to the TDS in the raw water, A, then valve B is closed, valve C is opened, and the recycling pump is started. The rinse recycling is continued, until the TDS in the effluent drops to the desired value; then valve C is closed, valve D is opened, and the recycling pump is stopped. This ends the rinse, and the anion unit is then put back in service.

presence of warm caustic soda. Gravel has been used for supporting cation resin, but anthracite also is used for this purpose, even though gravel is not attacked at low pH values.

It was found that the anthracite subfills under anion resin adsorbed caustic soda, which required extra rinsing to give a low solids content in the rinse effluent. To solve this problem, the underdrain was modified with fine openings, which prevent escape of the resin without the subfill. Several designs of this modern type of underdrain are described in Chapter 8, Section IIID.

IX. Ion Leakage and Endpoints of Exhaustion Phase

The reactions for the exhaustion phase given in the equations that appeared earlier in this chapter were written in a simplified form that seemed to indicate a complete exchange of the unwanted cations or anions. However, even with efficient fixed-bed columnar operations some of the unwanted ions escape into the effluent. This escape is known as "ion leakage."

Columnar operation is similar to the old Indian gantlet. In downflow operation the unwanted ions are progressively removed, as the water or solution percolates down through the bed. As a result, the exchanger captures more of the ions at the top than at the bottom. The purity of the exchanger at the bottom determines the purity of the effluent because as the liquid percolates down, the ions decrease in concentration, and their final reduction to trace amounts requires a deep enough bed (usually more than 24 in.) and pure enough (well regenerated) material at the bottom. The driving force for the greatest purification of a water or solution is the difference in concentration between the ions in the liquid and those in the lowest part of the exchanger bed. Unfortunately, for a complete freedom from the unwanted ions in the lowest part of the exchange bed the amount of regenerant needed would be uneconomical; therefore some ion leakage is to be expected. Several techniques for minimizing it, however, have been developed.

A. Strong-Acid Cation Exchangers

During regeneration with downflow of acid the top of the bed is more completely converted to the hydrogen form than the bottom, but unless uneconomical amounts of excess acid are employed, the bottom usually contains a band of sodium at the end of the regeneration. Figure 6.4 shows a cation exchanger bed before and after an acid regeneration.

As the next service run starts, the cations in the influent are exchanged for the hydrogen ions in the top of the bed. The hydrogen ions are then exchanged for the sodium in the bottom of the bed, releasing the sodium as cation leakage into the effluent. As the run progresses, this sodium cation leakage decreases, because the sodium band at the bottom is gradually consumed.

Figure 6.5 shows a typical service run. The cations in the water are converted to their corresponding acids. But the conversion is not complete. The difference between the total mineral acidity (corresponding to the sulfates and chlorides in the influent) and the free mineral acidity in the effluent is equal to the cation leakage.

At the end of the exhaustion run, at the breakthrough, the FMA drops, and when the resulting increased cation leakage reaches the allowable limit, the unit is regenerated. Usually, instead of FMA, its equivalent conductivity is determined. The curve in Fig. 6.5 is based on a constant amount of sulfates and chlorides (TMA) in the influent. If the TMA should vary during the

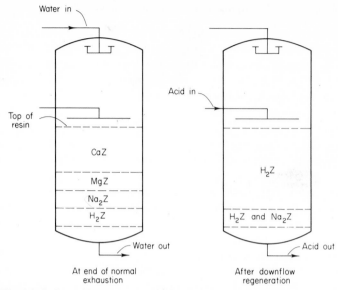

Fig. 6.4. Cation exchanger resin bed before and after regeneration with acid.

run, as it does in some surface supplies or mixtures of waters, the free mineral acidity will go up and down with the variations, so the effluent FMA alone will not serve to determine the breakthrough, and another means is utilized. A sample of water is taken by a screened probe located some inches above the bottom of the bed and its conductivity compared with the effluent conductivity. The difference between the two conductivities or their ratio (*12*) can be measured by a single instrument. During most of the exhaustion run the conductivity difference is zero, or the ratio is one-to-one, but at the end of the run the upper sample contains less free mineral acidity and shows less conductivity than the effluent. The difference or ratio has, then, increased, and when it reaches the allowable limit, the unit is regenerated. Another method of overcoming variations in the total mineral acidity is to measure sodium leakage directly by a flame photometer; this is an expensive instrument but is becoming popular in large demineralizer plants.

The amount of cation leakage can be reduced by increasing the acid level. The greater the excess of acid used, the greater the conversion of the exchanger to the hydrogen form, and the less the amount of sodium left in the bed and, therefore, the less the sodium leakage. Chapter 7, Section IB gives the amount of cation leakage to be expected with the major strong acid cation exchangers at different regenerant levels.

The amount of cation leakage is influenced also by the character of the influent. Waters high in sodium (in percent of total cations) cause high

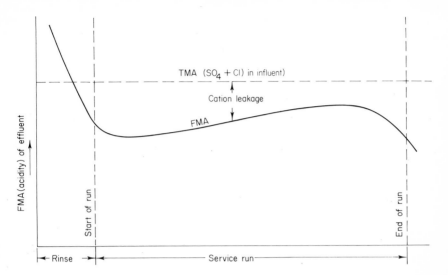

Fig. 6.5. Curves of typical service run of strong-acid cation exchanger. FMA, free mineral acidity; TMA, total mineral acidity.

cation leakage, and waters high in bicarbonate alkalinity, on the other hand, cause low cation leakage. Chapter 7, Section IB, gives the effect of sodium and alkalinity in the influent on the cation leakage.

Cation leakage is important because it affects the purity of the deminer-alizer effluent. A strong-base anion exchanger can remove only the acidity, not the sodium. It converts the sodium salts to sodium hydroxide by salt-splitting, which creates a high conductivity and pH value in the effluent. Therefore, for a low conductivity of demineralized water cation leakage must be reduced. Several methods have been devised for the purpose; they are described in the following paragraphs.

1. AIR-MIXING OF RESIN AFTER REGENERATION (UNIMIX)

Rohm and Haas Company has suggested the use of compressed air for mixing the cation resin after regeneration and has called the practice Unimix. Air mixing distributes the sodium band, shown in Fig. 6.4, throughout the bed, so that the greater sodium leakage at the start of the run, shown in Fig. 6.5, is decreased, and the free mineral acidity is more constant during the run. Air mixing requires, however, a considerable amount of air (5 to 10 scfm per square foot of area) and also involves additional steps for draining down to the top of the bed before introducing the air and refilling later, increasing the total outage time and the equipment costs; for this reason the technique is rarely employed.

2. COUNTERFLOW REGENERATION

With downflow exhaustion the acid regenerant may be passed upflow, or counterflow. This eliminates the sodium band at the bottom of the bed, because the excess pure acid, passing upward through the bottom of the bed, converts it to the hydrogen form. Upflow, however, presents the problem of an expanding bed (if the rate of flow is high) and channeling (improper contact of acid and resin). Expansion of the bed may be avoided by means of a screened pipe system near the top of the bed, for collecting the acid effluent, so that the acid is not allowed to rise into the freeboard. A "blocking flow" of water at the same time can be allowed to enter at the top of the shell, passing downflow through the freeboard and leaving through the same screened pipe system. An improved effluent quality and lower regenerant levels have been reported (13) with the blocking-flow technique, and a patent has been granted for its practice (14). However, upflow acid regeneration can be successful without the blocking flow. The laterals of the collector should be backflushed with water before the start of the acid flow, so that the screening does not become clogged by fine resin.

Counterflow regeneration is justified if the influent is high in solids and in sodium, because in such waters the sodium leakage is excessive, but for the usual influent, which is not high in these, downflow regeneration gives the same effluent quality and is usually preferred. It does not necessitate a collector and the distribution of acid is superior. Backwashing classifies the particles, bringing the finer ones to the top, where they impose resistance to downflow; this causes uniform distribution of the downflow acid across the bed, and channeling is avoided.

3. MULTIBED (FOUR-BED) DEMINERALIZERS

In demineralizer technical calculations (Chapter 9) the first step involves consideration of the purity desired in the product water or solution. This purity is usually expressed as parts per million electrolyte as total dissolved solids (or its equivalent conductivity) and as silica (for strong-base anion resin). Since the total dissolved solids, as explained in Section IXA, is determined by the cation leakage, the designer selects an acid regenerant level (pounds of acid per cubic foot of resin) that will keep the leakage low enough. If the level thus determined turns out to be excessive, the usual remedy is to demineralize the water two or more times in series. This is done in "multibed" plants, where a *primary* two-bed demineralizer (cation and anion exchange units) is followed by a *secondary* two-bed demineralizer. The cation leakage in the effluent of the primary pair is removed by the secondary pair. Less total acid is required than if the full demineralization is accomplished with a single pair. This is analogous to double and triple distillation, in which the distilled water is progressively purified. Primary and secondary pairs of units, or multibed plants, are also called "four-bed" demineralizers; they are described with other demineralizer systems in Section XI.

4. Mixed-Bed (Monobed) Demineralizers

In the mixed-bed (or Monobed) process developed by Rohm and Haas Company (15) the cation and anion exchangers are in the same shell rather than in separate shells. They are mixed together by compressed air after regeneration. The cation resin particles and anion resin particles, being thus next to each other, constitute a series of two-bed pairs of beads. Just as a four-bed demineralizer reduces cation leakage more, and produces a purer water, than a two-bed, so the mixed bed does better than the four-bed.

Figure 6.6 shows a mixed-bed unit. It indicates a shell with a flat lower head; in other designs an internal flat bottom is supported within the ordinary dished lower head. Prior to regeneration the two resins are separated by backwashing. The success of the mixed-bed technique was made possible by the difference in density between the two types of bead, which is sufficient to permit good classification and separation by backwashing. After separation the two resins are independently regenerated, as shown in Fig. 6.7. A screened interface pipe system, located between the two resins, collects the regenerant effluent. The acid usually flows upward and the caustic soda downward, as the figure shows, but the acid can be made to flow downward by being put into the interface system and out at the bottom. The cation resin regeneration can precede the anion resin regeneration, as in the figure, but the two may be simultaneous. The advantage of the sequential regeneration is that the calcium cations are eluted from the cation resin before carbonate anions are eluted from the anion resin, and this prevents the formation of calcium carbonate precipitates that might foul the interface screening.

A downward blocking flow of water proceeds from the top while the acid flows upward. Both the blocking water and the effluent acid escape through the interface collector. The blocking flow avoids expansion of the bed, but it mainly prevents the acid from entering the anion bed above the interface. An upward blocking flow of water or acid proceeds from the bottom while the caustic soda flows downward, so that the latter does not enter the cation resin. Blocking flow is covered by a patent (16).

Mixed beds are frequently used as secondary polishing units following a two-bed pair, as will be described in Section XI. The comparative effluent qualities of two-bed, four-bed, and combination two-bed and mixed-bed demineralizers are given in Table 6.2.

B. Weak-Acid Cation Exchangers

Figure 6.8 shows curves of typical service runs of carboxylic cation resin removing alkalinity from four waters of different total mineral acidities

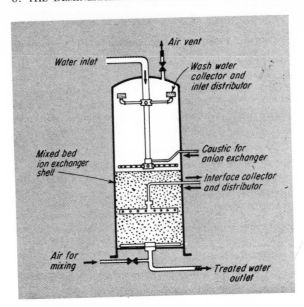

Fig. 6.6. Mixed-bed demineralizer. It houses mixture of cation and anion exchange resins. Air for mixing enters through bottom distributor. [Reproduced from *Power*, December, 1958 (*15a*)].

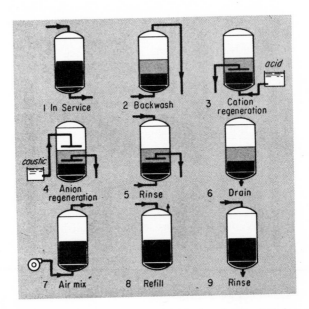

Fig. 6.7. Regeneration of mixed bed, from initial backwash to end of rinse and return to service, takes from 2 to 4 hr. [Reproduced from *Power*, December, 1958 (*15a*)].

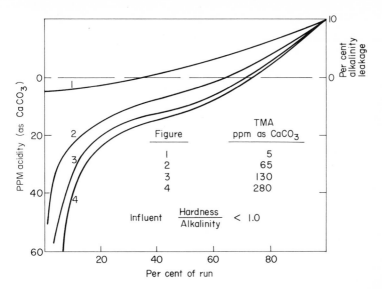

Fig. 6.8. Curves of typical service run of weak-acid cation exchanger (Amberlite IRC-84) with various TMA (total mineral acidities), in parts per million as $CaCO_3$, in influent and with influent hardness less than the alkalinity. Acid regenerant levels are 110 to 120% of theoretical. Endpoint of run shows alkalinity leakage that is 10% of influent alkalinity.

(sulfate plus chloride). The endpoint of the run is an effluent alkalinity leakage equal to 10% of the influent alkalinity. The acid regenerant level is 110 to 120% of theoretical; or the pounds of acid used equal 110 to 120% of the pounds of alkalinity removed.

The runs start with an acidity leakage, which is greater the higher the total mineral acidity present. As the curves show, the acidity leakage then decreases rapidly during the first 10 to 20% of the run. The curves flatten out at 20% of the run, and the acidity leakage drops to zero during the middle of the run. Then alkalinity starts to leak through, and the leakage reaches 10% of the influent alkalinity at 100%, or the endpoint of the run.

If the weak-acid cation units are being used for alkalinity removal for the purpose of saving acid in a demineralizer, they will be followed by anion units, which will satisfactorily remove the acidity from the cation effluent. If the weak-acid cation units are used for dealkalizing and not for demineralizing and there are no anion units, the varying effluent acidity may have to be neutralized by adding an alkali controlled by a pH meter. The application of carboxylic weak-acid cation resins for saving acid when treating high-alkalinity waters is just beginning in this country; it has been more actively applied in Europe and in Canada (*17*).

The service run in Fig. 6.8 applies only when the weak-acid cation resin is used for dealkalization alone. When it is used in double-layer cation units, a strong-acid cation resin being below it, as for demineralization, the run can be considerably lengthened. Then, instead of the run's ending when the effluent of the weak-acid cation layer shows an alkalinity leakage equal to 10% of the influent alkalinity, it continues until the effluent shows a hardness breakthrough. The alkalinity in the effluent of the upper layer increases in the form of sodium bicarbonate. This increased leakage of alkalinity is economically eliminated by the strong-acid cation resin lying below it, which has a high capacity for removing sodium bicarbonate alkalinity.

C. Weak-Base Anion Exchangers

Since divalent sulfate anions are more tightly held by weak-base anion resin than are monovalent bicarbonate and chloride, the leakage of anions in the effluent consists mainly of bicarbonate and chloride.

Figure 6.9 shows a typical weak-base anion exchanger rinse and service run. The rinse is given in two steps: in the first step the rinse water is run to waste until the total dissolved solids in the rinse effluent equals that of the water influent, and in the second step the rinse effluent is recycled back to the cation inlet, until the conductivity drops to the desired limit for starting the next run. At the end of the run acidity breaks through, and the effluent conductivity rises, because the acid is more conductive.

D. Strong-Base Anion Exchangers

Since the weakly dissociated silicic and carbonic acids are less tightly held by strong-base resins than are the strongly dissociated sulfuric and hydrochloric acids, they break through before the conductivity rises. Figure 6.10 shows a typical rinse and service run. A slight drop in conductivity often occurs at the breakthrough; it results from the neutralizing of the caustic soda in the normal effluent by the weak acids that suddenly appear, and the silicate and bicarbonate formed are less conductive than the caustic soda. The dip can serve to monitor the endpoint of the run.

Since silica in the effluent increases rapidly after the breakthrough (see Fig. 6.10), it is important to monitor it as the end of the run approaches. To avoid frequent testing for effluent silica it is possible to initiate the regeneration by a contactor on a flow meter to take place long before the silica breakthrough. Another possibility is to measure the conductivity of a sample from a screened probe, inserted in the bed above the bottom, whose elevation is adjusted so that the conductivity of the sample will rise before the silica break through; of course, a rise in conductivity may be caused by cation exchanger exhaustion, which must be similarly monitored. Automatic silica analyzers that directly monitor effluent silica are now available; although they are costly, they are gaining acceptance.

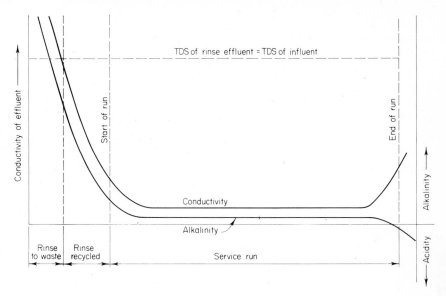

Fig. 6.9. Curves of typical service run of weak-base anion exchanger. TDS, total dissolved solids.

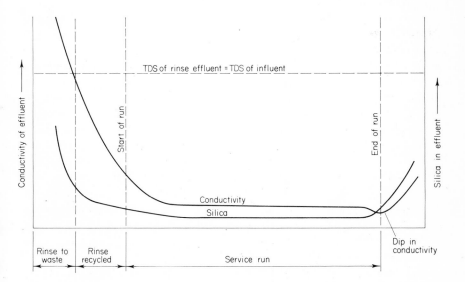

Fig. 6.10. Curves of typical service run of strong-base anion exchanger. TDS, total dissolved solids.

The amount of silica leakage during the exhaustion run is influenced by the ratio of silica to the total exchangeable anions in the influent. The higher this ratio (which is often expressed in percent of SiO_2 per total exchangeable anions, both as $CaCO_3$), the higher the silica leakage. For a lower silica leakage the caustic soda regenerant level, in pounds per cubic foot of anion resin, must be increased. Tables of capacities and silica leakages for various caustic soda levels and influent compositions are given in Chapter 7, Section IIB.

If the caustic soda level needed to give the desired silica level becomes excessive, four-bed or else two-bed plus mixed-bed units are indicated, but the strong-base anion resin then must be used in both the primary and secondary stages, the secondary removing the silica that leaks through the primary.

Premature silica breakthrough can be avoided with three-bed demineralizers, in which both weak-base and strong-base resins are regenerated simultaneously by a counterflow of caustic. The amount of strong-base resin used in the last unit may be so selected as to have considerable excess exchange capacity. The regeneration of both anion exchangers can be initiated by a conductivity rise in the effluent of the weak-base exchanger; the strong-base exchanger would then be only partially exhausted and premature silica breakthrough thus prevented.

E. Ion Leakage due to Low Flow Rates

If the flow rate is too low (under about 1 gal/min/ft^2) the effluent conductivity is increased. Also, if the flow through a demineralizer stops, the effluent quality is inferior when it is restarted; this is attributed to a regenerating effect, causing some elution of the unwanted ions. Frequently a short rinse is necessary before the restart of the service run. The deterioration in effluent quality is greater with two beds than with mixed beds, and the rinse required before restarting is shorter with mixed beds. The extra rinse will not be necessary, if the effluent can be recycled back to the cation resin inlet by a pump during idle or low flow periods; the pump can be started up automatically by a rate-of-flow meter with a low-flow contactor.

F. Ion Leakage due to Organic Fouling of Strong-Base Resins

Strong-base anion exchangers, by virtue of their ability to remove weakly dissociated acids, adsorb organic acids and salts from the effluent of the cation exchanger and are sometimes fouled by them. These "organics" are derived from organic matter in surface supplies. Despite pretreatment of the water (Chapter 4, Section III), even in well designed and operated pretreatment plants, some residual organic matter is to be expected; even municipally filtered city water has caused organic fouling. Unfortunately the organics adsorbed by the strong-base resin are not satisfactorily eluted in the caustic soda regeneration and, instead, accumulate in and block the pores and exchange sites, diminishing the capacity of the resin. In addition, the effluent quality deteriorates, resulting in leakage of the organic acids, greater leakage of total dissolved solids, equivalent higher conductivity and lower pH values. Consequently, the early replacement of fouled resin has often been necessary and, since anion resins are expensive, organic fouling has been a serious problem.

1. Fouling of Mixed Beds

The mixed-bed demineralizers are more vulnerable to organic fouling than are the two-bed. This is due partly to the fact that fouling is greater at the lower pH values that prevail in the effluent of mixed beds and partly to the fact that a better quality of effluent is expected from the mixed beds and therefore it takes much less fouling for a mixed bed to stop producing acceptable effluents. For example, an effluent conductivity of 0.1 to 1.0 µmho (10,000,000 to 1,000,000 ohm-cm specific resistance) normally is expected from mixed beds, but from two beds it is 5 to 10 µmhos (200,000 to 100,000 ohms-cm specific resistance), or 1 to 2 ppm total dissolved solids. When organic fouling of a two-bed demineralizer occurs, and some organics accumulate in the anion resin and start leaking into the effluent, the effect on the effluent quality is less significant than in mixed beds; in the latter the conductivity of the effluent soon rises to more than 1 µmho, and then the resin must be replaced. This was the experience at the Cromby Station despite frequent replacements of the pretreating granular carbon beds (18). The remedy was to install a two-bed demineralizer ahead of the mixed beds and use the latter as secondary polishing units only; then frequent replacements of the anion resin were no longer required, and a good effluent quality was maintained continuously.

2. Defouling

A method of cleaning organically fouled strong-base anion resin in two-bed demineralizers was developed (19) and has been found successful in prolonging the resin's life (20). The method originated from the observation that an intense, brown color appeared in the effluent during laboratory tests of the resin's basicity, or salt-splitting, capacity; the brown color was due to organic matter eluted when the fouled resin was treated alternately with caustic soda and sodium chloride solutions. The alternating treatments were applied on a large scale and shown to afford more exchange capacity and better effluent.

Warm (120°F) caustic soda and brine solutions work better than cold. First the resin is regenerated with the caustic soda, about 1.5 to 2.0 lb per cubic foot of resin being used; then the brine is passed through, 6.5 to 8.0 lb per cubic foot being used. The greatest intensity of brown color is observed when the brine starts flowing through. The cycle is repeated, until the color has faded sufficiently. The cleaning effect is both physical and chemical. The physical effect is that the resin shrinks and swells with the alternating caustic soda and brine, and some of the adsorbed organics are thereby released; it is as if the resin were a sponge that swells in adsorbing and then, when squeezed, expels. The chemical effect is that the chlorides in the brine also elute the organic foulants through ion exchange.

Usually two or three cycles suffice, provided they are applied frequently enough; they should not be delayed until the organic matter gets "fixed" in the resin. One or two treatments a year are often sufficient, but with badly contaminated raw waters, even well pretreated, a treatment may be needed every 10 or 20 runs [see Ref. (10), Chapter 4]. The treatments may not remove foulants other than organic matter; iron foulants, for instance, would require acid treatment of the resin.

3. MACRORETICULAR RESINS IN MIXED BEDS

Macroreticular anion resins (described in Chapter 7), with greater porosity and with larger discrete pores, than in previous resins, have been found to allow better elution of the organics (21). The addition of a small amount of the macroreticular weak-base anion resin Amberlite IRA-93 to mixed beds has prolonged the life of the anion resin significantly. The operation is called "sweetening."

In a case history (22) for example, two mixed beds required replacement of resin once or twice a year after every 200–300 runs when the effluent conductivity rose to over 1 μmho. But when the cation bed was replaced with macroreticular cation resin (Amberlite 200), and a few inches of macroreticular weak base anion resin (Amberlite IRA-93) were added to the gel-type strong base anion resin bed, the effluent conductivity remained below 1 μmho even after 1300 runs. Nevertheless, caustic soda, salt, and 15% hydrochloric acid were applied regularly after every 100 runs for the removal of other foulants. The organic fouling that had taken place in the strong-base resin was traced to organic "sloughage" from the cation resins and to organics in the water, but when the more stable macroreticular cation resin was substituted, it resisted oxidation, so that there was less of the sloughage. Macroreticular resins are more expensive than others and have somewhat smaller capacities, so that, although they alleviate the organic fouling, they are not a complete solution.

4. ORGANIC TRAPS

As described in Chapter 4, Section IIID, organic traps have been proposed as a pretreatment before demineralization and are beginning to be applied in the United States. They have been reported to protect large demineralizers abroad (21), and they also assure a better quality of final effluent. Brine is used for their regeneration on a daily basis.

The life of the resin in these traps and the cost of the brine regenerant must be evaluated and compared with the cost of the brine and caustic soda cleaning methods described in Section IXF2. The costs of anion resin replacements with and without the traps also must be compared, after some longer experience has been gained.

5. PRIMARY-STAGE STRONG-BASE ANION RESIN IN MULTIBED SYSTEMS

Strong-base anion resin in both the primary and the secondary stages of multibed demineralizers is recommended, so that the primary anion resin will remove the organics and protect the secondary units. This practice assures an excellent quality of final effluent continuously and for long periods. The large demineralizer at Linden, New Jersey [see Ref. (10), Chapter 4] has a primary three-bed system followed by secondary mixed beds. The anion resin in the primary system is cleaned with caustic and brine frequently, but the resin in the mixed beds is cleaned only about once a year. The final effluent has continued to have a specific resistance of 10,000,000 to 20,000,000 ohms-cm for many years.

X. Ten Major Demineralizer Systems

A number of demineralizer systems or arrangements of the following main building blocks are available: strong- and weak-acid cation exchangers, strong- and weak-base anion exchangers, and decarbonator or vacuum deaerator. Figure 6.11 shows ten major demineralizer systems. The weak-acid exchangers are not shown; they can be added to precede the strong-acid exchangers in any system, to save acid regenerant for waters high in alkalinity.

The decarbonators or vacuum deaerators shown in the figure are optional, depending on economic considerations. They reduce the free carbon dioxide in the effluent of the cation exchanger. Such mechanical reduction of the carbon dioxide is more economical than its chemical removal by the strong-base anion exchanger, whenever the influent alkalinity exceeds 50 to 100 ppm (as $CaCO_3$) and the demineralizer capacity exceeds 50 to 100 gal/min. The cost of the decarbonator or vacuum deaerator and the stainless-steel pumps that follow them must be compared with the savings in anion resin and caustic soda regenerant.

It is possible to place in the same unit both weak-acid and strong-acid cation resins, and the same is true of the weak-base and strong-base anion resins. The use of two resins as a double-layer in one unit is a recent development (23, 24) that can make for considerable savings in capital investment

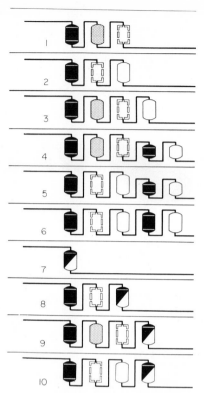

Fig. 6.11. Ten major demineralizer systems: black, strong-acid cation exchanger; white, strong-base anion exchanger; shaded, weak-base anion exchanger; half black and half white, mixed bed; broken rectangle, decarbonator or vacuum deaerator. (1) Two-bed with weak-base; (2) two-bed with strong-base; (3) three-bed; (4) four-bed, primary with weak-base; (5) four-bed, primary with strong-base; (6) parallel two-beds, as in system 2, or four-bed, as in system 5 (except for size of secondary unit); (7) mixed-bed; (8) cation bed, decarbonator, and mixed-bed; (9) two-bed, as in system 1, and mixed bed; (10) two-bed, as in system 2, and mixed-bed. The secondary units in systems 4 and 5, which are used only for polishing, may be smaller than the primary, as indicated. [Reproduced from *Power*, December, 1958 (*15a*)].

and operating cost, particularly in larger demineralizers. The two resins have enough difference in density so that they do not mix appreciably and remain stratified as a double layer. They are usually regenerated upflow (counterflow). This double-layer design is further discussed in Chapter 7, Sections IC and IIA2 and in Chapter 9, Section IID is given a technical calculation of a case using this design.

The selection of the demineralizer design from among these many systems is determined by the following factors: necessity of removing silica, effluent purity required, influent composition, size of plant, cost of regenerant.

A. Removal of Silica

If the application of the demineralized water in a given case can tolerate silica, then system 1 in Fig. 6.11 is used. This removes sulfates and chlorides (total mineral acidity) but not silica or carbon dioxide. The weak-base resin has about double the capacity for removing total mineral acidity that the strong-acid resin has, given equal caustic soda regenerant levels. Moreover, it can be regenerated with soda ash or ammonia, both of which are less expensive than caustic soda.

If the carbonic acid or resulting free carbon dioxide in the effluent of system 1 can be tolerated, the decarbonator or vacuum deaerator may be omitted, but in that case the pH value of the effluent will be low, because of the carbonic acid, and the effluent piping would have to be acid-proof. The decarbonator or vacuum deaerator can be located either before or after the weak-base exchanger, since the latter removes little, if any, carbonic acid. If it is located after, as shown in Fig. 6.1 and Fig. 6.11, it is not subjected to such low pH values. The effluent purity of system 1, expressed as total dissolved solids, is usually 2 to 5 ppm or, as equivalent conductivity, 5 to 12.5 μmhos.

If the demineralized water is used for boiler feed or some other industrial purpose in which the silica tolerance is low, strong-base anion resin must be used in any one of the other nine systems shown in Fig. 6.11.

B. Required Purity of Effluent

The required purity of demineralized water for different applications is usually expressed in terms of the amount of electrolyte in parts per million as total dissolved solids (TDS) in the effluent. These amounts are so small that it is very difficult to determine them by gravimetric analysis, but, fortunately, the easily measured specific resistance or specific conductance (conductivity) of the water may be used as the equivalent of the total dissolved solids, since the conductivity of a solution is in direct proportion to the solids content. The resistance is the reciprocal of the conductivity ("mho" is "ohm" spelled backwards). Specific resistance is expressed in ohms-centimeter (electrodes are 1 cm square and 1 cm apart) and specific conductance in mhos-cm (or, usually, micromhos-cm, that is, millionths of a mho-cm). Resistance, expressed in ohms, therefore equals 1,000,000 divided by the conductivity, expressed in micromhos. In measurements of the conductivity by the usual solubridge meter (galvanometer with a Wheatstone bridge circuit), the temperature must be taken into account. Usually the conductivity at 77°F (25°C) is the standard; in measurements at other temperatures correction factors must be applied. If gases, such as carbon dioxide or ammonia, are present, they affect the conductivity and therefore are usually removed ahead of the solubridge meter, or a correction factor is applied;

for example, each part per million carbon dioxide increases the conductivity by 0.05 μmhos.

1. CONDUCTIVITY VERSUS CONCENTRATION IN EFFLUENT OF VARIOUS DEMINERALIZER SYSTEMS

Table 6.1 gives the electrolyte content as total dissolved solids and its equivalent conductivity (or resistance) in the effluents of various demineralizer systems for three typical degrees of purity: "ultrapure," "very pure," and "pure" (25). The table shows that for two-bed strong-base systems each 1 ppm total dissolved solids is equivalent to 5 μmhos of conductivity,

Table 6.1

ELECTROLYTE CONTENT (AS TOTAL DISSOLVED SOLIDS) EQUIVALENT CONDUCTIVITY AND SPECIFIC RESISTANCE FOR VARIOUS REQUIRED PURITIES OF DEMINERALIZED WATER

Degree of purity	Spec. resistance (at 77°F), ohms-cm	Conductivity (at 77°F), μmhos	Electrolyte (TDS) (as $CaCO_3$), ppm	
			Mixed bed or two-bed with weak-base	Two-bed with strong-base
Ultrapure	10,000,000	0.1	0.04	0.02
Very pure	1,000,000	1.0	0.40	0.20
Pure	100,000	10.0	4.00	2.00

whereas for two-bed weak-base systems or for mixed-bed systems each 1 ppm is equivalent to 2.5 μmhos. The relation between parts per million and micromhos depends on the conductivities of the various sodium compounds to be expected in the effluent, as given in Fig. 6.12. In the two-bed strong-base system the effluent mainly contains sodium hydroxide, which has a high conductivity, but in the two bed weak-base system or the mixed-bed system the effluent pH is under 7, and sodium salts, such as sodium chloride, which have lower conductivities, predominate in the effluent.

2. QUALITY OF EFFLUENT IN MAJOR STRONG-BASE ANION DEMINERALIZER SYSTEMS

Table 6.2 gives the range of effluent total dissolved solids and silica, normally obtainable with the major silica-removing demineralizer systems treating raw waters of moderate salinity (under about 500 ppm TDS).

From this table it is evident that "pure" demineralized water (up to 100,000 ohms) is readily obtained from two-bed systems but that if "very pure" water (up to 1,000,000 ohms) is required, the use of four-bed or

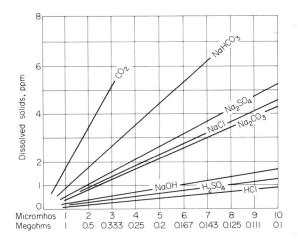

Fig. 6.12. Specific conductance of electrolytes.

mixed-bed systems is indicated, and if "ultrapure" water (up to 10,000,000 ohms) is needed, the combination two-bed or three-bed plus mixed-bed system (26) must be used (described in Sections XI and XII). Mixed-bed polishing units are therefore gaining acceptance in makeup demineralizers for high-pressure boiler plants.

The table also indicates that, when effluent silica is similarly considered, two beds may be expected to reduce the silica to about 0.02 to 0.1 ppm

Table 6.2

RANGE OF ELECTROLYTE CONTENT (AS TOTAL DISSOLVED SOLIDS) AND SILICA IN EFFLUENTS OF SOME MAJOR SILICA-REMOVING DEMINERALIZER SYSTEMS[a]

	Two- or three-bed	Four-bed	Mixed-bed	Two- or three-bed plus mixed-bed
Electrolyte (as TDS), ppm	2.0 to 3.0	0.2 to 1.0	0.2 to 0.5	0.04 to 0.10
Silica (as SiO_2),[b] ppm	0.02 to 0.1	(a) 0.02 to 0.1	0.02 to 0.1	(a) 0.02 to 0.1
		(b) 0.01 to 0.05		(b) 0.01 to 0.05
Conductivity, μmhos	10.0 to 15.0	1.0 to 5.0	0.5 to 1.25	0.10 to 0.25
Specific resistance, ohms-cm	67,000 to 100,000	200,000 to 1,000,000	800,000 to 2,000,000	4,000,000 to 10,000,000

[a] This table is based on the demineralization of waters of moderate salinity (under about 500 ppm TDS). Condensate high-rate mixed-bed demineralizers produce effluent TDS of under 0.04 ppm, or 0.1 μmho (10,000,000 ohms), and SiO_2 under 0.005 ppm.

[b] The two ranges given signify (a) with primary weak-base anion resin and (b) with primary strong-base anion resin.

(less silica may be produced if the caustic regenerant levels are increased, but this may be at the risk of excessive operating costs). If the amount of silica is to be 0.01 to 0.05 ppm, four beds or a combination of two beds and a mixed bed (with strong-base anion resin in both the primary and secondary stages) are generally recommended. Strong-base resin in the primary stage also serves to protect the secondary resin from organic fouling (see Section IXF above).

C. Influent Composition

Chapter 7 gives the cation leakage and silica leakage to be expected with various regenerant levels and raw waters of various compositions. The water analysis must be studied first for a calculation of the proportion of sodium and alkalinity, expressed in percent of total cations and anions, and the proportion of total mineral acidity (sulfates and chlorides) and silica, expressed in percent of total exchangeable anions.

Higher percentages of sodium and lower percentages of alkalinity increase the cation leakage and therefore require higher acid levels to keep this leakage within the limits set for the total dissolved solids. If the acid levels become excessive, four-bed or combined two-bed and mixed-bed demineralizers are recommended. Waters that have high percentages of alkalinity make the use of weak-acid cation resins economical, because it saves acid; for such waters a decarbonator or vacuum deaerator also becomes advisable.

Waters that have high percentages of silica cause much silica leakage and require high caustic soda levels; therefore strong-base anion resins in both the primary and secondary stages are recommended, to save caustic soda. If the percentage of total mineral acidity is high enough, a weak-base anion resin in a three-bed or the double-layer system is justified, to reduce the caustic soda requirements.

The demineralizer technical calculations in Chapter 9 include examples with different water analyses, in order that the advantages of the various options may be evaluated.

D. Size of Plant

The larger the plant, the greater the importance of reducing the operating cost, even though the capital investment is greater. In large plants it is possible to justify the selection of four-bed, instead of two-bed demineralizers and the inclusion of both weak-acid cation resin and weak-base anion resin by the saving in regenerant cost. In small plants the small capital investment is usually the controlling factor, and for this reason mixed beds alone are often preferred, even though the cost of the regenerant is high.

E. Cost of Regenerants

Hydrochloric acid as regenerant enhances the capacity of the cation exchanger in comparison with other acids and prevents fouling of the resin by calcium sulfate during regeneration. Therefore, despite its greater cost, it is often preferred for the small demineralizer. Even in larger plants, as indicated in Section VIIIB2, if they are located near an acid manufacturer, the cost of hydrochloric acid may be low enough to justify its use (with acid-reclaiming).

XI. Summary of Applications of the Ten Major Demineralizer Systems

The following paragraphs are a summary of the fields of application of the ten major demineralizer systems, with reference to Fig. 6.11.

System 1: Two-Bed with Weak-Base Resin. This system is for industrial plants requiring a reduction of electrolyte to 2 to 10 ppm but no reduction of silica; it is not applicable for boiler-feed purposes.

System 2: Two-Bed with Strong-Base Resin. This system will reduce the electrolyte to 2 to 3 ppm and the silica to 0.02 to 0.1 ppm.

System 3: Three-Bed. This system will save caustic soda regenerant with waters high in total mineral acidity (sulfates and chlorides). It also often will allow omission of the decarbonator. The caustic soda is passed counterflow through the strong-base and weak-base beds, when the effluent conductivity of the weak-base rises. The strong-base bed at that time will be only partially exhausted; therefore the latter often has enough excess capacity to remove the carbonic acid economically, even if the decarbonator is omitted. It also avoids early silica breakthrough.

System 4: Four-Bed with Primary Weak-Base and Secondary Strong-Base Resins. This system will reduce the electrolyte to 0.2 to 1.0 ppm and the silica to 0.02 to 0.1 ppm. The use of primary and secondary cation resins saves acid regenerant. The system is suited to waters with high percentages of sodium and low percentages of alkalinity, which cause greater sodium leakage. Weak-base resin also saves caustic soda with waters high in percentage of total mineral acidity. The secondary units, used only for polishing, can be smaller than the primary units.

System 5: Four-Bed with Primary and Secondary Strong-Base Resins. This system saves as much acid as does system 4, but the strong-base resins in both the primary and secondary stages reduce the silica to 0.01 to 0.05 ppm (see Table 6.2). The system also avoids organic fouling of the secondary resins.

System 6: Two-Bed/Four-Bed. This system is used when the output of demineralized makeup water must be increased for a short period (as when the condensate gets oily and must be wasted). Then the primary and secondary stages of the four-bed are run in parallel as a large two-bed system. The secondary units are made the same size as the primary, because during regeneration of the primary pair the secondary pair handles the full load. Some two-bed four-bed plants have been so designed that the freshly regenerated primary pair is always switched to the secondary position by opening certain valves in the piping interconnections. This was intended to improve

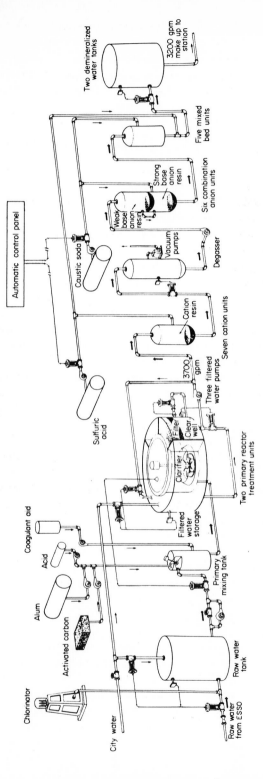

Fig. 6.13. Flow diagram of pretreatment and demineralizer at the Linden, New Jersey, station.

the effluent quality, but since organic fouling of the secondary units has interfered with obtaining this objective, it is best to keep the primary units always in the primary position, so as to protect the secondary anion resin from such fouling.

System 7: Mixed-Bed Alone. This system is used in the smaller plants to save investment cost, but the practice entails higher operating costs. The resin capacity in mixed beds is usually assumed to be 80 to 85% of the same resins in two-bed systems, so more acid and caustic soda are required for regeneration.

System 8: Cation Bed, Decarbonator, and Mixed Bed. This system will reduce the amount of acid and caustic soda needed compared to mixed bed alone for waters high in alkalinity. The cation bed also filters the water and thus acts as a pretreatment unit to protect the mixed beds.

System 9: Two-Bed with Weak-Base Resin and Mixed-Bed. This system will reduce the electrolyte to 0.04 to 0.10 ppm and the silica to 0.02 to 0.1 ppm. It saves as much acid as does system 8 but more caustic soda than does system 8 with waters high in total mineral acidity.

System 10: Two-Bed with Strong-Base Resin and Mixed-Bed. This system will reduce the electrolyte content as much as will system 9, to 0.04 to 0.10 ppm, but it will reduce the silica further, to 0.01 to 0.05 ppm. Having strong-base resin in both the primary stage and the mixed bed protects the latter from organic fouling. The mixed bed is regenerated infrequently.

XII. Three-Bed and Mixed-Bed System

Figure 6.13 is a flow diagram of the large, 3200 gal/min, Linden demineralizer (27).

The primary system was three-bed for the purpose of saving more caustic soda than would have been possible with system 10. Table 6.3 gives the operating results.

Table 6.3

OPERATING RESULTS AT THE LINDEN STATION (FIG. 6.13)

	Primary water treatment		
	Raw-water influent	Treated water effluent	Reduction % average
Turbidity, ppm	3 to 46	0.5	96
Color, ppm	40 to 160	2.0	98
Organics as O_2 consumed, ppm	10 to 15	3 to 4	72

Table 6.3 (*continued*)

	Raw-water influent	Demineralizing		
		Treated effluent		
		Specified	Average actual	Reduction % average
Tot. dissolved solids, ppm	100 to 520	0.2	—	99.99
Hardness as CaCO$_3$, ppm	66 to 284	0	0	100
Dissolved silica, ppm	3 to 12	0.01	0.005	99.5
Conductivity, μmhos	180 to 835	0.5	0.05	—
Spec. resistance, ohms-cm	5500 to 1200	2,000,000	20,000,000	—

REFERENCES

1. R. Kunin, "Elements of Ion Exchange." Reinhold, New York, 1960.
1a. R. Kunin, private communication.
2. Dowex: Ion Exchange. Published by the Dow Chemical Co., 1958.
3. H. L. Beohner and A. B. Mindler, Pectin production from grapefruit peel. *Ind. Eng. Chem.* **41**, 448 (1949).
4. S. J. Hussey, *U.S. Bur. Mines Rept. Invest.* No. 4374 (1949).
5. N. K. Hiester and R. C. Phillips, Ion Exchange. *Chem. Eng.* (October 1954).
6. J. K. Sargent and J. W. Stewart, Automatic water demineralization accelerates tin plate production. *Steel* (June, 1954).
7. L. Wirth, Jr., Demineralization operations at the Dow Chemical Co. *Proc. Ann. Water Conf., Engrs. Soc. West. Penn., 10th Ann. Conf.* p. 57 (1949).
8. H. E. Weaver, Discussion. *Proc. Ann. Water Conf., Engrs. Soc. West. Penn., 20th Ann. Conf.* p. 9 (1959).
9. S. B. Applebaum and F. Fast, Ammonia regeneration of weak base anion resin. *Water Sewage Works* (October 1960) (reprinted from Discussion at *Proc. 20th Intern. Water Conf., 1959*, p. 105.
10. B. L. Booher, Discussion of: Macroreticular anion exchange resins. *Proc. Intern. Water Conf. Engrs. Soc. West. Penn., October 1963*, pp. 89–90.
11. R. Riley, U.S. Patent 2,267,841 (1941).
11a. R. Osmun and L. Wirth, Jr., Silica removal with highly basic anion exchange resins. *Ind. Eng. Chem.* **43**, 1076 (1951).
12. M. E. Gilwood, Electrical determination of endpoints for ion exchange runs. *Ind. and Power*, (May 1954); U.S. Patent 2,628,194 (1953).
13. J. Thompson and A. C. Reents, Counterflow regeneration. *Proc. 27th Intern. Water Conf., Engr. Soc. West. Penn., November 1966*.
14. P. H. Caskey and A. C. Reents, U.S. Patent 2,891,007 (1959).
15. R. Kunin and F. X. McGarvey, U.S. Patent 2,692,244 (1954); also U.S. Patent 2,578,937 (1951).
15a. R. H. Marks, Water treatment. *Power* (December 1958).

16. D. M. Stromquist, A. C. Reents, and M. E. Veerman, U.S. Patent 2,771,424 (1956).

17. A. Himsley, Carboxylic resins in water treatment. *Proc. Intern. Water Conf., Engrs. Soc. West. Penn. 1962*, p. 91.

18. H. C. Farmer and S. B. Applebaum, Two bed primary system solves mixed bed demineralizer problems. *Proc. Am. Power Conf.* **21**, 670 (1959).

19. G. J. Crits, Discussion of paper—Organic fouling of anion exchangers. *Proc. Ann. Water Conf., Engrs. Soc. West. Penn., 20th Ann. Conf.* p. 119 (1959).

20. E. F. Davidson, Demineralized makeup for 1200 psi installation at East Millinocket Mill of Great Northern Paper Co. *ASME Meeting, Boston, June 1955.*

21. D. G. Downing and R. Hetherington, Macroreticular anion exchange resins. *Proc. Intern. Water Conf., Engrs. Soc. West. Penn., 1963*, p. 79.

22. G. J. Crits and J. Fischer, Discussion of paper by D. G. Downing and R. Hetherington, Macroreticular anion exchange resins, *Proc. Intern. Water Conf. Engrs. Soc. West. Penn., 1963*, p. 95.

23. I. M. Abrams and R. P. Poll, Progress in layered-bed cation exchange. *Proc. Intern. Water Conf., Engrs. Soc. West. Penn., December 1967.*

24. D. G. Downing, A. G. Susanin, and C. T. Orlando, Field experience with stratified beds of weakly basic and strongly basic anion exchange resins in the United States and abroad. *Proc. Intern. Water Conf., Engrs. Soc. West. Penn., December 1967.*

25. S. B. Applebaum and G. J. Crits, Producing high purity water. *Ind. Water Eng.* (September 1964).

26. C. Calmon and A. W. Kingsbury, Preparation of ultrapure water. *In* "Principles of Desalination" (K. S. Spiegler, ed.), Chapter 9. Academic Press, New York, 1966.

27. R. I. Smith and H. D. Reppin, Four years of operating experience with a 3200 gpm demineralizer. *Proc. Am. Power Conf.* **23**, 635 (1961).

7

The Major American Ion Exchange Materials

American producers of ion exchangers used in demineralization continue to develop new and improved materials. They have greater exchange capacity, resistance to physical attrition, stability toward oxidation and other chemical attack, and porosity, which lessens organic fouling.

I. Cation Exchangers

Table 7.1 gives the major cation exchangers produced by the four American manufacturers. Trade names and numbers are included. They are classified in three groups: sulfonated coal, sulfonic (strongly acidic) polystyrene resin, and carboxylic (weakly acidic) resin.

A. Sulfonated Coal (Zeo-Karb)

Zeo-Karb was the first commercial hydrogen cation exchanger produced. It is derived from coal, a natural product, and has therefore been called "carbonaceous." The crushed and screened coal is sulfonated with strong sulfuric acid, which attaches sulfonic acid exchange groups, $-SO_3H$, to the organic matrix of the original material. Carboxylic acid groups; $-COOH$, are also present; they are derived from the original coal and from the oxidation during the acid treatment. The carboxylic groups are helpful for dealkalization and for the efficient regeneration of the material with a single dose of weak sulfuric acid; a progressive increase in the acid strength is thus avoided, so as to prevent calcium sulfate precipitation on the exchanger. Hydrochloric acid is rarely used for the regeneration of Zeo-Karb, because its high cost compared to sulfuric acid is not compensated by any appreciable increase in exchange capacity.

172

Table 7.1

MAJOR UNITED STATES CATION EXCHANGERS

	DVB, %	Manufacturer and proprietary name				
		Diamond Alkali Co.,[a] Western Div.	Dow Chemical Co., (distributor, Nalco Chem. Co.)	Ritter Pfaudler Corp.		Rohm and Haas Co.
		Duolite	Dowex	Permutit	Ionac	Amberlite
Sulfonated coal				Zeo-Karb	C-150	
Sulfonic, strongly acidic, polystyrene resin						
Standard	8+	C-20	HCR	Q	C-240	IR-120
	10+	C-20 × 10	HGR	QB	C-250	IR-122
	12+	C-20 × 12	HDR	QC	C-255	IR-124
Strain-free white	8		HCR-W			IR-121
	10		HGR-W			
	12		HDR-W			
Macroreticular				Q220	C-355	200
Macroporous		C-250	MPC-1			
Carboxylic, weakly acidic resin		ES-80	CCR-1	Q210	C-265 C-275	IRC-84

[a] Corporate name recently changed to Diamond Shamrock Corp.

Zeo-Karb can be used for treating waters of up to 140°F in temperature and up to 11.0 in pH. There is no minimal pH. Since it is sensitive to oxidative attack by free residual chlorine in the water, the influent should be dechlorinated, if more than trace amounts of chlorine are present.

Table 7.2 gives the exchange capacity (in kilograins per cubic foot) and cation leakage (in percent of total cations) to be expected with various types of water. The waters are classified by their sodium content (in percent Na of total cations), their alkalinity (in percent alkalinity of total anions), and their parts per million total mineral acidity (sulfates and chlorides). The table is based on a regenerant level of 2.0 to 2.5 lb of sulfuric acid per cubic foot of exchanger.

As the table indicates, the best field of application for Zeo-Karb is in the treatment of waters of low solids and high alkalinity; the lower first cost and low acid requirements make it economical for such cases. It can be used

Table 7.2

ZEO-KARB H (IONAC C-150) HYDROGEN CATION EXCHANGER, CARBONACEOUS COAL
DERIVATIVE: CAPACITIES AT 2.0 TO 2.5 lb OF H_2SO_4, 66° Bé PER CUBIC FOOT OF
EXCHANGER AND CATION LEAKAGES FOR VARIOUS TYPES OF WATER

Na, %	TMA, ppm[a]	10% alkalinity		50% alkalinity		80% alkalinity	
		Capacity, kgr/ft^3	Cation leak., %	Capacity, kgr/ft^3	Cation leak., %	Capacity, kgr/ft^3	Cation leak., %
10	0–50	3.7–4.0	3.5–4.0	4.8–5.6	2.0–2.1	5.6–7.0	0.2–0.5
	100–200	3.5–3.7	3.6–4.1	4.6–5.2	2.1–2.2	5.2–6.5	0.3–0.6
50	0–50	3.8–4.0	3.7–4.5	5.1–6.0	2.3–2.4	6.7–7.6	0.6–0.7
	100–200	3.6–3.8	3.8–4.6	4.9–5.8	2.4–2.5	6.5–7.3	0.7–0.8
80	0–50	3.9–4.1	3.8–5.0	5.6–6.5	2.4–2.6	7.3–8.3	0.8–1.1
	100–200	3.7–3.9	3.9–5.1	5.3–6.2	2.5–2.8	7.0–7.9	0.9–1.2

[a] Total mineral acidity (TMA) greater than 200 ppm causes some reduction in capacity.

to advantage also in the secondary cation unit of a four-bed system, because
the amount of electrolyte in its influent would be very low and the cation
leakage negligible. Its exchange capacity, however, is generally less than
that of the polystyrene resins, which have come to be the major cation
exchangers used in demineralizers.

B. Sulfonic (Strong-Acid) Polystyrene Resins

Strong-acid cation exchangers of the polystyrene type are made by sulfonating a copolymer of styrene and divinylbenzene. As described in Chapter 6, Section I, the divinylbenzene acts as crosslinkage between the polymer
chains, and it determines many of the physical properties, such as the degree
of swelling, moisture content, and porosity. The number of crosslinks is
equal to the percent divinylbenzene added to the styrene during copoly-
merization. As the number of crosslinks decreases the swelling, the amount
of water that the resin will absorb and the speed of the exchange reaction
all increase. Too little crosslinkage, however, makes the resin jelly-like and
soft, so that it has poor hydraulic properties. Therefore the resin manufacturer must compromise between the kinetic and hydraulic performances
in selecting the percent divinylbenzene, or crosslinkage, in his products. Table
7.3 gives the moisture-holding capacity, amount of swelling, and amount of
crosslinkage for three standard polystyrene Amberlite resins; other manufacturers use about the same three degrees of crosslinkage for their standard
products.

If the resin is attacked by oxidation, especially at the higher water temperatures, it loses some of its crosslinkage, becomes softer, and suffers

Table 7.3

THREE STANDARD SULFONIC RESINS:[a] CROSSLINKAGE,
MOISTURE CONTENT, AND SWELLING

Crosslinkage, %	Moisture content, %	Swelling from 100% Na form to 100% H form, %
8.5	44 to 48	7.0
10.5	39 to 43	6.5
12.5	37 to 41	6.0

[a] Amberlite material.

greater attrition and loss of fine material in backwashing. It also loses capacity and finally must be replaced. This has been experienced particularly when the resin is used in hot-process sodium cation exchange; for this application the use of more crosslinked resins is beneficial, even though they are more costly than the usual material, 8 to 8.5% crosslinked. The resins that are 12 to 12.5% or 10 to 10.5% crosslinked last longer in processes of this kind, because the rate of deterioration follows a definite curve drawn between percent crosslinkage and time; they have a longer life expectancy than the 8% resins because of the time required for them to degrade to 8% along this curve, and this extra time is added to their life.

In the trouble shooting of resin deterioration problems samples of the resin are analyzed for percent moisture-holding capacity. This roughly determines the percent divinylbenzene, or crosslinkage, and thereby indicates when replacement of the resin should be made.

Figure 7.1 shows the chemical structural formula of a typical strong acid sulfonic polystyrene cation exchanger (such as Amberlite IR-120) taken from

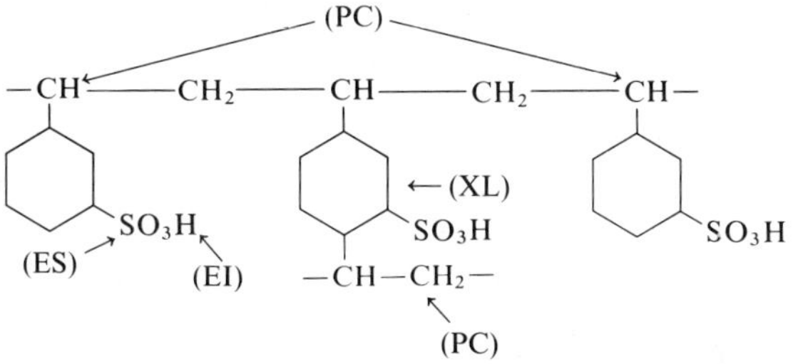

Fig. 7.1. Chemical structural formula of sulfonic strong acid cation resin (Amberlite IR-120). (XL): crosslink; (PC): polymer chain; (ES): exchange site; (EI): exchangeable ion.*

* Reprinted from *Chemical and Engineering News*, Vol. 32, August 2, 1954, page 3046. Copyright 1954 by the American Chemical Society and reprinted by permission of the copyright owner.

Kunin (*1*). On this diagram the crosslinks, the polymer chains, the exchange sites and the exchangeable ions have been located.

The sulfonic polystyrene resins do not swell excessively, as shown in Table 7.3. Therefore the freeboard commonly used is about 75% of the bed depth, preventing loss of material in backwashing.

1. CAPACITY AND CATION LEAKAGE

Table 7.4 gives the exchange capacity of Amberlite IR-120 resin (regenerated with sulfuric acid) and its cation leakage for various types of water.

Table 7.4

SULFONIC RESIN (AMBERLITE IR-120):[a] APPROXIMATE CAPACITIES[b] AND AVERAGE CATION LEAKAGES FOR VARIOUS TYPES OF WATER[c] AND 100% SULFURIC ACID REGENERANT LEVELS

Alk., %	Na, %	2.5 lb/ft³ (acid/resin)		5.0 lb/ft³ (acid/resin)		7.5 lb/ft³ (acid/resin)	
		Capac., kgr/ft³	Cation leak.,[d] %	Capac., kgr/ft³	Cation leak.,[d] %	Capac., kgr/ft³	Cation leak.,[d] %
0	0	8.3	0	11.4	0	13.1	0
	25	8.3	5	11.4	2	13.2	0
	50	8.3	10	11.5	4	13.6	2
	75	8.5	24	12.6	14	15.0	8
	100	10.3	62	16.9	42	20.0	29
50	0	8.6	0	11.9	0	13.5	0
	25	8.9	0	12.3	0	14.1	0
	50	9.2	5	13.1	2	15.0	2
	75	9.5	15	16.4	8	16.9	6
	100	11.5	39	19.2	25	22.7	16
100	0	9.0	0	12.2	0	14.0	0
	25	9.8	0	13.2	0	15.1	0
	50	10.8	0	14.8	0	16.9	0
	75	12.1	0	16.8	0	19.7	0
	100	13.5	2	21.4	1	25.5	0

[a] Standard 8% divinylbenzene; downward flow in steps of acid strength.

[b] Capacity figures are lower than Rohm and Haas Company ratings, to allow for rinse water and a safety factor.

[c] Magnesium (as $CaCO_3$) assumed to be about 33% of total hardness; more than that increases capacity.

[d] Zero signifies almost zero leakage.

Table 7.5 gives similar data for hydrochloric acid (HCl) regenerant. This table is expressed in terms of 100% HCl, but the acid is usually purchased as muriatic acid, which is 30% HCl. Multiply the 100% HCl acid levels by

Table 7.5

SULFONIC RESIN (AMBERLITE IR-120):[a] APPROXIMATE CAPACITIES[b] AND AVERAGE
CATION LEAKAGES FOR VARIOUS TYPES OF WATER[b] AND 100% HYDROCHLORIC ACID
REGENERANT LEVELS

Alk., %	Na, %	2.0 lb/ft³ (acid/resin)		4.0 lb/ft³ (acid/resin)		6.0 lb/ft³ (acid/resin)	
		Capac., kgr/ft³	Cation leak.,[c] %	Capac., kgr/ft³	Cation leak.,[c] %	Capac., kgr/ft³	Cation leak.,[c] %
0	0	11.9	1.5	18.9	0.4	23.7	0.2
	25	11.7	3.0	18.5	2.0	23.5	1.6
	50	12.2	6.5	19.4	3.9	23.8	3.0
	75	13.3	11.5	20.8	5.1	25.4	5.1
	100	14.9	29.0	22.9	13.1	27.9	7.9
50	0	12.4	1.0	19.5	0.5	25.1	0.4
	25	12.2	2.5	19.1	1.5	24.4	0.5
	50	12.6	4.0	20.2	1.7	24.8	1.0
	75	13.8	8.0	21.7	3.1	26.9	1.6
	100	15.3	20.0	23.9	5.9	28.9	2.2
100	0	12.7	0	20.4	0	25.7	0
	25	12.5	0	20.2	0	25.2	0
	50	13.1	0	20.8	0	25.9	0
	75	14.2	0	22.5	0	27.5	0
	100	16.0	0	24.7	0	29.7	0

[a] Standard 8% divinylbenzene; downward flow of acid at 0.5 gal/min/ft³ and 5 to 10% strengths (to convert 100% HCl to usual commercial 30% HCl multiply by 3.33).

[b] Capacity figures are lower than Rohm and Haas Company ratings, to allow for rinse water.

[c] Zero signifies almost zero leakage.

about 3.3, to express them in terms of 30% HCl. The table shows that the exchange capacity is higher with hydrochloric acid regenerant than with sulfuric acid (see Table 7.4); this is because dilute hydrochloric acid can be used in greater strengths than sulfuric acid without causing fouling precipitates on the resin. Nevertheless, sulfuric acid is the more commonly used for regeneration because it is less costly. In comparing Tables 7.4 and 7.5 it is to be noted that because of the lower molecular weight of the hydrochloric acid 1 lb of 100% H_2SO_4 is equivalent to 0.72 lb of 100% HCl.

The capacity and cation leakage of the more highly crosslinked resins (10 and 12%) are similar to those given in Tables 7.4 and 7.5 for the Amberlite IR-120; the sulfonic resins of the other manufacturers have capacity and cation leakage also similar. The higher crosslinked standard resins are somewhat denser and are recommended for the lower layer of double-layer units.

Cation leakage is aggravated by a band of sodium left in the bottom portions of the resin bed after regeneration. The band can be dispersed efficiently by an air mix given to the bed before and after the regeneration; this practice is known as Unimix (Chapter 6, Section IXA1). Instead of this expensive air mix some mixing can be accomplished by a second water backwash applied

Table 7.6

AVERAGE CATION LEAKAGES OF AMBERLITE IR-120 WITH SULFURIC ACID REGENERANT IN STANDARD FLOW, UNIMIX, AND SECOND BACKWASH FOR VARIOUS TYPES OF WATER

		Standard,[a] at lb/ft^3 (acid/resin)			Unimix,[b] at lb/ft^3 (acid/resin)			Second backwash,[c] at lb/ft^3 (acid/resin)		
Alk., %	Na, %	2.5	5.0	7.5	2.5	5.0	7.5	2.5	5.0	7.5
0	25	5	2	0[d]	3	2	0[d]	4.0	2.0	0[d]
	50	10	4	2	9	3	2	9.5	3.5	2.0
	75	24	14	8	21	7	4	19.0	10.5	6.0
	100	62	42	29	36	14	9	49.0	28.0	19.0
50	50	5	2	2	3	2	1	4.0	2.0	1.5
	75	15	8	6	12	3	2	13.5	5.5	4.0
	100	39	25	16	27	9	4	33.0	18.0	13.2

[a] Standard downward acid flow in steps of acid strength and high enough flow to avoid $CaSO_4$ fouling.

[b] Unimix is the Rohm and Haas Company name for air mixing before and after regeneration.

[c] Second backwash after regeneration: cation leakage halfway between standard downward flow and Unimix.

[d] Zero signifies almost zero leakage.

after regeneration. Table 7.6 shows the reduction in cation leakage that is achieved by Unimix, by a second backwash, below standard regeneration.

Tables 7.4 and 7.5 apply to the cation units of multibed demineralizers only. In the designing of mixed beds the cation leakage given in these tables is disregarded. Because of their multiple cation–anion exchanger effects the mixed beds do not suffer from appreciable amounts of cation leakage, and therefore they produce very pure effluents. In figuring the exchange capacity of mixed beds it is customary to use only the 100% alkalinity columns in Tables 7.4 and 7.5 and to multiply the capacities in those columns by 0.8 to 0.85. This loss of 15 to 20% in the capacity of mixed beds compared to that of multibeds is caused by the lower regeneration efficiency obtained with mixed beds. The hydraulic classification and separation of the cation and anion resins in mixed beds are not 100% complete; therefore not all of the cation or anion resin receives its proper regenerant.

2. DOWEX STRAIN-FREE RESINS

To reduce attrition losses, the Dow Chemical Company developed sulfonic cation exchange resins beads more perfectly spherical, more transparent, and whiter than previous resins. The letter W was added to their commercial designations, giving the names Dowex HCR-W, HGR-W, and HDR-W. The beads have fewer potential cracks, which induce splitting. It has become customary in the trouble shooting of resin problems to examine the used material under the microscope and count the broken beads; the fragments are smaller and are more likely to be lost in backwashing. Tougher resin, resisting such attrition losses, is particularly desirable for external regeneration systems, in which the resin may be hydraulically or pneumatically transferred through considerable lengths of piping.

Table 7.7 gives the physical properties of 8% crosslinked "strain-free" cation resin (Dowex HCR-W), backwash flow rates required for 50% expansion of the bed, and pressure losses at various service flow rates and temperatures. The higher crosslinked resins HGR-W and HDR-W have

Table 7.7

STRAIN-FREE SULFONIC RESIN (DOWEX HCR-W), 8%
CROSSLINKED: BACKWASH RATES, AND PRESSURE LOSSES
FOR VARIOUS SERVICE FLOW RATES AND WATER TEMPERATURES

Shipping weight, 53 lb/ft³ backwashed and drained Moisture content, 45%		Bead mesh size, 16–50 Degree of swelling from Na to H form, 5%	
Water temp., °F	Backwash rate for 50% bed expansion gal/min/ft²	Service flow rate, gal/min/ft²	Pressure loss, psi per ft of bed depth
40	5	6	0.9
60	6	6	0.7
80	7	6	0.5
40		8	1.3
60		8	1.0
80		8	0.7

similar physical properties but they have greater chemical stability and resistance to oxidative attack. The capacities and cation leakages of these strain-free materials approximate those given for Amberlite IR-120 in Tables 7.4 and 7.5.

All the sulfonic resins can be used at pH values of 0 to 14 and at temperatures of as much as 250°F.

3. MACRORETICULAR RESINS

Macroreticular resins, commercially introduced in 1959, have large, discrete pores that permit the removal of high-molecular-weight ions from solutions or water and their more complete elution from the resin during regeneration. They have an open structure and are made with tougher copolymers than are the standard gel-type resins. Amberlite 200 has more than 20% divinylbenzene by weight in its copolymer and therefore provides greater resistance to attrition and oxidative attack. Its cost is somewhat greater, and exchange capacity somewhat less than the gel type, but when the gel-type resin suffers from rapid deterioration, its use or that of similar competitive types* is recommended.

Amberlite 200 also has found application in mixed-bed demineralizers that have been vulnerable to organic fouling of the anion resin. This fouling in many cases reduced the capacity of the bed and decreased the effluent purity. When the effluent conductivity exceeded about 1 μmho, the resin beds were replaced, often more than once a year. At a utility plant [see Applebaum and Crits (25) of Chapter 6] it was found that the fouling of the anion resin was due partly to the deterioration products of the previously

Table 7.8

MACRORETICULAR CATION RESIN (AMBERLITE 200): PHYSICAL PROPERTIES, BACKWASH RATES, AND PRESSURE LOSSES FOR VARIOUS SERVICE FLOW RATES AND WATER TEMPERATURES

Shipping weight, 50 lb/ft^3 Moisture capacity, 46 to 51% Bead mesh size, 15–50%		Effective size, 0.4 to 0.5 mm Fines through 50-mesh screen size not over 2%	
Water temp., °F	Backwash rate for 50% expansion, gal/min/ft^2	Service flow rate, gal/min/ft^2	Pressure loss, psi per ft of bed depth
40	4.5	6	0.7
60	5.8	6	0.5
80	7.5	6	0.3
40		8	0.9
60		8	0.7
80		8	0.5
40		10	1.3
60		10	0.9
80		10	0.6

* Diamond Alkali Company and Nalco-Dow call their competitive resins "macro-porous" (see Table 7.1).

Table 7.9

MACRORETICULAR STRONG-ACID RESIN (AMBERLITE 200):[a] FOR VARIOUS TYPES OF
WATER AND SULFURIC ACID (100% BASIS) REGENERANT LEVELS

		2.5 lb/ft³ (acid/resin)		5.0 lb/ft³ (acid/resin)		7.5 lb/ft³ (acid/resin)	
Alk., %	Na, %	Capac.,[b] kgr/ft³	Cation leak.,[c] %	Capac.,[b] kgr/ft³	Cation leak.,[c] %	Capac.,[b] kgr/ft³	Cation leak.,[c] %
0	0	6.3	2	9.0	1	10.9	0
	25	6.2	4	9.0	2	10.9	1
	50	6.3	7	9.0	3	10.9	2
	75	6.3	16	9.2	6	11.0	4
	100	8.1	49	14.4	28	16.6	18
50	0	7.2	0	9.9	0	11.7	0
	25	7.2	2	9.9	1	11.7	0
	50	7.2	4	9.9	2	11.7	1
	75	7.2	9	9.9	5	11.7	4
	100	11.7	28	17.1	15	18.9	10
100	0	7.7	0	10.4	0	12.2	0
	25	8.6	0	10.8	0	12.6	0
	50	9.0	0	11.7	0	13.5	0
	75	10.3	1	13.0	0	15.3	0
	100	13.5	2	18.5	1	21.5	0

[a] With downward regeneration in steps of acid strength.
[b] Capacity figures are lower than Rohm and Haas Company ratings, to allow for rinse water.
[c] Zero signifies almost zero leakage.

used gel-type cation resin; this is called "organic sloughage." When Amberlite 200 was used in the mixed beds instead of the gel-type resin, the life of the bed was lengthened considerably (2). The addition of macroreticular anion resin prolonged still further the life of the mixed bed, as discussed in Chapter 6, Section IXF3.

Table 7.8 gives the physical properties of Amberlite 200, the backwash rates required to expand the bed 50%, and the pressure losses during service runs at various flow rates and temperatures. Table 7.9 shows the capacities and average cation leakage of this resin for various types of water and sulfuric acid regenerant levels.

C. Carboxylic (Weak-Acid) Resins

The first carboxylic weak-base cation resin, Amberlite IRC-50, introduced by Rohm and Haas Company in 1948, was a copolymer of macroacrylic acid and divinylbenzene. This resin had certain limitations. It had too low an exchange capacity for waters containing an alkalinity greatly exceeding the hardness; in such waters there was a high amount of sodium bicarbonate. Its capacity was reduced too much when the flow rate (in gallons per minute per cubic foot of resin) was increased; the resin was called "flow-sensitive." Finally, the pH of the effluent during the service run fluctuated too widely.

In 1965 an improved carboxylic resin, Amberlite IRC-84, was developed with a tenfold increase in acidity in the resin, which overcame the limitations of the earlier product. This is a crosslinked acrylic resin. Figure 7.2 is a

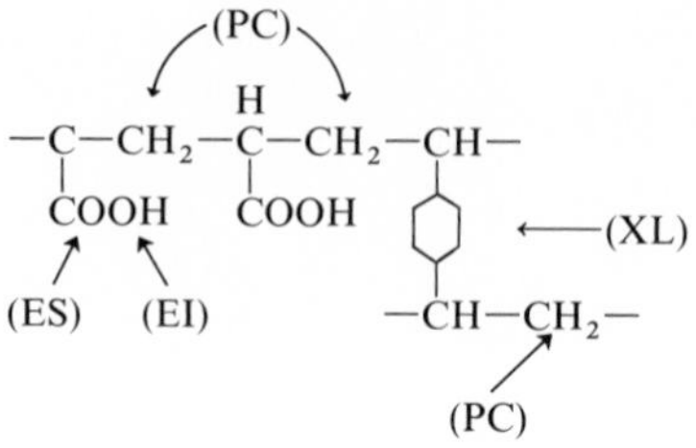

Fig. 7.2. Chemical structural formula of carboxylic weak acid cation resin (Amberlite IRC-84). Code is as in Fig. 7.1.

diagram of its chemical structural formula, on which have been indicated the location of the polymer chains, exchange sites, exchangeable ions and crosslinks. Table 7.10 gives its physical properties, backwash rates for

Table 7.10

CARBOXYLIC RESIN (AMBERLITE IRC-84): PHYSICAL PROPERTIES, BACKWASH RATES, AND PRESSURE LOSSES AT VARIOUS WATER TEMPERATURES AND SERVICE FLOW RATES

Shipping weight, 47 lb/ft³	Moisture capacity, 43 to 50%
Water pH, 4 to 14	Bead mesh size, 16–50
Maximal temperature, 250°F	Effective size, 0.38 to 46 mm

Water temp., °F	Backwash rate for 50 to 60% expansion gal/min/ft²	Service flow rate, gal/min/ft²	Pressure loss, psi per ft of bed depth
40	1.5	6	1.5
60	2.1	6	1.2
80	3.0	6	0.9
40		10	2.9
60		10	2.3
80		10	1.6

expanding the bed 50 to 60% and pressure losses during the service run at various flow rates and water temperatures.

Table 7.11 gives the capacity of Amberlite IRC-84 for alkalinity removal for waters of different compositions and at two water temperatures, 75 and 55°F. These temperatures are representative of well waters in the south and

Table 7.11

CARBOXYLIC RESIN (AMBERLITE IRC-84):[a] CAPACITY FOR ALKALINITY REMOVAL FOR VARIOUS TYPES OF WATER

Hardness / Alkalinity	Total mineral acidity as $CaCO_3$, ppm	Capac.[b] kgr of alk. removed per ft^3 of resin	
		At 75°F	At 55°F
0	5	12	8
	65	13	10
	130	16	10
	280	18	14
0.5	5	12	9
	65	15	11
	130	20	13
	280	22	17
0.9	5	13	10
	65	17	12
	130	23	16
	280	26	19
1.0 or more	5 to 280	50	40

[a] Standard downward flow of sulfuric acid regenerant in several steps of acid strength (1 to 4%); 110 to 120 lb of acid for each 100 lb of alkalinity removed; endpoint at alkalinity leakage of 10% of influent alkalinity.

[b] The capacities do not provide for rinse water, and they apply only when the resin is used alone for dealkalization; when the resin is used in double-layer cation units, with Amberlite IR-124 or 200 below it, higher capacities for Amberlite IRC-84 are obtained. The capacities in this table are based on flow rates of up to 2 gal/min/ft³.

north, respectively. The lower temperature decreases the capacity. The factors that influence the capacity are the amount of total mineral acidity (sulfates plus chlorides) and the ratio of the hardness to the alkalinity in the influent; the higher the total mineral acidity and the ratio of hardness to alkalinity, the greater the capacity. Table 7.11 applies only when the weak-acid cation resin is used for dealkalization alone; when it is used in double-layer units with strong-acid cation resin below it, as for demineralization, the capacity rating of the weak-acid resin will be greater than that given in the table. As explained in Chapter 6, Section IXB, the service run through the upper layer (weak-acid resin) can be prolonged until the effluent of this layer shows a hardness breakthrough. During this prolongation of the run the sodium bicarbonate alkalinity in the effluent of the upper layer increases. The lower layer (strong-acid resin), however, has a high capacity for removing sodium bicarbonate alkalinity. An increase in capacity of 25 to 50 % beyond the ratings in Table 7.11 may be realized from this overrun. Laboratory tests are required to determine this increased capacity, because the water composition influences the results (see Chapter 9, Section IID).

Table 7.12
SWELLING OF AMBERLITE IRC-84 VERSUS DEGREE OF CONVERSION
FROM HYDROGEN FORM

Conversion to Na form, %	Swelling, %	Conversion to Ca and Mg form, %	Swelling, %
0	0	0	0
50	30	50	10
100	65	100	25

Amberlite IRC-84 is subject to reversible swelling during the exhaustion cycle. Table 7.12 shows this swelling (in percent) when the resin is converted from the hydrogen form to the sodium and to the calcium and magnesium forms. The resin also swells irreversibly by about 8 % during the first few runs. These amounts of swelling, particularly the swelling reversible, must be taken into account in determining the depth of the freeboard above the bed. As Table 7.12 shows, the swelling may reach 65 % if the resin is converted from the hydrogen form to a 100 % sodium form. Fortunately, the conversion to the sodium form alone is less than 100 % complete. Therefore it is customary to allow for about 25 % of reversible swelling. For example, if a technical calculation calls for a bed 4 ft deep in the unswollen condition, one should allow for 25 % swelling, or a depth of 5 ft, in the swollen condition; then the freeboard should be 100 % of the swollen depth, or 5 ft, too. This will make the straight shell height about 10 ft, if no subfill is used above the underdrain. The acid distributor must be located about 6 in. above the top of the bed in its swollen condition, so that it is not submerged in the resin at the start of the regeneration.

When the weak-acid column is followed by a strong-acid column, both columns are regenerated at the same time. The acid is passed countercurrent, first through the sulfonic column and then through the carboxylic column, in series. The spent acid from the sulfonic column is usually pure enough to accomplish a good regeneration of the carboxylic column. This results in the greatest acid efficiency and lowest total acid requirement.

The use of both carboxylic and sulfonic resins in one double-layer column is a recent development (Chapter 6, 23, 24). Owing to its lower density, the carboxylic resin can be brought to the top by backwashing. The acid is passed upward through the combined bed. The combination of the two resins in one double-layer column obviates separate columns for them and therefore reduces the capital investment. It has proved to be a valuable tool in reducing acid levels for demineralizers when the alkalinity of the water is appreciable.

The double-layer column also will solve the problem of neutralizing the acid rinse waters from demineralizers. Antipollution regulations call for neutral waters to enter sewers or streams; therefore the waste rinse waters from regenerations often require a neutralizing system (see Chapter 8, Section VIII). The technical design calculations should determine whether the amount of waste excess acid from the regeneration of the cation units is equivalent to the amount of waste excess alkali from the regeneration of the anion units, so that they are in balance in the neutralizing system; otherwise an acid or alkali must be added in the neutralizer, increasing the operating cost. Since the alkali (caustic soda) is more costly than the acid, a three-bed demineralizer is often selected (if the water contains enough sulfates and chlorides), because it will save caustic soda regenerant. Then, however, there may be an imbalance of excess acid and excess caustic soda, requiring alkali to be added in the neutralizer, and in that case the saving in caustic soda with the three-bed system is offset by the extra amounts needed for neutralization. By reducing the acid levels, as in double-layer carboxylic and sulfonic columns, this imbalance often may be avoided. The technical calculations in Chapter 9, Section IID, include a typical example of the balancing of excess acid and caustic soda for selecting regenerant levels.

Another application of carboxylic weak-acid cation resin is in a posttreatment column, which follows a two-bed demineralizer and removes the leakage of caustic soda in the effluent. Amberlite IRC-84 has a high capacity for removing caustic soda. The posttreatment permits using less acid for regenerating the sulfonic cation resin of the two-bed, allowing more cation leakage, which the third column removes economically. Thus acid is saved, and the operating cost is reduced.

II. Anion Exchangers

Two classes of anion exchangers exist, weakly basic and strongly basic (a few of the weak-base exchangers are "intermediate," containing some strong-base groups).

A. Major Weak-Base Exchangers

Table 7.13 lists the chief weak-base anion exchangers produced by the four United States manufacturers and gives their trade names and numbers. Five types are represented: polystyrene polyamine, phenolic polyamine, epoxy polyamine, acrylic polyamine, and macroreticular tertiary amine resin.

Table 7.13

MAJOR UNITED STATES WEAK-BASE AND INTERMEDIATE-BASE RESINS

	Manufacturer and proprietary name				
	Diamond Alkali Co.,[c] Western Div.	Dow Chemical Co., (distributor, Nalco Chemical Co.)	Ritter Pfaudler Corp.		Rohm and Haas Co.
	Duolite	Dowex	Permutit	Ionac	Amberlite
Polystyrene polyamine					IR-45
Phenolic polyamine	A2, A4, A6, A7		Deacidite[a] CCG	A-260	IR-4B
Epoxy polyamine	A30-B, ES-57	WGR	A[b]	A-300, A-310	
Acrylic polyamine					IRA-68
Macroreticular resin			S-440	A-320	IRA-93

[a] Described as an aliphatic amine.
[b] Described as an aminated amine.
[c] Corporate name recently changed to Diamond Shamrock Corp.

The first three types are not used often today, because they require excessive rinsings when caustic soda is the regenerant, but they can be used successfully without excessive rinsing, as they age, when ammonia is the regenerant (see Chapter 6, Section VIIIC1). Currently the exchangers used in demineralizers are usually the epoxy polyamine and the macroreticular tertiary amine types.

1. EPOXY POLYAMINE INTERMEDIATE-BASE RESIN (DUOLITE A30-B)

Duolite A30-B was the first improved intermediate-base resin developed that solved the problem of excessive rinsings. Only 50 gal of water are needed to rinse each cubic foot of new resin and on aging of the resin the amount becomes only about 100 gal/ft^3.

Table 7.14 gives this resin's capacity for adsorbing sulfuric and hydro-chloric acids or, as they are usually called, "TMA" (total mineral acidity). The total mineral acidity is equal to the sulfates plus the chlorides. The capacity is higher for divalent sulfuric acid than for monovalent hydro-chloric acid; the table shows that, as the proportion of chlorides in the total mineral acidity increases, the capacity decreases. The capacities given here are conservatively reduced from the manufacturer's ratings for new resin, to allow for some decrease with age and for rinse water. The resin is commonly guaranteed to operate with a capacity reduction of not more than 20 to 25% either after 18 months of use or after treating 750,000 gal of water per cubic foot of resin, whichever comes first.

Table 7.14

CAPACITY OF DUOLITE A30-B FOR REMOVAL
OF TOTAL MINERAL ACIDITY (SULFATES PLUS
CHLORIDES)[a]

Cl, % of TMA (both as $CaCO_3$)	Capacity, kgr/ft^3
0 to 40	20
40 to 60	19
60 to 80	18
> 80	17

[a] Regenerant (lb/ft^3): caustic soda (NaOH), 4 or soda ash (Na_2CO_3), 6 or ammonia (NH_3), 2.

When the resin replaces older weak-base anion resin of lower density, the backwash rates may have to be increased. Its bulk density is 43 lb/ft^3. The backwash rates needed to expand the bed 50 to 60% are about 2.5 to 3.0 $gal/min/ft^2$ at 40°F, 3.0 to 3.2 at 60°F, and 4.0 to 4.2 at 80°F; therefore it is best to allow for 3.5 to 4.0 $gal/min/ft^2$ for proper backwashing.

Clumping of Duolite A30-B has been experienced in some cases; the resin particles become agglomerated and form large clumps. A reduced capacity due to channeling may result. This difficulty has been attributed to electrostatic charges on the resin particles. Treatment with a slurry of clay has been found helpful. Organic fouling has also contributed to this difficulty: in three-bed systems, in which the caustic soda first passes through the strong-base anion resin, then through an anthracite subfill, and finally into the weak-base anion resin, "organics" leached from the anthracite may foul the last resin. Clumping may require removal of the bed and breaking up of the lumps outside, followed by increased backwash rates.

The service-run flow rates may vary from 2 to 3 gal/min/ft^3 of resin; if the rate goes up to 5, the capacity may decrease by 25 %. The dilute regenerant flow rates may vary from 0.2 to 2.0 gal/min/ft^3; a good average rate is 0.5. The regenerant strength may vary from 4 to 10%, but 4% is the strength commonly used.

2. MACRORETICULAR RESIN (AMBERLITE IRA-93)

Amberlite IRA-93 is a tertiary amine resin of high porosity, developed to resist organic fouling and the increased rinse requirements that occur with age. Its chemical structural formula is shown in Fig. 7.3 on which are indicated the location of the polymer chains, cross links, exchange sites and exchangeable ions.

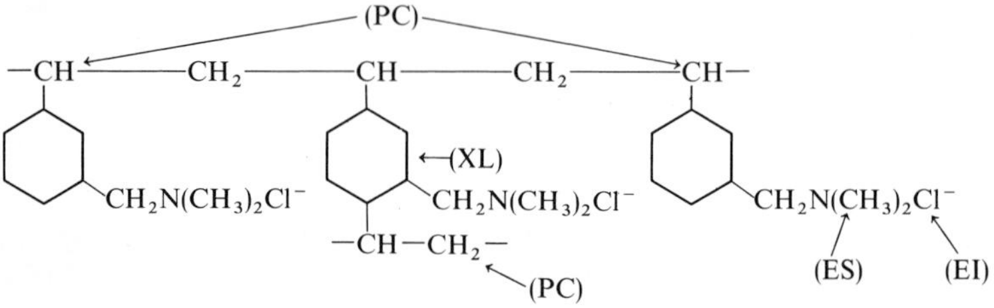

Fig. 7.3. Chemical structural formula of macroreticular weak base anion resin (Amberlite IRA-93). Code is as in Fig. 7.1.

The capacity of this resin, when new, is somewhat less than that of Duolite A30-B, but after a year or two of use its performance has been found superior in some cases (3). Its capacity for monovalent chloride and nitrate is claimed to be not appreciably less than for divalent sulfate. It is customary to rate it at a capacity of 20 kgr/ft^3 with 4 lb of caustic soda per cubic foot of resin.

The swelling characteristics of the resin are somewhat high: it swells about 25 to 35 % when converted from a 100 % hydroxyl form to a 100 % chloride form. However, the conversion is never that complete, so that it is customary to allow a swelling of about 25 % in calculating the required freeboard and location of the regenerant distributor. The latter should be about 6 in. above the top of the bed in its swollen condition.

The resin can operate at water temperatures of up to 212°F and at a pH range of 0 to 9. The backwash rates for 50 % expansion of the bed in hydroxide-regenerated form is only 1.2 to 1.5 gal/min/ft^2 at 80°F, but in the chloride-exhausted form it is 2.5 to 2.8 at the same temperature. Therefore one should backwash only after exhaustion and use a rate of 2.0 to 2.5 gal/min/ft^2 at 80°F. At lower water temperatures the rate should be reduced to less than 2.0 gal/min/ft^2, to avoid losses of the resin. The bulk density of the resin is 38 lb/ft^3.

The pressure drop during service, when the resin is in the hydroxyl-regenerated form, is 0.2 to 0.3 psi per foot of depth of the bed at 5 gal/min/ft^2 and 80°F. The pressure loss is 0.5 to 0.7 psi at a flow rate of 10 gal/min/ft^2. The usual flow rate during service is 1 to 3 gal/min/ft^3, and the regenerant rate is 0.5 to 1.0 gal/min/ft^3.

Amberlite IRA-93 has found application as a "sweetening" upper layer above a mixed bed containing strong-base anion resin, protecting the latter from organic fouling. Adding it in a proportion of only 10 or 15% of the volume of the strong-base resin has prolonged the life of a mixed bed appreciably (2).

In larger proportions it has also been applied in combination with strong-base resin in double-layer anion units of demineralizers. Because of its lower density compared with that of the strong-base resin in the regenerated form it is possible to classify the two resins by backwashing after regeneration and bring the lighter Amberlite IRA-93 to the top. In that location it will remove organic matter and so protect the strong-base resin. It will also remove the total mineral acidity more economically and thereby save caustic soda regenerant, as in three-bed systems. Regeneration is conducted with an upward counterflow of the caustic soda solution through the strong-base and the weak-base layers and then through a screened collector located above the bed in its swollen condition.

3. ACRYLIC RESIN (AMBERLITE IRA-68)

Amberlite IRA-68 has been developed for demineralizing brackish water by the Kunin process. In this application it reduces the regenerant operating cost, because it can operate in the bicarbonate form and can exchange its bicarbonate for the large amounts of chloride in the brackish water. Its use in the Kunin process is discussed in Chapter 12, Section VIIIA.

B. Major Strong-Base Exchangers

Table 7.15 gives the chief strong-base anion exchangers produced by the four United States resin manufacturers. There are five types: standard and porous Types I and II, and macroreticular type. The macroreticular has three sub-groups indicated in the table.

1. STANDARD TYPE I RESINS

The chemical structural formula of Type I strong-base anion resin is shown in Chapter 6, Sect. I. It is the most strongly basic type. It has less porosity than the resins developed later, such as Dowex SBR-P, and therefore does not resist organic fouling as well, but the beads possess good physical stability, so that they can withstand attrition satisfactorily. It has been the work horse of many two-bed makeup demineralizers.

Table 7.15

MAJOR UNITED STATES STRONG-BASE EXCHANGERS

	Manufacturer and proprietary name				
	Diamond Alkali Co.,[b] Western Div.	Dow Chemical Co., (distributor, Nalco Chemical Co.)	Ritter Pfaudler Corp.		Rohm and Haas Co.
	Duolite	Dowex	Permutit	Ionac	Amberlite
Type I (standard)		SBR	S-1	A-540	IRA-400
Type II (standard)		SAR	S-2	A-550	IRA-410
Type I (porous)	A101-D	SBR-P	SK	A-580	IRA-402
Type II (porous)	A102-D				
Macroreticular or Macroporous					
Type I			S-450	A-641	IRA-900
Type I (for organic traps)[a]			S-460	A-642	IRA-904
Type II			S-470, S-480	A-651	IRA-910
					IRA-911

[a] For organics removal Dow–Nalco recommend their Dowex 11, which is not macroreticular but is a haloalkylated resin, and Diamond Alkali recommend their weak-base anion resin Duolite A-7.

[b] Corporate name recently changed to Diamond Shamrock Corp.

Amberlite IRA-400 has a bulk density, or shipping weight, of 44 lb/ft^3. It is made in beads of 16-50 mesh screen size and 0.38 to 0.45 mm effective size. Its moisture content is 42 to 48 %. It swells about 19 % when fully converted from the exhausted chloride form to the regenerated hydroxyl form, but since the conversions are not that complete, a swelling of about 10 % is rarely exceeded. It is to be noted that the resin swells during regeneration and shrinks during exhaustion, unlike the weak-base anion resin, which shrinks during regeneration and swells during exhaustion.

Type I can operate without excessive attack at water temperature of 140°F in the hydroxyl form and over the entire pH range, 0 to 14. It has a higher crosslinkage than the porous type. Its chemical stability is relatively high, so that its capacity is guaranteed to decrease not more than 25 %, either after 24 months of use or after 1,000,000 gal of water have been treated per cubic foot of resin, whichever occurs first.

2. STANDARD TYPE II RESINS

As described in Chapter 6, Section I (which has the chemical structural formula), the Type II strong-base anion resins differ from the Type I in that one of the methyl groups of the latter has been replaced by an ethanol group. Type II has somewhat more exchange capacity and less basicity than Type I, but it is less stable chemically (4). Its capacity is guaranteed to decrease not more than 25%, either after 18 months of use or after 750,000 gal have been treated per cubic foot of resin, whichever comes first.

The bulk density, or shipping weight, of Amberlite IRA-410 is 44 lb/ft^3. It is made in beads of 16-50 mesh size and of 0.38 to 0.45 mm effective size. It swells about 13% when converted completely from the chloride to the hydroxyl form. It can withstand water temperatures of up to 105°F when in the hydroxyl form.

Type II resins are used for demineralizing waters that contain silica in amounts that are not more than 25 to 30% of the total exchangeable anions. Since the silica leakages from these resins are higher than from Type I resins, then if a low effluent silica, less than 0.05 ppm, is desired, the Type I is usually preferred.

3. POROUS-TYPE

The greater porosity of the porous strong-base anion resins gives them better resistance to organic fouling. The porosity is increased by decreasing the crosslinkage. The resulting resin contains pores large enough to permit penetration of the large molecules of organic matter into the interior of the resin particle. Thus the exchange sites are more easily reached and are not so readily blocked off after a relatively small amount of organic matter has been adsorbed. Likewise, the "organics" are more readily eluted from the resin during regeneration. The capacity of the porous types is somewhat greater than that of the standard types. The characteristics and capacity of Dowex SBR-P (type I) are given in detail below. This resin was one of the earliest porous type materials developed, and it is in wide use today.

Table 7.16 gives the physical properties of Dowex SBR-P, the backwash rates for 50 to 60% expansion of the bed, and the pressure loss at various service flow rates. High flow rates, up to 50 gal/min/ft^2, are included in this table, because they prevail in condensate demineralization.

Table 7.17 gives the exchange capacity and average silica leakages to be expected at various caustic soda regenerant levels at 120°F and with various types of water. The waters are characterized by the proportions of silica and of weak acids (silicic and carbonic) to the total exchangeable anions present, all the constituents being expressed as $CaCO_3$.

The usual form of water analysis expresses the amount of silica present as SiO_2; this is multiplied by 0.83, to convert it to silica expressed as $CaCO_3$.

Table 7.16

POROUS-TYPE STRONG-BASE RESIN (DOWEX SBR-P): PHYSICAL
PROPERTIES, REQUIRED BACKWASH RATES, AND PRESSURE LOSSES
AT VARIOUS WATER TEMPERATURES AND SERVICE FLOW RATES

Shipping weight, 43 lb/ft^3	Bead mesh size, 16–50
Moisture content, 55 to 58%	Effective size, 0.52 mm
Swelling, 25% from Cl to OH form	Amount over 16 mesh, 2%
Maximal temperature, 120°F	Amount passing 40 mesh, 3%

For 50 to 60% expansion		At 75°F	
Water temp., °F	Backwash rate, gal/min/ft^2	Service flow rate, gal/min/ft^2	Pressure loss, psi per ft of bed depth
40	1.5 to 2.0	5	0.5
70	2.0 to 2.5	10	0.9
100	2.5 to 3.0	30	2.2
		50	4.0

Table 7.17

POROUS-TYPE I STRONG-BASE RESIN (DOWEX SBR-P):[a] CAPACITIES AND AVERAGE
SILICA LEAKAGES VERSUS CAUSTIC SODA REGENERANT LEVELS (100% BASIS) AT VARIOUS
WEAK-ACID PERCENTAGES AND SILICA PERCENTAGES

Regen. level, lb/ft^3	Capacity, kgr/ft^3			Average silica leakage, ppm				
	% weak acid[b]			% silica[c]				
	25	50	75	10	30	50	70	90
4	10.8	11.8	12.6	0.05	0.19	0.30	0.41	0.53
5	11.7	12.7	13.5					
6	12.2	13.4	14.2	0.02	0.05	0.08	0.12	0.14
8	13.4	14.2	15.0	0.01	0.03	0.05	0.07	0.09

[a] Endpoint of run is 0.2 ppm SiO$_2$ (cation leakage assumed to be 2 ppm). Silica leakages must be increased about 10% for each ppm cation leakage above 2 ppm. Higher water temperatures increase SiO$_2$ leakage 10% for each 10°F above 75°F. Capacity based on percentage of chloride (as CaCO$_3$) in total exchangeable anions from 0 to 15%; if chloride is 50% decrease capacity 15%; if chloride is 75%, decrease capacity 25%.

[b] Calculated as (SiO$_2$ + CO$_2$) × 100 in ppm as CaCO$_3$ per total exchangeable anions or SiO$_2$ + CO$_2$/TEA (in ppm as CaCO$_3$) × 100.

[c] Calculated as (SiO$_2$ × 100) in ppm as CaCO$_3$ per total exchangeable anions; or SiO$_2$/TEA (in ppm as CaCO$_3$) × 100.

The standard analysis also states the amount of carbonic acid expressed as free carbon dioxide, CO_2; this is multiplied by 1.13, to convert it to carbonic acid expressed as $CaCO_3$.

Thus the total exchangeable anions (TEA) are calculated from the usual form of water analysis as follows:

$$
\begin{aligned}
HCO_3 \text{ (as } CaCO_3) \times 1.0 &= HCO_3 \text{ (as } CaCO_3) \\
SO_4 \text{ (as } CaCO_3) \quad \times 1.0 &= SO_4 \text{ (as } CaCO_3) \\
Cl \text{ (as } CaCO_3) \quad\ \times 1.0 &= Cl \text{ (as } CaCO_3) \\
Free\ CO_2 \text{ (as } CO_2) \times 1.13 &= CO_2 \text{ (as } CaCO_3) \\
SiO_2 \text{ (as } SiO_2) \quad\ \times 0.83 &= SiO_2 \text{ (as } CaCO_3) \\
\hline
Sum &= TEA \text{ (as } CaCO_3)
\end{aligned}
$$

The weak carbonic and silicic acids (as $CaCO_3$) are calculated in like manner.

Table 7.17 is based on a cation leakage of 2 ppm, a water temperature of 75°F, and a proportion of monovalent anions (Cl or NO_3) equal to 10 to 15% of the total exchangeable anions. As the footnotes to Table 7.17 show, increasing the cation leakage and water temperatures above those limits causes an increase of the silica leakage. Higher proportions of monovalent anions (chloride or nitrate) than the 15% assumed decrease the capacity.

The only porous type II is the Diamond Alkali Company's A102-D (see Table 7.15) and it is recommended instead of standard type II where organic matter is present.

4. MACRORETICULAR RESINS

As Table 7.15 shows, Rohm and Haas Company have developed several macroreticular strong-base anion resins: Type I (Amberlite IRA-900 and 904) and Type II (Amberlite IRA-910 and IRA-911). Ritter Pfaudler have competitive types (see Table 7.15); these have greater porosity than the so-called porous types and the pores are larger and more discrete.

a. Amberlite IRA-900

Amberlite IRA-900 is the most strongly basic and is used, therefore, when the lowest silica leakage is required. It has a high porosity of discrete pores, affording a more complete removal of large-sized organic ions and a greater elution of them during regeneration.

The physical characteristics of this resin are as follows: shipping weight, $42\ lb/ft^3$; moisture content, 60 to 64%; screen size, 16-50 mesh; effective size, 0.43 to 52 mm; backwash rates for expanding the bed, 50 to 60%, about 3 $gal/min/ft^2$ at 86°F (colder waters require backwash rates below this, to avoid resin losses in backwashing).

Table 7.18

MACRORETICULAR TYPE I STRONG-BASE RESIN (AMBERLITE
IRA-900): PRESSURE LOSSES AT VARIOUS SERVICE FLOW
RATES AND TEMPERATURES

Water temp., °F	Flow rate, gal/min/ft^2	Pressure loss, psi per ft of bed depth
40	5	1.0
	10	1.9
	30	5.8
	50	10.0
60	5	0.7
	10	1.3
	30	4.1
	50	7.0
80	5	0.5
	10	1.1
	30	3.1
	50	5.1

The pressure losses at various flow rates and water temperatures are given in Table 7.18. The resin can withstand operating temperatures during service of up to 140°F in the hydroxyl form.

The usual service flow rate is 1 to 3 gal/min/ft^3; the regenerant flow rate, 0.5 gal/min/ft^3; the displacement flow rate, 0.5 gal/min/ft^3; the rinse flow rate, 1.5 to 2.0 gal/min/ft^3. The exchange capacity is about 20% less than that of Dowex SBR-P (given in Table 7.17).

The Rohm and Haas Company ratings at a flow rate of 2 gal/min/ft^3 are as follows:

100% NaOH per cubic foot of resin, lb	Capacity, kgr/ft^3
4	9.2
5	10.5
6	11.2
8	12.1

These ratings should be multiplied by 0.9, to be conservative and to allow for rinse water.

b. Amberlite IRA-904

Amberlite IRA-904 has little regeneration efficiency in the hydroxide phase of the cycle, but because of its large pore volume and surface area it is recommended for organics scavenging in the chloride form. The regeneration is effected with sodium chloride (see Chapter 4, Section IIID).

The resin has a shipping weight of $42\,lb/ft^3$ and a moisture capacity of 56 to 62 %, and its beads have an effective size of 0.4 to 0.5 mm. It swells only 5 % when converted from the chloride to the hydroxide form.

c. Amberlite IRA-910

Amberlite IRA-910 is a recently developed macroreticular Type II strong-base anion resin of somewhat greater capacity and regeneration efficiency than those of Amberlite IRA-900. For example, Rohm and Haas Company gives the following exchange capacity ratings:

100% NaOH per cubic foot of resin, lb	Capacity, kgr/ft^3
4	16
5	16.7
6	17.3
8	17.9

These ratings should be multiplied by 0.9, to be conservative.

The pressure losses are similar to those of Amberlite IRA-900 (given in Table 7.18), and so are the physical characteristics and required backwash rates (see preceding paragraphs). Amberlite IRA-911 is more porous than IRA-910 but it has lower capacity and is not so widely applied.

In general, Amberlite IRA-910 is recommended when Type II resins suffice for the degree of silica removal desired but greater resistance to organic fouling is needed.

REFERENCES

1. R. Kunin, Recent developments in ion exchange. *Chem. Eng. News* **32**, 3046 (1954).
2. G. J. Crits, and J. Fischer, Discussion of paper by D. Downing and R. Hetherington, Macroreticular anion exchange resins. *Proc. Intern. Water Conf. Engrs. Soc. West. Penn., October 1963*, pp. 95–97.
3. B. L. Booher, Discussion of paper, *ibid.*, pp. 89–90.
4. L. Wirth, Jr., The expected life of anion exchangers. *Combustion* **25** (May 1954).

8

Demineralizer Equipment Designs

The designer of demineralizers has a number of options when he decides on the components of his equipment. The final design selected must be reliable in performance, require a minimum of maintenance, and be economical in cost.

The equipment designs discussed in this chapter are for the fixed-bed columnar plants currently used for the demineralization of water. The operation steps that this equipment must control are the following, in their order: exhaustion, or service run, backwashing for cleansing the exchanger, regenerant dilution and injection, displacement of regenerant through the exchanger bed, or "slow rinse," and finally fast rinse to waste. When the demineralizer is applied in chemical processing (Chapter 14), two additional steps are required: "sweetening off," in which a valuable liquid in the exchange unit is displaced by water and recovered before backwashing and regeneration, and "sweetening on," in which the water contents in the exchange unit are replaced by the valuable liquid after regeneration and before the next service run (these "sweetening" terms are derived from the demineralization of sugar).

The demineralizer systems (described in Chapter 6) consist of various arrangements of what might be called their building blocks. These are the weak-acid and strong-acid cation exchanger units, the weak-base and strong-base anion exchange units, and the decarbonator or vacuum deaerator. The components of the equipment common to all demineralizers are the shell, the tank or container for the exchange material, the subfill (when used) under the exchange material, the internal distributors, the external valves and piping, the equipment for regenerant-handling and storage, the means of diluting and injecting the regenerants into the exchange bed, the instrumentation for monitoring the plant performance, the influent and effluent quality, and the start and end of the service runs, the automatic control devices with the panel or the cabinet for housing them and finally, the regeneration waste-water neutralizer. The decarbonator or vacuum deaerator designs are not described in this chapter, having been fully described in Chapter 5.

I. The Shell

The exchanger shells may be of the gravity or the pressure type. During World War II, when steel and rubber linings were difficult to procure, a number of gravity plants with wood shells or tanks were installed (*1*). Currently demineralizers are of the vertical pressure type in sizes that range from 2 to 12 ft in diameter. The horizontal type, found in filters (Chapter 4, Section IA) are rarely used. The shells are constructed of steel, with dished heads, and in large part conform to the ASME Code for Unfired Pressure Vessels. The pressure is usually 50 to 100 psi, although condensate demineralizers have been built for much higher pressures.

In the past, when gravel or anthracite subfills were commonly used, the lower dished head of the shells contained one of these materials. When the subfills were abandoned (for reasons discussed below), it was desirable to have a flat surface on which a horizontal underdrain system could be placed. The lower head then was made flat and was reinforced on the outside by beams, which were welded on so as to withstand the internal pressure. This construction was found to be costly with large diameters and high pressures; a more recent design has an internal flat bottom supported by steel cylinders welded into the lower dished head (see Fig. 8.1).

Since demineralizer shells must withstand acid regenerants and acid water, they must be acid-proof or lined with acid-proof material. Generally, sheet-rubber lining is used, $\frac{1}{8}$ to $\frac{3}{16}$ in. thick. Thinner linings, such as acid-proof paints, are unreliable. For smaller shells sprayed polyvinyl chloride coatings have been applied successfully. The $\frac{3}{16}$ in. rubber lining, however, is the usual standard.

II. Subfill under Exchange Materials

To support the exchange resins and prevent their escape through the orifices in the underdrain system, several layers of gravel or anthracite have been used as subfill. Anthracite has been the preferred support for anion resin, because it is nonsiliceous and therefore does not give up silica even in waters of high pH value. In the cation units siliceous gravel or quartz, which is not attacked by acid water, has been used, but anthracite has been preferred as subfill in the cation units too.

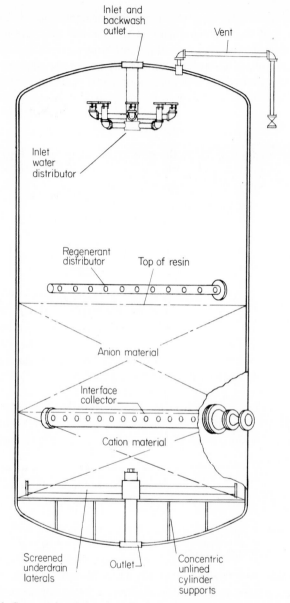

Fig. 8.1. Cross sectional elevation of ion exchange unit, showing internal distributors.

The subfill is placed in the lower head to a depth of 12 to 16 in. in the straight of the shell. Several layers are used, starting with a $\frac{1}{2}$ to 1 in. layer at the bottom, a $\frac{1}{4}$ to $\frac{1}{2}$ in. layer above it, and a $\frac{1}{8}$ to $\frac{1}{4}$ in. layer at the top.

The advantage of the subfill is that the orifices in the underdrain system can be made large enough to prevent their being clogged. On the other hand, the subfill has several disadvantages, as follows.

(a) It absorbs caustic soda and thereby increases the rinse water required to reach a conductivity low enough for starting the next service run. In some cases, when a conductivity of $5\,\mu$mhos was necessary at the start of the run, the rinsing required has lasted several hours. Omitting the subfill shortened these excess rinses substantially. With 10 to 20 μmho starting conductivity the effect was less pronounced.

(b) The subfill can be upset by high backwash rates suddenly applied or by air bubbles in the backwash water. The upset causes hills and valleys in the subfill layers, and resin can escape through the valleys. Channeling, variable run lengths, and poor effluent quality may also result.

(c) Cation resin escaping through an upset subfill in the cation unit enters the anion resin bed. The caustic soda regenerant then places sodium on this cation resin. The sodium leaks off into the final effluent, and poor-quality water is delivered. It is difficult to separate and remove this cation resin completely from the anion resin bed.

For all these reasons it is currently good practice to omit subfills and, instead, to use underdrains with fine openings, which prevent escape of the resin.

III. Internal Distributors and Collectors

To avoid channeling and ensure uniform contact of the water and regenerants with all parts of the resin bed, well designed and properly constructed distributors and collectors are essential.

A. Top Inlet Distributor

The influent enters the top of the shell through an inlet distributor. The distributor also acts as a collector of the dirty backwash water to be discharged from the top of the shell to waste. As an inlet distributor it also serves to prevent disturbance of the top of the resin bed due to impingement by the influent stream. Such disturbance has resulted in the gouging out of cavities in the resin bed, so that the top of the bed no longer had a flat, level surface but consisted of hills and valleys. The disturbance became more severe with higher flow rates and lighter resins. For example, when heavy greensand was replaced with lighter sulfonated coal, this trouble suddenly developed. Likewise, when flow rates increased from the old 6 to 8 gal/min/ft^2 to 10 to 15 and, later, to 50 gal/min/ft^2, as in condensate demineralizers, the impingement effect increased appreciably. Cavities in the resin bed resulted in short service runs and poor effluent quality.

The inlet distributor must dampen the dynamic effect of the large influent flow by breaking the flow up into a number of smaller streams of low velocity (4 to 5 ft/sec). These smaller streams must be directed away from the top dished head and the side walls, because they tend to follow the walls and gouge out depressions in the bed around the periphery.

Figure 8.1 shows the design developed for this purpose. The central hub has a number of radial horizontal laterals ending in elbows and vertical umbrella heads. The latter are located far enough away from the top and the periphery, so that the streams discharged horizontally in a radial pattern do not impinge on the head or side of the shell. The materials used for the inlet distributor are polyvinyl chloride or stainless steel, the latter being preferred for the high flow rates that prevail in condensate demineralizers.

B. Regenerant Distributor

The regenerant is introduced into the bottom of the freeboard about 6 in. over the resin. This location avoids diluting of the regenerant by the water in the freeboard space and reduces the displacement water volume required for the slow rinse that follows. To distribute the regenerant uniformly over the area of the top of the resin bed, a pipe system containing orifices is used. A central hub with radial orificed laterals has been used, but the orifices can be spaced more evenly with a horizontal pipe header, to which the orificed laterals are connected at right angles on equal centers. The regenerant distributor must be supported and braced by horizontal rubber-covered beams welded to the shell, so that it will not be broken by the rising resin during backwashing. The materials used for the distributor are polyvinyl chloride or stainless steel; the latter is the stronger and resists strains better.

C. Interface Distributor

Interface distributors are used only in mixed-bed demineralizers. As the name implies, they are located at the interface between the beds of cation and anion resin that are formed after the backwash classifies the two resins. They collect the spent caustic soda that has passed down through the upper anion resin and also collect the spent acid that has passed up through the lower cation resin bed. They can also be used for distributing the acid, if it is to be passed downward through the cation resin bed. The blocking flow (described in Chapter 6) also is collected by these distributors. They usually consist of a header and orificed laterals, similar in design to the regenerant distributor. The orifices must, however, be covered by stainless-steel screening to prevent escape of the resin. Because of their location within the bed they are subject to great strains from the swelling and shrinking of the resins and are therefore usually made of stainless steel. It is important, too, that they be braced rigidly by rubber-covered beams above and below them, so that they will resist upward or downward pressures.

D. Underdrain System

When subfills are used, the underdrain consists of a hub located in the center of the lower dished head directly over the outlet nozzle and of orificed curved laterals radiating from the hub. The materials used are polyvinyl chloride or hard rubber. The laterals follow the curvature of the lower head.

When the subfills are omitted, either a flat lower head externally reinforced, as described above, or an internal flat bottom is used (Fig. 8.1). The internal flat bottom is rubber-lined only on its upper surface. The lower surface, the steel cylindrical supports, and the lower dished head are unlined, because no acid or acid water enters the space below the internal flat bottom.

Over the flat bottom is an underdrain pipe system consisting of a header across the diameter, with orificed laterals at right angles on equal centers. To cover the orifices in the laterals and prevent escape of the resin, fine stainless-steel screening is attached. The materials used for the distributor are polyvinyl chloride or stainless steel.

Instead of the use of screening over the orifices, the laterals can be made of Johnson well-screen construction, using a helically wound stainless-steel wire welded to some support rods. The spaces between the successive helical loops are made fine enough to prevent escape of the resin. This is a rigid, strong design, less likely to clog and break than the design with screening; its cost, however, is somewhat higher.

Another design that avoids header and laterals is an internal dished stainless-steel false bottom, supported at the periphery and located within the lower rubber-lined dished bottom. The radius of curvature of the false bottom is greater than that of the dished real bottom (2). Large orifices in the false bottom are supplied with strainers containing fine openings that prevent resin escape. The strainers can be made of polyvinyl chloride or stainless steel. This construction avoids beams. The false bottom is not as flat or level as is the internal flat bottom described above. Therefore the bottom of the resin bed may not be as uniformly utilized or regenerated. Additional resin may be required to offset this inefficiency.

Figure 8.1 shows a cross-sectional elevation of a typical shell with internal flat bottom and the four internal distributors in place, as used in a mixed-bed unit.

In condensate demineralizers with external regeneration special underdrains are required to facilitate resin transfer (see Chapter 10, Section VIIIA1).

IV. External Valves and Piping

The external valves may consist of either a nest of individual valves or a single control multiport valve.

A. Valve Nest

Six main individual valves are in the valve nest: inlet, outlet, backwash inlet, backwash outlet, rinse outlet, and regenerant inlet. In addition to these smaller vent and drain valves are included. Mixed-bed units have, besides the other valves, an interface outlet valve. Figure 8.2 is a photograph of two anion exchange units with typical valve nests.

Fig. 8.2. Valve nests on the front of two anion exchange units.

The external piping and valves must be acid-proof; either steel that is lined with rubber or Saran or stainless steel may be used. Small valves may be made of polyvinyl chloride entirely. The design of large valves must be suitable for rubber-lining. Therefore, the four types generally used are the following: Saunders diaphragm, butterfly, eccentric plug, and ball valves. For manual control handwheels are provided. For remote manual or automatic control the valves are supplied with pneumatic diaphragm or piston operators. The automatic operators may be equipped with hand jacks for emergency manual operation. For throttling service limit stops are included. Position indicators may be attached, which indicate when the valves are wide open or closed. Microswitches, connected to the position indicators, may be wired to lights on the main panel for indicating which valves are open or closed.

For automatic valve nests the pneumatic supply to the operators is controlled by solenoid valves. These either are located alongside each main operating valve or are clustered in a cabinet in front of the ion exchange unit. They also may be located on the main panel, but that involves running considerable lengths of air tubing between the panel and each main valve. It is more economical to employ an electrical panel, the solenoid valves located near the ion exchange unit, and to use electric wiring for connecting the panel control devices and the solenoid valves. Keeping the air supply and tubing out of the panel itself is preferable. Larger main valves can have motor operators instead of pneumatic operators. Although more costly, these are more reliable.

B. Single Control Valve

Instead of a nest of individual main valves, one single control valve may carry out all the operations. This reduces the possibility of error that results from opening and closing the wrong individual valves of a valve nest. The various steps of operation are clearly indicated on a dial.

A number of designs of single control valves are available. For the smaller demineralizers, particularly the packaged shop-assembled units, a "Solo" lift-turn* valve is popular. The internal disk is lifted off its port plate for easy turning and then rotated to a new position for the next step in operation. For the larger demineralizers the two types chiefly used are the Permutit single multiport valve, rotary-disk design, and the Cochrane Hydromatic valve.

In the rotary-disk type the inner disk is kept in close contact with the port plate at all times and is not lifted off for turning, as in the solo valve. Lubricant is injected, to facilitate rotation. In the Hydromatic type the rotary-disk principle is confined to a small pilot valve. This hydraulically actuates a group of individual single-seated diaphragm-operated valve members located inside a large rubber-lined body casting. Leakage through the individual inner valves is avoided by the use of soft rubber disk seats that are compressible. Pilot water, distributed to the various diaphragm operators, opens and closes the valves in the proper sequence. The higher pressure of the pilot water, aided by spring pressure, results in tight seating of the individual valves. The rotary-disk pilot valve is only a few inches in diameter and is easily machined to avoid leakage. For automatic operation a small, fractional-horsepower motor is ample for turning the pilot valve from one position to the next. Figure 8.3 shows schematically how the pilot valve distributes the pilot water so as to pressurize and keep closed four individual diaphragm valves. The latter are connected to the pilot-valve area within the bonnet but outside the rotary slide. At the same time the area under the slide exhausts and opens two other valves involved in any step of operation. The enlarged view

---

* Made by Aquamatic, Rockford, Illinois.

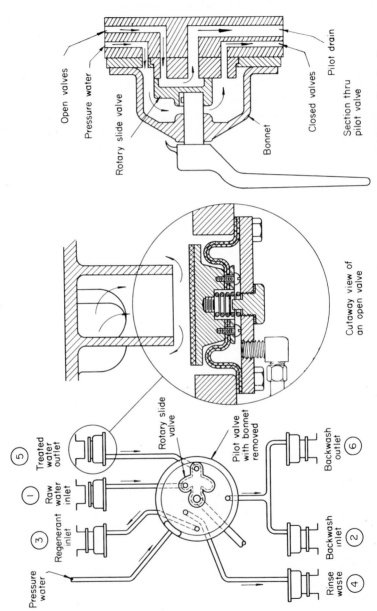

Fig. 8.3. Diagram of Cochrane Hydromatic single control valve. The main valves are operated from a pilot circuit.

illustrates one of the diaphragm valves in a wide-open position. The pressure below the diaphragm has been exhausted through the pilot valve to the drain, and the pressure of the water itself, applied to the upper side of the valve, has opened it completely. Integral backwash and rinse-rate controllers are included, designed to compensate for variations in water pressure. This rate control is accomplished by automatic throttling of the inner backwash and rinse valves, controlled by pressure drop through an orifice.

The Hydromatic valve has external tubing between the pilot valve and the six individual diaphragm operators. The valve is made in 2, 3, 4, and 6 in. sizes. For automatic operation a control cabinet containing the program timer, relays, and switches for controlling the sequence and duration of each step is furnished. Interlocks are included, so that only one unit can be regenerated at a time.

C. External Interconnecting Piping between Units

There are a number of possible piping arrangements for interconnecting the cation and anion exchange units of a demineralizer. Five schemes are described and illustrated, as follows.

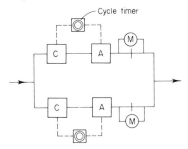

Fig. 8.4. Type A piping arrangement: train type of interconnecting piping of a two-bed demineralizer with simultaneous regeneration of cation and anion units.

Type A. Figure 8.4 shows this type, in which the cation exchange units (C) and the anion exchange units (A) are connected together in trains. One meter (M) serves each train of units of this two-bed demineralizer. The cation and anion units are regenerated at the same time. While the anion unit is receiving its caustic soda, which takes 60 to 90 min, the cation unit can be fully regenerated (Chapter 9, Section II 3g gives this simultaneous regeneration schedule).

The advantages of this type are as follows: the outage time for regeneration is reduced, the cation units need not be enlarged in area to provide the backwash and rinse water for the anion units, one meter is saved on each train, two pipe headers (cation outlet and anion inlet) are eliminated, and fewer cycle timers and control valves are required for automatic operation.

Type B. Figure 8.5 shows this type, in which the units are not connected in trains. The cation unit outlets are joined by a header and then split again in two branches to the anion unit inlets. The units are regenerated individually and separately. Each unit has a meter.

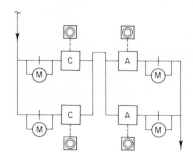

Fig. 8.5. Type B piping arrangement: nontrain type of interconnecting piping of a two-bed demineralizer with independent timer controls for separate regenerations of cation and anion units.

The advantages of this type are as follows: it provides greater availability, because in emergencies the cation unit (C) of one pair can be connected to the anion unit (A) of the other pair, it can be used with a decarbonator between the cation and anion units, and it can save operating cost, because each unit is run to exhaustion. The disadvantages are as follows: its first cost is greater, and the cation units must be enlarged in size to backwash or rinse the anion units, unless adequate demineralized storage is provided.

Type C. Figure 8.6 shows this type with a decarbonator. Nontrain piping interconnections are used, as in Type B, but simultaneous regenerations are used, which save meters and cycle timers. This type combines some of the advantages of Types A and B.

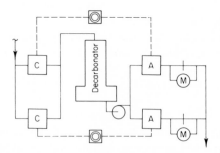

Fig. 8.6. Type C piping arrangement: nontrain type of interconnecting piping, but with simultaneous regenerations of cation and anion units even with decarbonator.

Type D. Figure 8.7 shows this type, in which the Type A train scheme is supplemented with manual valves for emergency nontrain operation and with separate cation and anion unit regenerations. It combines the advantages of Types A and B but has fewer pipe headers. However, it cannot be used if a decarbonator is required.

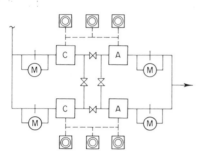

Fig. 8.7. Type D piping arrangement: train type of interconnecting piping but with extra manual valves for emergency nontrain operation.

Type E. Figure 8.8 shows this type, which is for three-bed demineralizers. The cation units are non-train connected and separately regenerated. The weak-base and strong-base anion pairs have train interconnecting piping and train regeneration controls, in order that the countercurrent regeneration, which saves caustic soda, may be used.

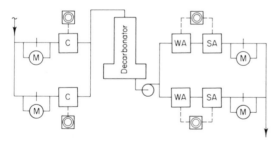

Fig. 8.8. Type E piping arrangement for three-bed demineralizer. The cation units are non-train; the weak-base (WA) and strong-base (SA) units have train interconnections and simultaneous regeneration.

V. Regeneration Systems

Demineralizer regenerations are commonly conducted with liquid sulfuric acid (66°Bé) and liquid caustic soda (usually 50% NaOH). Since these are dangerous chemicals, certain precautions must be followed in their handling and storage (*3*).

A. Handling of Regenerant

Personnel who work with regenerant chemicals should be provided with protective clothing, goggles, boots, gloves, and gas masks. The deluge type of safety showers should be near by for emergency use. Unloading of the tank cars should follow the recommendations of the Manufacturing Chemists Association.

B. Storage Tanks for Strong Sulfuric Acid

Strong sulfuric acid storage tanks are made of unlined steel. Since some slow corrosion takes place, a steel thickness of $\frac{3}{8}$ in. should be used, and the welded joints should be stress-relieved. Horizontal tanks are preferable, because they provide large bottom areas for the settling out of suspended impurities. Such foreign matter in the strong sulfuric acid can block small orifices. Screens or filters for removing these impurities are inadvisable, because they clog too rapidly and their cleaning is hazardous. Therefore the equipment should be designed to pass the particles rather than to remove them. But the acid purchased should be as clean as possible, containing not more than 20 ppm Fe, 0.5 ppm Cu, 0.2 ppm Mn, and 10 ppm Cl.

When the strong acid is diluted, its corrosiveness is greatly increased. Therefore water must not be allowed to back up into the storage tanks. If the air which enters the vent, while the acid level drops, is moist, it increases corrosion of the tank. To avoid this, a dry breather pot is often connected into the vent. The moisture absorbents used in this pot are calcium chloride, silica gel, or the strong sulfuric acid itself.

The acid storage tanks should be located in an area surrounded by a dike, with a limestone fill and the bottom sloped to a drain. Strong 66°Bé acid freezes at a temperature under 29°F; therefore, protection against freezing must be provided, if the tank is located outdoors. The drain connection of the tank should be made near a manhole, to permit easy rodding out of a plugged drain. It is recommended that the unloading pipe from the tank car to the storage tank be as short as possible and have a uniform slope. Usually it is supplied with a vent and a drain, easy to replace. These unloading pipes last only a few years.

C. Storage Tanks for Caustic Soda

Caustic soda storage tanks are usually constructed of unlined steel; however, this invites corrosion at higher temperatures, and the iron picked up by corrosion fouls the anion resin. Therefore, in large demineralizer plants, as at the Linden Station, the storage tanks are lined with epoxide resin plastic coating (Shell YP100), 4 to 6 mils thick, baked on.

Since 50% NaOH freezes at a temperature under 56°F, protection against freezing is necessary, if the tank is located outdoors. Either external or internal tubular steam heaters may be used. The internal type should have nickel tubing to withstand the hot caustic soda. Overheating may cause severe corrosion of the unlined steel storage tank, so thermostatic control of the steam valve is advisable. To avoid iron fouling of the anion resin besides protecting the steel tank, a pure rayon-grade mercury-cell type of caustic soda should be purchased, containing not more than 0.5 % Na_2CO_3, 0.5 % NaCl, 0.5 % Na_2SO_4, 10 ppm SiO_2, 10 ppm Fe, and 100 ppm chlorates.

D. Dilution and Injection of Regenerants

For controlling the dilution and measuring the amounts of regenerant injected during each regeneration several schemes are available.

1. DILUTION TANKS FOR ACID

Dilution tanks can be used to hold a single charge of 20 % acid required for a unit regeneration. A hydraulic ejector can then be employed to dilute the acid to below 4 % strength during the injection. An internal, perforated, lead pipe is used for mixing the strong acid and dilution water with compressed air during the preparation of the 20 % acid. This system was developed for sulfonated-coal cation exchangers, which can be regenerated with a single strength of 2 to 3 % H_2SO_4. However, it is not readily adapted to providing acid in several steps of increasing strength, such as 2, 4, 6 %. These steps are required for sulfonated styrene resins, if fouling of the exchanger by calcium sulfate is to be avoided. The 20 % acid also is corrosive. Lead lining of the dilution tank has been used, but even this lasts only a short time. The preparation of the 20 % acid requires that the dilution water be added first and then, slowly, the strong acid, to avoid overheating and spattering. This must be carefully controlled, and the devices to make it automatic are subject to corrosion. For these reasons, the use of dilution tanks has been largely abandoned.

2. STRONG-ACID MEASURING TANKS

Measuring tanks that hold a single charge of 66°Bé acid are a good means of measuring the amount of acid used during each regeneration. They also protect the strong-acid storage tanks against backup of water. They can be lead-lined, but in time the lead dissolves in strong acid. Therefore unlined steel tanks are better; they are replaced after several years, and this is more economical than replacing the lead lining.

Figure 8.9 shows an acid regeneration system with a measuring tank such as is used at Oak Ridge (4). Two steps of acid strength were obtained by changing the dilution-water flow rates with two rate-setting valves on the dilution lines and keeping the strong-acid flow rate constant. This is no longer the preferred method of step strength control, however, because

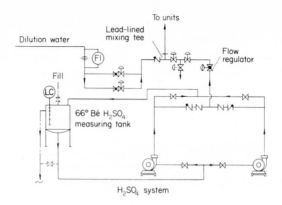

Fig. 8.9. Acid regenerating system with measuring tank.

cutting the dilution flow rate in half in changing from 2 to 4 % often introduces distribution problems for the regenerant distributor. The current method is to change the strong-acid rate and keep the dilution rate constant. Doubling the strong-acid rate in changing from 2 to 4%, changes the dilute-acid rate very little and thus avoids nonuniform distribution (see the calculation of the acid regeneration schedule in Chapter 9, Section IIA3f).

The disadvantages of strong-acid measuring tanks are that they require double pumping of the acid and the use of level-control devices, which are difficult to maintain. The trend today is to omit even the measuring tanks and to use instead the closed in-line dilution systems, as described below.

3. Strong Caustic Soda Measuring Tanks

Figure 8.10 shows a caustic soda regeneration system with a measuring tank. Usually one strength of dilute caustic soda (4%) is used, so that the

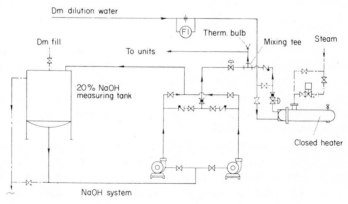

Fig. 8.10. Caustic soda regenerating system with measuring tank.

problem with steps of increasing acid strength is avoided. Nevertheless double pumping is still required, and level control causes maintenance problems, so with caustic soda, as with acid, the use of closed in-line dilution systems without measuring tanks generally is preferred today.

4. CLOSED IN-LINE ACID-DILUTING SYSTEM

Figure 8.11 shows an in-line dilution system. The volume of acid introduced is measured by maintaining a constant flow rate of strong acid and by using the duration of the pumping step to control the total volume. This has been

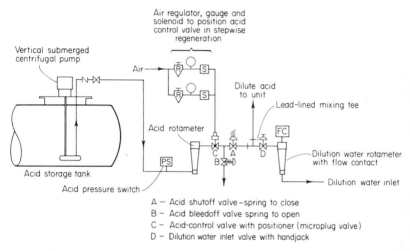

Fig. 8.11. Closed in-line acid dilution-control system.

found quite accurate. A flow-rate indicator (rotameter) is used on the strong-acid line. The strong-acid valve C in Fig. 8.11 has a positioner which controls its throttling. To obtain several strengths of acid in steps, compressed air, its pressure controlled by a regulator, is fed to the valve positioner through solenoid valves. For the 2 % strength the upper solenoid valve is opened; for the 4 % strength the lower one is opened and the upper one closed. This is done automatically. To control the dilution flow rate a rotameter is also provided on the dilution-water inlet ahead of the dilution-water inlet valve D. This valve is provided with a hand jack for manual throttling, to set the desired flow rate.

A more refined method of controlling the dilution is by the use of ratio controllers. A flow transmitter from an orifice plate in the dilution-water line throttles a valve in the strong-acid line and maintains the desired ratio of the two flows for dilution control. This scheme is expensive and usually is not justified, because the simpler dilution control shown in Fig. 8.11 is sufficiently accurate. To check the dilution obtained, a conductivity cell (not shown) can be inserted in the dilute-acid line connected to a solubridge conductivity indicator calibrated in percent acid.

To avoid backup of dilution water into the large strong-acid storage tank, as shown in Fig. 8.11, three valves, A, B, and C, are used. B is a bleedoff-to-waste valve, which is automatically opened when the other two valves, C and A, are closed. Any leakage of dilution water through A will bleed to waste rather than back up into the acid storage tank. Likewise, any leakage of strong acid through C will bleed to waste through B. When valves C and A are opened, valve B is closed automatically.

In addition to the protection afforded by the three-valve arrangement, a strong-acid pressure switch and a dilution-water flow contact are provided, as indicated. The sequence in the automatic control of an acid regeneration is as follows. Dilution valve D opens. When the correct dilution flow rate is obtained, the flow contact on the dilution-water rotameter closes. This automatically starts the acid pump. When the pump has created sufficient discharge pressure, the pressure switch closes. This opens valve A and the upper solenoid valve, which causes valve C to open to the correct strong-acid flow rate. Valve B remains closed. When the program timer ends the acid-injection step, dilution valve D remains open for the displacement step, but valves A and C are closed and B is opened. The acid pump is kept running for a delayed period. This continued operation of the pump ensures against even a momentary backflow of dilution water into the strong-acid storage tank while valves A and C are closing.

Steel piping is generally used for the strong acid and rubber-lined piping for the dilute acid. A lead-lined mixing tee is used, followed by a certain length of lead-lined pipe. Lead lining is needed to resist the heat generated as the dilution water mixes with the strong acid. Rubber lining has been known to fail owing to this heat. However, beyond this length of lead-lined pipe rubber-lined pipe is satisfactory.

The strong-acid valves A, B, and C usually are made of Durimet 20 or its equivalent. The joints at the fittings should be welded to avoid leakage. In some cases the entire strong-acid pipe assembly system is made of Carpenter 20 material with all joints shop-welded and stress-relieved so as to aid in withstanding corrosion.

5. STRONG-ACID PUMPS

Reciprocating, volumetric metering, strong-acid pumps made with Carpenter 20 heads of the plunger or the diaphragm type are often used, but they present pressure-relief problems when operating against closed valves, and they are also quite costly in large sizes.

The trend today is toward the use of cast-iron vertical centrifugal pumps of the sump type, submerged in the strong-acid storage tank (see Fig. 8.11). This avoids the problems with leakage through pump glands and with sticking of pump check valves by impurities in the acid when reciprocating pumps are used. Vertical centrifugal pumps operate well against dead ends due to closed valves and are therefore well suited to the in-line dilution-control scheme.

6. Closed In-Line Caustic Soda-Diluting System

Figure 8.12 shows an in-line dilution system for caustic soda. It is similar to that for the acid system, but the rotameter cannot be made of glass, as is used for the acid, because glass is attacked by strong caustic soda. The rotameter

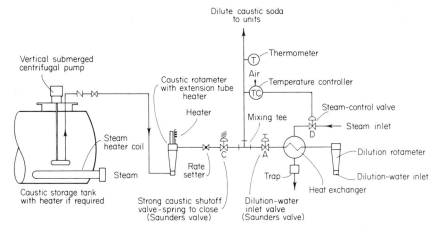

Fig. 8.12. Closed in-line caustic soda dilution-control system.

has an extension tube for the float stem with a heater that prevents freezing and plugging around the float stem. Since a single concentration of caustic soda (usually 4 %) is employed, a simple manual rate-setter valve is used.

For optimal elution of the silica from the anion resin the dilute caustic soda should be warm (usually 120°F); the dilution water therefore should be heated. This can be done in several ways. (a) The water may be heated by a direct-contact steam-jet heater; this is the least expensive, but there is some danger of steam's passing through and damaging the anion resin and rubber lining, if the dilution-water flow should stop. (b) It may be heated by a closed tubular steam-heat exchanger, as shown in Fig. 8.12; a thermometer (T) and temperature controller (TC) actuates the diaphragm operator of the steam inlet valve (D). (c) It may be heated by an electric heater. The last (electric heater) is selected when steam for heating the dilution water is not available locally. The electric heater is used with a hot-water storage tank, in which a thermostat maintains a constant high temperature of hot water. The hot water is then mixed with cold water through a blend valve, thermostatically controlled by a thermometer and temperature controller to give the desired 120°F temperature of the dilute caustic soda.

VI. Instrumentation for Monitoring Performance

In monitoring the performance of a demineralizing plant a number of instruments are used. These are conductivity and pH meters and various analyzers for checking the effluent and influent quality, determining when to regenerate a unit, and controlling the steps of regeneration.

A. Effluent Quality

Conductivity is the chief test of effluent quality. Sometimes the pH value is measured, but it is less important in determining the endpoints of runs, and the maintenance of pH meters can be burdensome. In most plants pH measurement of individual-unit effluents is omitted, and only the combined effluent is monitored for pH, to make sure that this final water is not acid. In the larger plants continuous automatic analyzers for determining sodium and silica breakthroughs and the endpoints of service runs also are finding increasing acceptance.

B. Influent Quality

Conductivity and sometimes the pH value are measured in the influent. This practice is of value when the water varies in composition. A rise or drop in dissolved solids will cause a corresponding change in conductivity. The operator will thus be alerted to expect a corresponding decrease or increase in the total gallons to be treated between regenerations.

C. Endpoint of Service Runs

1. CATION UNITS

If the influent composition is fairly constant, the cation-unit service run ends when the effluent free mineral acidity drops a predetermined amount (usually 5 to 10%); cation leakage increases when this happens (see Fig. 6.5), the drop in the acidity may be measured reliably by conductivity. If, on the other hand, the influent composition varies, it may cause the effluent conductivity to rise or fall and thus mask the results. The problem may be solved by comparing a sample of cation effluent with a sample withdrawn from a screened probe located a short distance above the bottom of the resin bed (as discussed in Chapter 6, Section IXA). The conductivities of the two samples may be compared either by ratio or by difference. During the run the two conductivities are equal, but at the end of the run the probed sample will show a drop in conductivity before the final effluent conductivity is affected, and this increases the conductivity difference. A contact in the conductivity-difference meter sounds an alarm or initiates the regeneration, when the difference increases appreciably. If there are a sufficient number of cation units in a battery, it is possible to omit the probed-sample technique and to compare instead the conductivity of any unit effluent with the conductivity of the combined effluent of the battery. In large plants sodium analyzers also are being installed more and more frequently; they measure the breakthrough of sodium, which leaks through before the other cations do.

2. WEAK-BASE ANION UNITS

During the run the effluent contains a few parts per million alkalinity. The amount depends on the cation leakage and on the percentage of alkalinity in the influent. At the endpoint the effluent alkalinity drops to zero, and free mineral acidity begins to appear (see Fig. 6.9). The rise in acidity causes the conductivity to rise and the pH value to fall. Conductivity measurement is usually depended on for determining this endpoint.

3. STRONG-BASE ANION UNITS

As Fig. 6.10 shows, silica breaks through before the conductivity rises; in fact, there is usually a short conductivity dip at the silica breakthrough. Therefore, effluent-silica analyzers are being installed in the larger plants for endpoint determination. Another method is to measure the conductivity of samples with screened probes located slightly above the bottom of the resin bed. The location is so selected enough above the bottom for the conductivity in the probed sample to rise just before silica breaks through in the final effluent. In many plants the flowmeter, which measures the volume of water treated by the unit, can be used to end the run, if the meter integrator contact is adjusted with a sufficient factor of safety to anticipate the full capacity of the resin bed.

4. MIXED-BED UNITS

Exhaustion of either the cation or anion parts of the mixed bed will result in a conductivity rise, so a measurement of the conductivity usually suffices to determine the end of the run.

D. Conductivity Indicators and Recorders

Conductivity indicators of the solubridge type are used for the smaller plant. These are usually field-mounted and not on a panel. Indicators, calibrated in percent acid or caustic soda, also may be used for measuring the acid and caustic soda strengths in transit to the units being regenerated. Conductivity indicators are also used on the rinse effluent for determining the end of rinse. For anion exchange units they are helpful in determining the beginning and end of the rinse recycling.

When recorders are desired, the conductivity cells are located in the piping and wired to the recorder on the panel. The cells should be inserted with valves and fittings to permit easy withdrawal for cleaning and maintenance.

Temperature compensators must be provided, since conductivity is affected by the water temperature. To save space on the panel, multipoint recorders may be used for recording the conductivities of samples from a number of units in a battery.

E. Flowmeters and Flow Indicators

Individual unit meters are used for determining the total volumes of water treated. The flowmeters may be of the displacement type (either disk or turbine) and be located in each cation unit inlet and each anion unit outlet (except in train arrangements). The meters are equipped with integrators and contacts for endpoint control. If flow recorders are desired, orifice plates are used with transmitters, to convey the pressure differentials across the orifice to the recorder. Multipoint recorders can be used for measuring flow through a number of units, saving space on the panel.

Flow indicators, such as rotameters, are often used on the unit inlets as an aid in valve adjustment for dividing the load evenly between the various units. In large plants rate-of-flow controllers accomplish the load division automatically. The flow indicators also help in adjusting backwash and rinse flow rates.

F. Pressure Loss

The determination of pressure loss through the resin beds is important for indicating when the resin has become dirty and whether backwashing has cleaned the bed adequately. Separate inlet and outlet pressure gauges mounted on each unit will serve this purpose, but single gauges that show the differentials between inlet and outlet pressures also are available. Occasionally differential pressure recorders are mounted on the panel.

VII. Automatic Control Devices and Panel

A sequence controller and timers program the sequence and duration of the regeneration steps: backwash, regenerant introduction, displacement, and rinse. Various types of program controllers are available. The trend is toward the use of stepping switches with individual timers for each step, because they permit easy change of the duration of any one step without the others being affected.

The panel, or "control cubicle," must be carefully designed and shop-assembled, the instruments mounted in place and wired up. The finished panel should be shop-tested before shipment; this final test must simulate the activity of all field-mounted equipment, and the steps of operation must be carefully checked out, to make sure that the design and wiring are correct.

The panel may be of the graphic design, including a flow diagram of all the units, their piping and valves, and the switches and lights at each valve. The

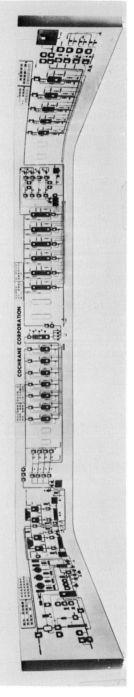

Fig. 8.13. Large graphic panel of an eastern utility demineralizer.

graphic design is favored for large demineralizers because it aids the operator in controlling the operations. Figure 8.13 shows the large graphic panel of an eastern utility demineralizer.

In addition to automatic control, it is customary to provide for emergency manual operations of valves by manual override on solenoid valves or by manual switches on the control panel. Annunciators are included, showing the location of any desired alarm point.

Panel cubicles may have either rear doors or end doors for entrance to the interior. Sometimes both sides of the panel have instruments mounted on them.

Panels are generally designed for indoor location, but they may be built for outdoor service with sealed glass doors, which protect the instruments and yet afford good visibility. Some outdoor panels contain internal passageways between the instrument face and the front wall, all under one weatherproof roof.

Instruments are being improved steadily and being miniaturized so as to save panel space without sacrificing reliability. Electronic and solid-state designs are being introduced. Improved drum-type sequencing controllers have been developed, to reduce the number of relays and wiring required; they also reduce the size of the panel and increase its reliability. The "hardware" must be continually refined in design with the aim of avoiding failures and making it more rugged, long-lasting, and capable of trouble-free operation.

Automatic monitoring of the program of regeneration is being adopted. This scheme checks the various steps as they are being performed. For example, it verifies whether a valve has opened or closed as scheduled. If any valve operation has failed to take place, as required, the automatic monitor stops the regeneration and rings an alarm.

The engineering design of the control panel, including the wiring and circuitry for the automatic controls and instrumentation on the panel, must include the following.

(a) Preparation of regeneration schedules giving flow rates and duration of each step, expected demineralizer effluent conductivities, pH values, and flow rates. Panel-mounted instruments required for these measurements are listed.

(b) Flow diagram of the demineralizer, showing location of field-mounted orifice plates, conductivity cells, and other items.

(c) Schematic wiring in a "ladder" type of diagram, showing all the equipment to be controlled and the controlling means. All relays, solenoids, timers, indicating lights, motor controls, and switches must be included. Separate schematic wiring diagrams generally are prepared for the different batteries of units. A separate alarm wiring diagram may be required.

(d) Interconnecting wiring diagrams, showing connections to the field-mounted cells and transmitters.

(e) Schematic air piping, showing the pneumatic controls, including field-mounted and panel-mounted items, connections, and required air pressures.

(f) Hydraulic schematic diagrams, showing pumps, cylinders, and similar items.

(g) The panel detailed drawings of the steel enclosures, structural details, cutouts, name plates, supports, stiffeners, and removable plates and doors.

(h) Physical panel wiring drawings showing equipment in place, wiring specifications, and colors of the different wires.

With the growing hourly cost of operating labor and the steady rise in effluent purity required, automatic controls for demineralizers are becoming the adopted standard. Sophisticated designs that provide reliable performance are essential.

VIII. Neutralizers of Regeneration Waste Waters

The regeneration of demineralizers produces waste waters that are alternately acid and alkaline. Our national concern with pollution abatement has resulted in government regulations requiring neutralization of this waste water before its discharge into rivers. Acid or alkaline waste waters may be harmful to fish life in rivers, and they also increase the complexity of water purification for downstream users. City Health Departments allow only "neutral" wastes to enter municipal sewers, because acid water corrodes them. Besides, low or high pH wastes harm the bacteria that are responsible for the successful operation of municipal sewage treatment plants.

A. The pH Range of Acceptable Neutralized Water

Figure 8.14 shows the pH values for various amounts of free mineral acidity and alkalis in water and also the pH values of the usual cation and anion exchanger effluents and their regeneration waste waters. A pH range of 5 to 10.5 is usually acceptable, because it does not interfere with potability (6), is not harmful to aquatic life (7, 8), and will not cause excessive corrosion.

B. Alternate Neutralization Schemes

Various arrangements have been used for neutralization, as follows.

(a) In large plants acid waters may be neutralized in continuous flow basins by the addition of lime monitored by pH and flow measurements. The basins may be fairly small, because the required reaction time is short. However, continuous agitation and addition of the lime in several successive steps are desirable (9). Modulating pH recorder-controllers, properly maintained for defouling the electrodes, are essential.

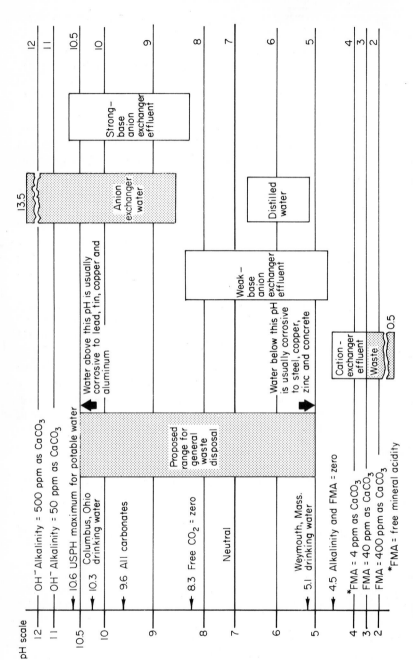

Fig. 8.14. Acceptable range of pH values in waste water, and the pH of effluents and regeneration waste waters from cation and anion exchanger regenerations [from Crits and McKeown (5)].

(b) Acid waters can be neutralized by being passed through limestone beds (*10*). To avoid fouling of the limestone, upflow at high rates is necessary. Recycling pumps are used, when the flow is too low.

(c) Where waste waters are alternately acid and alkaline, as from de-mineralizer regenerations, two tanks for intermittent fill and drain can be used, in which the acids and alkalis are allowed to neutralize each other. When one of the tanks fills, however, the contents must be mixed thoroughly by agitators. The pH is measured and the corrective alkali or acid added, to bring the pH value within the desired neutral range. Then the tank is drained to the sewer, and the other tank collects the wastes from the next regeneration.

In large demineralizer plants this scheme involves both big tanks and costly instrumentation. In one case, for a demineralizer located in a city, two tanks of 150,000 gal each were required. The cost of the corrective chemicals to be added amounted to about $50,000 a year, and the labor of attention was also costly. The high costs were due to the fact that the excess acid and caustic were not kept in chemical balance (or equivalence) during regenerations. The need for such balance is stressed in Chapter 9, Section IIC3h, in the technical calculations of demineralizers.

(d) Small neutralizing fill-and-drain tanks may be used to hold only the displacement effluent and the stronger part of the rinse. The backwash and the later weaker part of the rinse are bypassed to the sewer. This does not keep the pH value accurately within the desired range but approximates it. It neutralizes the bulk of the acid and alkali.

(e) Continuous-flow basins, always kept full, may also be used. They are made in a size sufficient to hold the waste water from only one regeneration of either a cation or an anion unit. The alkaline water in the basin from an anion-unit regeneration acts as a buffer, neutralizing the acid water from the next cation-unit regeneration. Pumps, recycling from outlet to inlet, are used for agitation. Nevertheless calcium sulfate precipitates form and settle out in the basin and must be periodically removed, and the pH is not kept accurately within the desired range at all times.

(f) The regenerant waste water may be discharged into condenser once-through cooling-water tunnels, when the fresh water is sufficiently high in flow and alkalinity to provide dilution and neutralization (*11*), but this often requires long acid-proof sewers from the demineralizer to the tunnels.

(g) The regeneration waste water may be discharged to a central waste-treatment plant used for other waste waters; this also may require long acid-proof sewers, because the neutralizer may be far from the demineralizer.

C. Ion-Exchange Neutralizer

The disadvantages of the neutralizers, cited in the last paragraphs, led to the development in 1960 of an ion-exchange neutralizer (*12, 13*), which contains a weak-acid carboxylic cation resin, such as Amberlite IRC-50 or IRC-84. The shell is rubber-lined and is equipped with internal inlet and underdrain distributors. The shell may be of the gravity or pressure design, preferably the latter, which avoids repumping if the sewer is elevated. Even if the sewer is below the shell, the depth of gravity units may not provide enough head to maintain the desired flow at all times. Gravel is the subfill. External acid-proof valves and piping permit occasional backwashing. Normally the neutralizer does not have to be regenerated, provided the excess acid from a cation-unit regeneration is chemically equivalent to the excess caustic soda from an anion-unit regeneration, but provision for occasional regeneration when necessary may be included.

The cation-exchanger backwash is usually bypassed around the neutralizer, because it may be turbid and therefore foul the neutralizer resin. The neutralizer and cation unit should be backwashed at the same time, and the two backwash streams should mix on the way to the sewer. The cation backwash may be slightly acid and the neutralizer backwash slightly alkaline, so that the mixture is within the desired pH range.

Weak-acid carboxylic cation resin is used because it does not split the neutral salts, chlorides, and sulfates present in the regenerant waste water. If strong-acid sulfonic cation resin were used, it would split the salts, and its capacity therefore would be consumed, but the weak-acid cation resin allows them to pass through unchanged. Weak-base anion resin also can be used successfully.

D. Chemical Reactions of the Neutralizer

After the acid waste water from cation-unit regeneration passes through the neutralizer resin, the latter is in the hydrogen form. Then when the caustic soda waste water from an anion-unit regeneration passes through, the

Table 8.1

REACTIONS OF THE ION EXCHANGE NEUTRALIZER

Reactions with acid:

$$2\,RNa \;+\; H_2SO_4 \;\longrightarrow\; 2\,RH \;+\; Na_2SO_4$$

sodium	sulfuric	hydrogen	sodium
resin	acid	resin	sulfate

Reactions with alkali:

$$RH \;+\; NaOH \;\longrightarrow\; RNa \;+\; HOH$$

hydrogen	sodium	sodium	water
resin	hydroxide	resin	

Reactions with neutral salts:

$$2\,RNa \;+\; CaCl_2 \;\longrightarrow\; \text{does not react}$$
$$2\,RH \;+\; Na_2SO_4 \;\longrightarrow\; \text{does not react}$$

neutralizer resin is changed to the sodium form. The neutralizer effluent is neutral, because the acid and caustic soda are alternately absorbed. Table 8.1 shows the chemical reactions involved.

E. Resin Capacity, Required Freeboard, and Flow Rates

The Amberlite IRC-50 carboxylic resin swells about 80% when it goes from the hydrogen form to the sodium form. A freeboard depth equal to 75% of the resin-bed depth in the swollen condition should be allowed, to permit backwashing without loss of resin. The depth of the gravel below the resin should be about 12 in. The capacity of the resin is 3 or 4 lb of acid or its chemical equivalent in caustic soda (expressed as $CaCO_3$) per cubic foot of resin; thus the excess acid from a cation unit regeneration or the chemical equivalent in excess caustic soda, expressed in pounds and divided by these capacity figures, gives the volume of neutralizer resin required. The allowable flow rates are 3 to 4 gal/min square foot of area; thus the cation or anion rinse rate, divided by these rates, gives the required area of the neutralizer.

F. Description of First Ion-Exchange Neutralizer

One of the first ion-exchange neutralizers was installed in 1961 at the Southwark Station in Philadelphia. The demineralizer consisted of three pairs of two-bed units, each 30 in. in diameter. Each anion unit contained 17.2 ft^3 of strong-base resin (Amberlite IRA-402), which was regenerated with 86 lb of caustic soda. The capacity of the bed was 125 kgr, equivalent to 15 lb, of caustic soda. Subtracting 15 lb from the 86 lb of caustic soda introduced gave 71 lb of excess caustic soda (as NaOH). Dividing this by 0.8 gave 89 lb of excess caustic (expressed as $CaCO_3$) to be neutralized. The amount of carboxylic resin (Amberlite IRC-50) required was therefore 25 ft^3; slightly more, 30 ft^3, was used. The cation or anion rinse rates were 30 to 35 gal/min, so the neutralizer area needed was 10 to 12 ft^2. A neutralizer unit 48 in. in diameter was furnished. Figure 8.15 is a flow diagram of the installation.

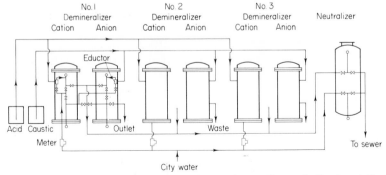

Fig. 8.15. Flow diagram of two-bed demineralizers and neutralizer at the Southwark Station, Philadelphia.

During its years of operation since 1961 the pH of the neutralizer effluent has been kept within the desired range of 5.0 to 9.5 continuously.

G. Advantages of Ion-Exchange Neutralizer

The advantages of the ion-exchange neutralizer are as follows.

(a) A saving in first cost may be realized when the neutralizer is compared with a fill-and-drain tank system. For the Southwark Station the capital saving was estimated to be $20,000 (14).

(b) The sewer from the neutralizer need not be acid-proof and is not attacked.

(c) Chemicals for correcting pH are not required.

(d) Floor space is saved by the neutralizer in comparison with a fill-and-drain tank system, because the neutralizer resin operates on the weights of the acid–alkali constituents rather than on their solution volumes. Table 8.2 gives

Table 8.2

COMPARATIVE VOLUMES OF REQUIRED NEUTRALIZER RESIN
AND SOLUTIONS OF ACID AND ALKALI

Soln. H_2SO_4 or equiv. alk. %	Concn., ppm	Approx. vol. soln. per 100 lb acid or alk. cont.		Vol. neut. resin, ft^3
		ft^3	gal	
0.1	1,000	1600	12,000	20 to 30
0.5	5,000	320	2,400	20 to 30
1.0	10,000	160	1,200	20 to 30
4.0	40,000	40	300	20 to 30
7.5	75,000	20	150	20 to 30

the comparative volumes of the neutralizer resin and the solutions. For example, the volume of resin required to neutralize 100 lb of sulfuric acid or its equivalent in alkali in 0.5 % solution is only $\frac{1}{16}$ of the volume of the solution. Actually, the same resin volume will neutralize not only 100 lb of acid but also 100 lb of alkali, so the impounding-tank volume for a 0.5 % solution of acid plus alkali would have to be 32 times as great as the required neutralizer resin volume.

REFERENCES

1. S. B. Applebaum and F. Fast, Ammonia regeneration of weak base anion resin. *Water Sewage Works* (October 1960), reprinted from discussion at *Proc. Intern. Water Conf. 20th, October 1959*, p. 105.
2. R. C. Adams, U.S. Patent 3,004,668 (1961).

3. T. P. Harding, Handling and feeding acid to demineralizers. *Proc. Ann. Water Conf. Engrs. Soc. West Penn., 19th Ann. Conf.* (1958).

4. G. W. Brush, S. B. Applebaum, and G. J. Angele, Mixed bed demineralizer operations at A.E.C. Facilities, Oak Ridge, Tenn. *Proc. Ann. Water Conf. Engrs. Soc. West Penn., 17th Ann. Conf.* (1956).

5. G. J. Crits and M. C. McKeown, Neutralize acid and alkaline wastes. *Power* (February 1961).

6. "APHA Standard Methods for the Examination of Water, Sewage and Industrial Wastes," 10th ed. 1955.

7. Water quality criteria. SWPCB, Publ. No. 3. State of California, 1952.

8. Water quality criteria, Addendum No. 1. SWPCB, Publ. No. 3. State of California, 1954.

9. B. W. Dickerson and R. M. Brooks, Neutralization of acid wastes. *Ind. Eng. Chem.* **42**, 599 (1950).

10. A. L. Reidl, Limestone used to neutralize acid wastes. *Chem. Eng.* (July 1947).

11. R. P. Logan, "Industrial Wastes," Monogram Ser. No. 18, p. 239 of Rudolph's Book, Reinhold, New York, 1953.

12. G. J. Crits, U.S. Patent 3,062,739 (1962).

13. G. J. Crits and M. C. McKeown, Ion exchange acid-alkali neutralizer for demineralized waste waters. *Proc. Intern. Water Conf., Engrs. Soc. West Penn., October 1961*, p. 119.

14. W. B. Willsey, Discussion of paper by Crits, G. J., and McKeown, M. C., Ion exchange acid-alkali; neutralizer for demineralized waste waters, *Proc. Intern. Water Conf., Engrs. Soc. West. Penn., October, 1961*, p. 126.

9

Demineralizer Technical Design Calculations and Typical Examples

The purpose of demineralizer technical calculations is to determine the dimensions of the ion exchange units, the amounts and kinds of exchange resin and their regenerant levels, and the design of the pretreatment equipment that may be required. A number of alternative systems may have to be compared for first cost and regenerant operating cost, before the most economical system can be selected. The data on which the calculations are based include the following: the required purity of effluent, the maximal and average amounts of impurities in the various available water supplies, the maximal and average flow of the water to be treated and the length of the service runs, the availability of adequate storage for demineralized water, the local cost of regenerants, and the equivalence of excess acid and alkali used for regeneration.

The following abbreviations, common in the literature on demineralization, will hereinafter be employed without further identification: TDS, total dissolved solids (electrolyte content); TMA, total mineral acidity (sulfates and chlorides); TC, total cations; TA, total anions; TEA, total exchangeable anions. M in the calculations will signify the numeral 1000.

I. Normal Procedure and Steps to Be Followed

The steps to be taken proceed in a logical sequence, as follows.

A. Determine the Effluent Purity Required

The required degree of purity of the final demineralized product greatly influences the complexity and cost of the system selected. It is uneconomical to request a greater effluent purity than is actually required. By consulting Tables 2.5–2.7, 3.4, and 3.5, which give water-quality tolerances, silica tolerances, and required effluent electrolyte, for various applications, the final purity may be determined. These are the three main criteria for selection of a demineralizer system.

B. Study the Analyses of the Available Water Supplies

A well-water supply of adequate capacity, if obtainable, is preferable to a surface supply, because well water is usually clearer, lower in organic content, and more constant in composition. Many well waters can be used without pretreatment. If surface waters must be used, the range of analysis, minimum to maximum, should be obtained and made a basis for determining the length of service runs between regenerations at all times. A single analysis may be misleading, because the composition is affected by rainfall and varies with the seasons. If only one analysis is available, the date of sampling and condition of the river should be taken into account.

Sometimes it is advisable to run a pipeline to a distant better water supply rather than to use, for instance, a creek at the site, because the creek may be acid at times, owing to mine drainage, and it may contain higher amounts of solids during droughts. The cost of a pipeline to a pond or lake some distance away may be offset by the lower first cost and operating cost of the demineralizer and pretreatment plant required to treat the water of lower solids content.

C. Select the Type of Pretreatment Needed

When the water supply has been decided on, the type of pretreatment, if any is required, must be determined. Chapters 3 and 4 describe the various possible pretreatments. If the hardness and alkalinity are both high enough, lime presoftening may be indicated. Otherwise, for surface supplies coagulation without presoftening is usually employed before the final clarification with filters. If the organic content of the water is high, the various methods of reducing it (discussed in Chapter 4, Section III) should be compared and a selection should be made; this is important for the avoidance of organic fouling of the anion resins. In the case of well waters that contain high amounts of iron and manganese a pretreatment for their removal may be required to avoid iron fouling of the resins. The pretreatment selected causes a change in the analysis because of the chemicals added. After the dosage of chemicals is selected, their effect in modifying the analysis is calculated, in order to establish the "design analysis," on which the demineralizer must be based.

D. Decide on the Type of Demineralizer System and the Resins

The desired effluent purity and the influent design analysis determine the demineralizer system required. These systems are described in Chapter 6,

Sections X and XI, and Table 6.2 gives the effluent TDS and silica to be expected from them. If the required TDS is more than 2 ppm, a two-bed system may suffice. If silica is not to be reduced, weak-base anion resin is used, but for silica removal the strong-base anion resin is necessary. For less than 2 ppm TDS the multibed type with secondary, or polishing, units is usually selected.

If the influent contains high amounts of alkalinity, a decarbonator or vacuum deaerator will reduce the free carbon dioxide in the cation exchanger effluent. High alkalinity also may justify the use of weak-acid cation exchangers for saving acid regenerant. If high amounts of TMA are present, weak-base exchangers preceding the strong-base exchanger will save caustic soda regenerant. This can be done with three-bed systems, or else the weak- and strong-base resins may be used in the same unit (double-layer design). Examples given later in the chapter show the regenerant savings realized by these alternatives.

E. Establish the Regenerant Levels and Exchange Capacities

The effluent TDS specified establishes the cation leakage permissible, and this in turn determines the acid regenerant level required. The effluent silica desired similarly indicates the allowable silica leakage and the required caustic soda regenerant level. The tables in Chapter 7 give the regenerant levels, for various resins, that will keep the TDS and silica leakages below the desired limits for various types of water.

From the design analysis of the influent the proportion of sodium, in percent of TC, is calculated. Higher percentages of sodium increase the cation leakage and require higher acid levels to depress this leakage. Likewise, the proportion of alkalinity, in percent of TA, is computed. Lower percentages of alkalinity also increase the cation leakage and the required acid level. The proportion of silica in percent of the TEA is also figured. Higher percentages of silica increase the silica leakage and the required caustic soda level. The proportion of weak acids (carbonic and silicic), in percent of TEA, is then estimated. The higher this percentage, the greater the anion exchange capacity.

After the regenerant levels are selected, the corresponding exchange capacities of the resins are taken from the tables in Chapter 7. The capacities are expressed in kilograins of ions removed per cubic foot of resin (kgr/ft^3). The total kilograins to be removed by a resin bed is the product of the thousands of gallons treated between regenerations and the grains of TC or TEA per gallon. The parts per million TC or TEA in the analysis is divided by 17.1, to give the grains per gallon present.

It has recently been found necessary to calculate, after selection of the regenerant levels, whether the excess acid and excess caustic soda discharged to waste from the regenerations are chemically equivalent, or "in balance," because antipollution regulations require that liquid wastes discharged into rivers be neutral. Most industrial facilities have neutralizing systems for this purpose. If the excess acid is greater than the excess caustic soda, ordinarily it is necessary to add expensive alkali in the neutralizer; therefore the regenerant levels selected must be checked for whether the excesses are in balance. One of the sample calculations (Case 3) given later in the chapter shows that a three-bed demineralizer would save considerable caustic soda, but the excesses of acid and caustic soda in the regeneration waste water are not in balance, so it becomes necessary to modify the demineralizer design and regenerant levels to correct the imbalance.

The final adjusted regenerant levels are used in calculations of the cation and anion regeneration schedules. These include the following steps: backwash, regenerant dilution and introduction, displacement (slow rinse), and final (fast) rinse. The schedule includes the flow of strong and dilute regenerants and water, in gallons per minute, the duration in minutes, and the total gallons of water required for each of these steps. These determine the size of piping, valves, and pumps for regeneration and the total regeneration water to be provided.

F. Specify the Length of Service Runs and Flow Rates

The area of the ion exchange units is determined by the flow rates and the volume of resin by the length of the service run selected.

The flow rates, in gallons per minute per square foot of area of the exchange unit in the past were limited to 6 gal/min/ft^2, when all units in a battery were in operation, and to 8 gal/min/ft^2 when one unit was being regenerated; the trend recently is to increase the flow rates to 8 to 10 with all units on and 12 to 15 with one unit out. Secondary, or polishing, units can operate at higher rates, 15 to 25 gal/min/ft^2. Condensate mixed-bed demineralizers are designed for rates of 50 gal/min/ft^2.

The length of service run specified in the past has usually been 24 hr between regenerations. The long run was justified with manually operated plants, because it minimized operating labor requirements, but with the reliable automatic designs now available shorter runs, of 4 to 8 hr, are practical. They reduce the first costs and resin volume inventory in fixed beds. Recently a renewed interest in the continuous designs has appeared (see Chapter 13). The continuous demineralizers operate for very short, intermittent periods. Every few minutes some of the exhausted resin is transferred to external vessels or zones for regeneration, while some of the regenerated resin is moved back into the main service sections. For waters of high solids, the resin volume inventory and regenerant requirements are usually less in continuous than in fixed-bed plants. For equitable comparisons of the fixed-bed and continuous designs, however, the shorter runs and higher flow rates of the fixed beds, mentioned above, should be taken into consideration.

If the influent design analysis varies widely from minimum to maximum, a short service run, of 4 to 8 hr, should be used, based on the maximum; for the minimum and average the run will then be much longer.

G. Consider the Availability of Storage for Demineralized Water and for Regenerants

Without storage for demineralized water the pretreatment and primary exchange units must provide the backwash and rinse flows required by the secondary units plus the peak service rates, and this often means enlarging the areas of the primary units. The storage avoids such enlargement, and it also provides for short maintenance outages.

Adequate storage of regenerant reduces their cost, because it permits their being purchased in tank cars rather than in drums or carboys. In the larger demineralizer plants the saving in operating cost thus realized is appreciable.

H. Make Design Calculations Working from Outlet to Inlet

After the questions in the foregoing paragraphs A to G have been settled, the calculations proper are undertaken, in a backwards order, that is, by working from the outlet end back to the inlet end; for example, in a two-bed system the anion unit is designed first and then the cation unit. The reason for this is that the cation unit must provide the water for regenerating the anion unit, and this water must be included in the calculation of cation unit's capacity; likewise, the pretreatment plant must provide for the regeneration water for both the cation and anion units.

II. Typical Examples of Design Calculations

Four examples of design calculations are given in the following sub-sections A to D; they are called Cases 1, 2, 3, and 4.

A. Case 1: Prechlorination and Lime Softening Pretreatment Followed by Two-Bed Demineralization and Vacuum Deaeration

1. DESIGN DATA

The total flow is 266 gal/min without demineralized-water storage for makeup to high-pressure boilers (2400 psi).

The influent is from a reservoir of fairly constant analysis; see column A in Table 9.1.

The effluent quality required: TDS, 2 ppm; conductivity, 10 μmho; and the silica, 0.03 ppm (as SiO_2).

2. MODIFICATION OF WATER ANALYSIS AFTER ADDITION OF PRETREATING CHEMICALS

(a) The first step is to calculate the effect of adding the chlorine (a chlorine demand of 5 ppm is assumed in this case). As Table 3.1 shows, 1 ppm chlorine added increases the chlorides by 1.4 ppm, decreases the alkalinity by 1.4 ppm, and increases the free carbon dioxide by 1.3 ppm. Multiplying these figures by 5, for the chlorine dose added, results in column B in Table 9.1.

(b) The second step is to modify the analysis in column B by the coagulant added. A dosage of 12 ppm ferric sulfate is selected for this lime softening pretreatment. The ferric hydroxide floc precipitates well at the high pH values present. As Table 3.1 shows, 1 ppm ferric sulfate decreases the alkalinity by 0.75 ppm, increases the free carbon dioxide by 0.66 ppm, and increases the sulfates by 0.75 ppm. Multiplying these figures by 12 for the coagulant dose added results in column C in Table 9.1.

(c) The third step is to show the effect of the lime. Since the HCO_3 alkalinity exceeds the calcium in column C, the rules given in Chapter 3, Section 1A and 4C, are followed. This results in column D, which becomes the *design analysis* for the demineralizer.

The lime dosage required is calculated as follows:

Alkalinity: 92 ppm as $CaCO_3$
CO_2 (22.5 × 2.3): 52 ,, ,, ,,
Mg: 24 ,, ,, ,,
168 ppm as $CaCO_3$

Lime: (168 × 74)/93 = 132 ppm as 93% $Ca(OH)_2$
Lime: 168/150 = 1.1 lb of 93% $Ca(OH)_2$ per 1000 gal

3. DESIGN CALCULATIONS

a. Determination of Demineralizer System

To produce an effluent TDS of the 2 ppm specified a two-bed system with strong-base resin suffices. Since the alkalinity in column D, Table 9.1, is 69 ppm, a vacuum deaerator will be placed between the cation and anion units, to reduce the carbon dioxide to 5 ppm and the dissolved oxygen to under 0.5 ppm.

The figures in columns E, F, and G in the table each apply after one of the stages of treatment: column E, after the cation unit; column F, after the vacuum deaerator; column G, after the anion units (final demineralized water).

b. Selection of Resins, Capacities, and Regenerant Levels

Cation resin

TC as $CaCO_3$ = 112 ppm:

$$\frac{112 \text{ ppm}}{17.1} = 6.6 \text{ gr/gal}$$

% Na: $\dfrac{55 \text{ ppm}}{112 \text{ ppm}} = 49\%$

% alk: $\dfrac{69 \text{ ppm}}{112 \text{ ppm}} = 62\%$

Cation leakage required:
  2 ppm:

$$\frac{2 \text{ ppm}}{112 \text{ ppm}} = 1.8\%$$

Resin: strong-acid, such as
  Amberlite IR-120 or Dowex
  HCR-W, or equal.

Therefore, from Table 7.4, use an
acid level of 5 lb/ft^3, H_2SO_4/resin,
and a capacity of 13.6 kgr/ft^3.

Anion resin

TEA as $CaCO_3$

CO_2 after vac. deaer.:

	5 ppm × 1.13 =	6 ppm
SiO_2:	7.4 ppm × 0.83 =	6	„
TMA:	$\dfrac{SO_4 + Cl}{21 \ + \ 22}$	= 43	„

$$\overline{ 55 \text{ ppm}}$$

TEA: $\dfrac{55 \text{ ppm}}{17.1} = 3.2 \text{ gr/gal}$

% weak acids: $\dfrac{12 \text{ ppm}}{55 \text{ ppm}} = 22\%$

% Cl: $\dfrac{22 \text{ ppm}}{55 \text{ ppm}} = 40\%$

% SiO_2: $\dfrac{6 \text{ ppm}}{55 \text{ ppm}} = 11\%$

Desired SiO_2 leakage: 0.03 ppm

Resin: porous strong-base such
  as Dowex SBR-P or Amberlite
  IRA-402 or equal.

Therefore, from Table 7.17, use a
caustic soda level of 5 lb/ft^3,
NaOH/resin, and a capacity
11.7 × 0.9 (for Cl) = 10.6 kgr/ft^3.

c. Design of Anion Units

The area of the units and the resin volumes are first calculated. The total flow is 266 gal/min continuously without demineralized-water storage. Therefore use two units.

A flow rate of 12 gal/min/ft^2 through one unit, while the other is regenerating, gives

$$\frac{266 \text{ gal/min}}{12 \text{ gal/min/ft}^2} = 22.2 \text{ ft}^2$$

Use 5 ft 6 in. diameter (23.5 ft^2).

Table 9.1

CASE 1: OPERATING RESULTS [a]

	Impurities ppm as $CaCO_3$ (except [b])						
	A	B	C	D	E	F	G
Ca	56	56	56	35	0	0	0
Mg	24	24	24	22	0	0	0
Na	55	55	55	55	2	2	2
H	0	0	0	0	41	41	0
TC	135	135	135	112	43	43	2
HCO_3	108	101	92	0	0	0	0
CO_3	0	0	0	69	0	0	0
OH	0	0	0	0	0	0	1
SO_4	12	12	21	21	21	21	0
Cl	15	22	22	22	22	22	1
TA	135	135	135	112	43	43	2
CO_2[b] (as CO_2)	8	14.5	22.5	0	30	5	0
SiO_2[b] (as SiO_2)	7.4	7.4	7.4	7.4	7.4	7.4	0.03
pH	7.5	7.2	6.9	10.2	2.9	3.0	9.0
Turbidity	100			0	0	0	0
Color[b]	30			5	5	5	5

[a] The columns are as follows:
A, raw water.
B, after adding 5 ppm chlorine.
C, after adding 12 ppm ferric sulfate.
D, after adding 132 ppm lime as 93% $Ca(OH)_2$ (this is the design analysis of the demineralizer).
E, cation effluent.
F, after vacuum deaerator.
G, after anion unit.

Assuming two* regenerations of each unit daily,

$$\frac{266 \text{ gal/min} \times 1440 \text{ min}}{2 \text{ units} \times 2 \text{ regenerations}} = 96,000 \text{ gal per unit run}$$

$96M$ gal $\times$ 3.2 gr/gal TEA: 307 kgr

$$\frac{307 \text{ kgr}}{10.6 \text{ kgr/ft}^3} = 29 \text{ ft}^3, \qquad \frac{29 \text{ ft}^3}{23.5 \text{ ft}^2} = 1.2 \text{ ft resin bed depth}$$

* Note that the anion units are each regenerated once daily as the further calculation shows.

This is too shallow. Use a minimum of 24 to 30 in. If 30 in., or 2.5 ft, are used, then

$$23.5 \times 2.5 = 59 \text{ ft}^3 \text{ of Amberlite IRA-402, Dowex SBR-P or equivalent.}$$

The straight shell height, with 100% freeboard, is computed:

Depth of resin:	2.5 ft
100% freeboard:	2.5 „
Total straight height:	5.0 ft

Therefore use two anion units each 5 ft 6 in. in diameter by 5 ft 0 in. in height. Capacity: $59 \text{ ft}^3 \times 10.6 \text{ kgr/ft}^3 = 625 \text{ kgr}$

$$\frac{625 \text{ kgr}}{3.2 \text{ gr/gal}} = 195M \text{ gal}, \qquad \frac{195M \text{ gal}}{133 \text{ gal/min} \times 60 \text{ min}} = 24.4 \text{ hr anion run so}$$

that each anion unit will be re-generated only once daily instead of twice daily

Caustic soda: $5 \text{ lb} \times 59 \text{ ft}^3 = 295 \text{ lb}$

$$\frac{295 \text{ lb}}{195M \text{ gal}} = 1.5 \text{ lb NaOH (100\% basis) per 1000 gal}$$

d. Regeneration Schedule for Anion Unit

4% NaOH at 120°F will be used.

4% caustic soda contains 0.348 lb NaOH per gal
50% caustic soda contains 6.364 lb NaOH per gal

The steps of the regeneration schedule are as follows.

(1) Backwash: Use 3 gal/min/ft² for 15 min:
$$3.0 \times 23.5 \text{ ft}^2 = 71 \text{ gal/min} \times 15 = 1070 \text{ gal}$$
(2) Caustic soda injection: Assume 50% liquid caustic soda to be used.

Total pounds NaOH (100% basis): $5 \text{ lb} \times 59 \text{ ft}^3 = 295 \text{ lb}$

$$a = \frac{295 \text{ lb}}{6.364 \text{ lb/gal (50\%)}} = 46 \text{ gal 50\% NaOH}$$

$$b = \frac{295 \text{ lb}}{0.348 \text{ lb/gal (4\%)}} = 848 \text{ gal 4\% NaOH}$$

The dilution water is $b - a = 848 - 46 = 802$ gal in 60 to 90 min. Use demineralized water or cation effluent for dilution water.

The caustic soda injection rate should be 0.25 gal/min/ft^3.

$$\text{Dilute caustic rate:} \quad 0.25 \text{ gal/min/ft}^3 \times 59 \text{ ft}^3$$

$$= 15 \text{ gal/min}; \qquad \frac{848 \text{ gal}}{15 \text{ gal/min}} = 56 \text{ min}$$

$$\text{Dilution-water rate:} \quad \frac{802 \text{ gal}}{56 \text{ min}} = 14.3 \text{ gal/min}$$

$$50\% \text{ NaOH rate:} \quad \frac{46 \text{ gal}}{56 \text{ min}} = 0.82 \text{ gal/min}$$

(3) Displacement, or slow rinse: The flow rate is the same as the dilution rate, or 14.3 gal/min. The total volume is equal to the voids in the resin bed plus the 6 in. space from the regenerant distributor to the top of the bed.

$$\text{Voids:} \qquad 40\% \times 59 \text{ ft}^3 = 23.6 \text{ ft}^3$$

$$6 \text{ in. space: } 0.5 \text{ ft} \times 23.5 \text{ ft}^2 = \underline{11.7 \,{}_{\prime\prime}}$$
$$35.3 \text{ ft}^3$$

$$35.3 \text{ ft}^3 \times 7.5 = 265 \text{ gal}; \qquad \frac{265 \text{ gal}}{14.3 \text{ gal/min}} = 18.5 \text{ min}$$

(4) Rinse to waste: The rate can be 5 to 6 gal/min/ft^2. If 6 gal/min/ft^2 are used, then

$$23.5 \text{ ft}^2 \times 6 = 141 \text{ gal/min}$$

The total volume usually is 100–130 gal/ft^3; then 59 ft^3 × 100 = 5900 gal:

$$\frac{5900 \text{ gal}}{141 \text{ gal/min}} = 42 \text{ min}$$

(5) Rinse recycle: Instead of discharging all the 5900 gal to waste, about one half can be recycled back to the cation inlet.

SUMMARY OF ANION REGENERATION SCHEDULE

Steps	Flow rate, gal/min	Duration, min	To waste, gal	Amt. recycled, gal
Backwash	71.0	15.0	1070	
Caustic soda dilution	14.3	56.0	802	
Displacement	14.3	18.5	265	
Rinse to waste	141.0	21.0	2950	
Rinse recycle	141.0	21.0		2950
TOTAL		131.5	5087	2950

The cation effluent is used for backwashing and rinsing of the anion unit. Demineralized water is used for diluting the caustic soda and for displacement.

e. Design of Cation Units

The cation unit must provide the water for the anion regeneration. The recycled anion rinse will have about one half of the solids of the raw water; therefore assume that only one half of 2950 gal, or 1475 gal must be included.

Anion regeneration water to waste:	5,087 gal
1/2 of recycled rinse:	1,475 „
Anion regeneration water:	6,562 gal
Service water:	96,000 gal
Anion regeneration water:	6,562 „
TOTAL:	102,562 gal

$$102.6M \text{ gal} \times 6.6 \text{ gr/gal TC} = 678 \text{ kgr}$$

$$\frac{678 \text{ kgr}}{13.6 \text{ kgr/ft}^3} = 50 \text{ ft}^3 \text{ of cation resin}$$

Use 5 ft 6 in. diameter, as with anion unit, and a minimal bed of 30 in. depth, or 59 ft^3. The other dimensions will be as follows:

Resin:	2.5 ft
75% freeboard:	1.9 „
Straight height:	4.4 ft (use 5 ft 0 in.)

Use two cation units each 5 ft 6 in. in diameter by 5 ft 0 in. in height.
Capacity: 59 ft^3 × 13.6 kgr/ft^3 = 800 kgr

$$\frac{800 \text{ kgr}}{6.6 \text{ gr/gal}} = 121M \text{ gal}$$

$$\frac{-7M \text{ gal for anion regeneration}}{114M \text{ gal net}}$$

$$\frac{114,000 \text{ gal}}{8,000 \text{ gal/hr}} = 14.3 \text{ hr cation runs (instead of the 12 hr originally assumed)}$$

Acid: 5 lb × 59 ft^3 = 295 lb H_2SO_4

$$\frac{295 \text{ lb}}{114M \text{ gal net}} = 2.6 \text{ lb } H_2SO_4 \text{ per 1000 gal}$$

f. Regeneration Schedule for Cation Unit

(1) Backwash: Use 6 gal/min/ft^2 × 23.5 ft^2 = 141 gal/min for 15 min = 2120 gal total.

(2) Sulfuric acid injection: Use two steps, 2% and 4%, to avoid resin fouling by calcium sulfate. Since Ca/TC = 35/112 = 31%, use dilute-acid rate of 31/50 = 0.6 gal/min/ft^3.

$$0.6 \times 59 \text{ ft}^3 = 35.4 \text{ gal/min}$$

2% acid contains 0.17 lb of H_2SO_4 per gallon;
4% acid contains 0.34 lb of H_2SO_4 per gallon;
66°Bé acid contains 15.3 lb of H_2SO_4 per gallon

Assume that one half of the total acid will be at 2% and one half at 4%:

$$\frac{295 \text{ lb acid}}{2} = 147.5 \text{ lb acid at 2\% and 147.5 lb acid at 4\%}$$

For 2% acid:

$$a = \frac{147.5 \text{ lb}}{0.17 \text{ lb/gal}} = 870 \text{ gal of 2\% acid}$$

$$b = \frac{147.5 \text{ lb}}{15.3 \text{ lb/gal}} = \underline{\quad 96 \quad ''} \text{ of 66°Bé}$$

Dilution, $a - b$: 774 gal

Duration of acid: $\dfrac{870 \text{ gal}}{35.4 \text{ gal/min}} = 24.5 \text{ min}$

Dilution rate: $\dfrac{774 \text{ gal}}{24.5 \text{ min}} = 31.6 \text{ gal/min}$

For 4% acid:

$$a = \frac{147.5 \text{ lb}}{0.34 \text{ lb/gal}} = 433 \text{ gal}$$

b = strong acid = $\underline{\quad 96 \quad ''}$
Dilution: 337 gal

Dilution rate is fixed at 31.6 gal/min

Time: $\dfrac{337 \text{ gal}}{31.6 \text{ gal/min}} = 10.7 \text{ min}$

(3) Displacement: The rate is the same as the dilution rate, or 31.6 gal/min.

Voids: 40% × 59 ft^3 = 23.6 ft^3
6 in. space: 0.5 ft × 23.5 ft^2 = $\underline{11.7 \text{ ''}}$
35.3 ft^3

$$\text{Volume:}\quad 35.3 \text{ ft}^3 \times 7.5 = 265 \text{ gal}$$

$$\text{Time of displacement:}\quad \frac{265 \text{ gal}}{31.6 \text{ gal/min}} = 8.4 \text{ min}$$

(4) Rinse: The rate is 6 gal/min/ft^2 = 6 × 23.5 = 141 gal/min.
Volume: 50 to 75 gal/ft^3
Taking 50 gal/ft^3:   59 ft^3 × 50 gal/ft^3 = 2950 gal;

$$\frac{2950 \text{ gal}}{141 \text{ gal/min}} = 21 \text{ min}$$

SUMMARY OF CATION REGENERATION

Steps	Flow rate, gal/min	Duration, min	Total, gal
Backwash	141	15	2120
Acid injection, 2% dilution	31.6	24.5	774
Acid injection, 4% dilution	31.6	10.7	337
Displacement	31.6	8.4	265
Rinse	141	21	2950
TOTAL		79.6	6446

g. Simultaneous Regeneration of Cation and Anion Units

The outage times for the separate cation and anion regenerations given in the summary tables of the schedules were (cation) 79.6 min and (anion) 131.5 min, or a total of 211.1 min. This may be reduced by simultaneous cation and anion regenerations as follows.

Cation unit		Anion unit	
Steps	Minutes	Steps	Minutes
Wait		Backwash	15.0
Backwash	15.0	Caustic	56.0
Acid, 2%	24.5		
Acid, 4%	10.7		
Displacement	8.4		
Rinse	21.0	Displacement	18.5
	79.6		89.5
Wait	9.9		
	89.5		
Use cation effluent to rinse anion.		Rinse	42.0
		TOTAL	131.5

Thus the cation regeneration is completed while the caustic soda is flowing through the anion unit. This reduces the total outage from 211.1 min to 131.5 min, saving 79.6 min.

h. Design of Vacuum Deaerator

Service flow:	266 gal/min
Anion rinse:	141 "
	407 gal/min

Use 4 ft 6 in. diameter by 9 ft 0 in. height and rubber-lined steel shell with Raschig rings and rotary vacuum pumps.

i. Summary of Plant Design

Two cation exchange units, each 5 ft 6 in. in diameter and 5 ft 0 in. in height, and each with 59 ft^3 of strong-acid resin.

Two anion exchange units, each 5 ft 6 in. in diameter and 5 ft 0 in. in height, each with 59 ft^3 of strong-base resin.

One vacuum deaerator, 4 ft 6 in. in diameter and 9 ft 0 in. in height.

j. Regenerant Cost

Assuming the cost* of sulfuric acid, 100% basis, to be 1¢ per pound and the cost of caustic soda, 100% basis, to be 3¢ per pound, the regenerant cost is as calculated below:

			Cents per 1000 gal of net output
Acid:	2.6 lb at 1¢ per lb	=	2.6
Caustic soda:	1.5 lb at 3¢ per lb	=	4.5
	Total:		7.1 per 1000 gal

4. DESIGN OF PRETREATMENT EQUIPMENT

The capacity in gallons per minute is calculated as follows:

Final effluent rate: 266 gal/min

Total anion waste, 5087 gal per unit (once a day):

$$1 \times 5087 \text{ gal} \times 2 \text{ units} = \frac{10,174 \text{ gal}}{1440 \text{ min}} = 70 \quad "$$

Total cation waste, 6446 gal per unit (twice a day):

$$\frac{2 \times 6446 \text{ gal} \times 2}{1440 \text{ min}} = \frac{25,800 \text{ gal}}{1440 \text{ min}} = \underline{179 \quad "}$$

	515 gal/min
Filter waste, 5%:	26 "
Total:	541 gal/min

*These assumed costs of acid and caustic soda are subject to change.

A solids-contact Reactor and two gravity filters are therefore provided for an average total flow of 550 gal/min. The clearwell below the gravity filters shown in Fig. 9.1 will provide for the high filter backwash, demineralizer backwash, and rinse rates.

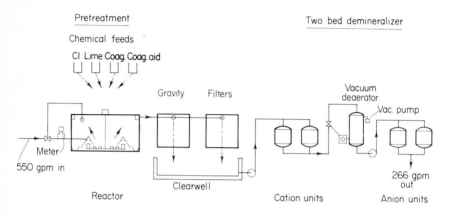

Fig. 9.1. Flow diagram of pretreatment plant and demineralizer, Case 1.

The Reactor is designed for a rise rate of 1.1 gal/min/ft². Use 25 ft 6 in. diameter by 13 ft 6 in. height.

The two gravity filters are designed for a rate of 2.2 gal/min/ft². Use two filters each 12 ft 6 in. in diameter and 12 ft. in height.

Chemical feeds of the solution type for chlorine, lime, ferric sulfate, and coagulant aid are as shown in the diagram.

B. Case 2: Prechlorination and Coagulation Pretreatment Followed by Primary Two-Bed Demineralization, Vacuum Deaeration, and Secondary Mixed-Bed Demineralization

1. DESIGN DATA

The total flow is 1000 gal/min without demineralized-water storage for makeup to once-through supercritical boiler (3500 psi).

The influent is from a river high in color, turbidity, and organic matter; see column A, Table 9.2, for the maximum and column B for the average.

The effluent quality required: TDS, 0.4 ppm; conductivity, 1.0 μmho; SiO_2, 0.01 ppm (as SiO_2).

2. MODIFICATION OF WATER ANALYSIS AFTER ADDITION OF PRETREATMENT CHEMICALS

The dosages of chemicals in parts per million are as follows:

	Average	Maximum
Chlorine:	5	10
Alum sulfate:	34	51
93 % lime hydrate:	9	16

The high dosages of chlorine and alum assumed are required for the high color, turbidity, and organic matter present. The lime dosage is selected to result in a pH value of 6.5, which should be optimal for coagulating this water.

The raw-water maxima and averages are modified stepwise as in Case 1: first, for the effect of the chlorine, then for the alum, and finally for the lime. This results in column C (maximum) and column D (average), Table 9.2, for the pretreatment effluent analyses. Column D is the demineralizer-design analysis, but column C must be considered, to make sure the service runs of the primary units are not too short.

Table 9.2
CASE 2 AND CASE 3: OPERATING RESULTS SHEET[a]

	Impurities, ppm as $CaCO_3$ (except [b])					
	A	B	C	D	E	F
Ca	150	100	172	112	0	
Mg	75	50	75	50	0	
Na	150	100	150	100	20	
TC	375	250	397	262	20	0.4
HCO_3	50	40	35	30	0	
CO_3	0	0	0	0	0	
OH	0	0	0	0	10	
SO_4	175	120	198	135	0	
Cl	150	90	164	97	10	
TA	375	250	397	262	20	0.4
SiO_2 (as SiO_2)[b]	30	20	30	20	0.10	0.01
Turbidity	400	100	0	0	0	0
Color	80	40	5	5	5	5
CO_2 (as CO_2)[b]	10	10	22	18	0	0
pH[b]	7.0	6.9	6.5	6.5	7.0	7.0
Organic matter[b] (KMnO₄ consumed)	40	30	3	2	0	0

[a] The columns are as follows:

A, maximum river water.
B, average river water.
C, pretreated maximum.

D, pretreated average (design analysis).
E, after primary units.
F, final demineralized.

3. DESIGN CALCULATIONS

a. Determination of Demineralizer System

The "very pure" effluent quality required dictates the use of a multibed system, with primary units and secondary polishing units. Mixed beds are selected for the polishing, because they produce effluents of the lowest conductivity. Since the influent contains considerable organic matter, strong-base resin is used in the primary stage, to protect the secondary anion resin from organic fouling.

Because the total flow is high, 1000 gal/min, a vacuum deaerator is included, to reduce the free carbon dioxide in the primary cation effluent and so reduce the caustic soda regenerant needed for the primary anion units.

b. Selection of Resins, Capacities, and Regenerant Levels

PRIMARY UNITS

Cation resin	Anion resin
Based on pretreated average water (Column D)	Based on pretreated average water (Column D)

Cation resin

Based on pretreated average water (Column D)

$$TC: \quad \frac{262 \text{ ppm}}{17.1} = 15.4 \text{ gr/gal}$$

$$\% \text{ Na}: \quad \frac{100 \text{ ppm}}{262 \text{ ppm}} = 38\%$$

$$\% \text{ alk}: \quad \frac{30 \text{ ppm}}{262 \text{ ppm}} = 11.5\%$$

Cation leakage: To obtain 0.4 ppm TDS from the secondary units, it will be conservative to reduce the total cations in the primary effluent to about 20 ppm.

The cation leakage for the primary cation will be:

$$\frac{20 \text{ ppm}}{262 \text{ ppm}} = 7.6\%$$

This can be obtained with 4.0 lb/ft³ acid/resin, with strong-acid resin, such as Amberlite IR-120 or Dowex HCR-W, or equal, and the capacity is 11.0 kgr/ft³, based on Table 7.4.

Anion resin

Based on pretreated average water (Column D)

TEA after vac. deaer.:

CO_2	5 ppm × 1.13	= 6 ppm
SiO_2:	20 ppm × 0.83	= 17 „
TMA:	135 ppm + 97 ppm	= 232 „
		255 ppm

$$TEA: \quad \frac{255 \text{ ppm}}{17.1} = 14.9 \text{ gr/gal}$$

$$\% \text{ SiO}_2: \quad \frac{17 \text{ ppm}}{255 \text{ ppm}} = 6.7\%$$

% weak acids:

$$\frac{CO_2 + SiO_2}{TEA} = \frac{(6 + 17) \text{ ppm}}{255 \text{ ppm}} = 9\%$$

$$\% \text{ Cl}: \quad \frac{97 \text{ ppm}}{255 \text{ ppm}} = 38\%$$

Assume primary SiO_2 leakage of 0.1 ppm, so that the % SiO_2 in the secondary influent will be low. This can be obtained with 4 lb/ft³ NaOH/resin, with strong-base porous resin, such as Dowex SBR-P, Amberlite IRA-402, or equal.

The resin capacity will be 10.5 kgr/ft³ × 0.9 (for Cl) = 9.5 kgr/ft³, based on Table 7.17.

SECONDARY MIXED BED

Cation resin	Anion resin
TC: $\dfrac{20 \text{ ppm}}{17.1} = 1.2$ gr/gal	TEA: $= \dfrac{20.08 \text{ ppm}}{17.1} = 1.2$ gr/gal
% alk: 50% % Na: 100%	% weak acids: $= 0$ (nearly) % SiO_2: $= 0$ (nearly)
However, for mixed beds the cation leakage and capacity are based on 100% alkalinity in the tables: cation leak. $= \dfrac{0.4 \text{ ppm}}{20.0 \text{ ppm}} = 2\%$ Use strong-acid resin, such as Amberlite IR-120, Dowex HCR-W, or equal.	% Cl: $= \dfrac{10 \text{ ppm}}{20 \text{ ppm}} = 50\%$ Use porous strong-base resin, such as Amberlite IRA-402, Dowex SBR-P, or equal.
From Table 7.4, use 5 lb/ft^3, and a capacity of 21.4 kgr/ft^3 $\times$ 80% = 17.1 kgr/ft^3. The 80% is used for mixed beds, as previously discussed.	From Table 7.17, use 6 lb/ft^3 NaOH/resin and a capacity of 12 kgr/ft^3 $\times$ 0.85 (for Cl) = 10.2 kgr; but 10.2 kgr/ft $\times$ 80% = 8.2 kgr/ft^3. The 80% is used for mixed beds.

c. Design of Mixed Beds

Use a flow rate of 15 gal/min/ft^2:

$$\frac{1000 \text{ gal/min}}{15 \text{ gal/min/ft}^2} = 63 \text{ ft}^2, \text{ or 9 ft 0 in. diameter}$$

For one regeneration every three days:

$$1{,}440{,}000 \text{ gal/day} \times 3 \text{ days} = 4{,}320{,}000 \text{ gal}$$

$$\frac{4{,}320{,}000 \text{ gal}}{2 \text{ units}} = 2{,}160{,}000 \text{ gal per unit}$$

Cation bed	Anion bed
$2160M$ gal $\times$ 1.2 gr/gal = 2592 kgr	$2160M$ gal $\times$ 1.2 gr/gal = 2592 kgr
$\dfrac{2592 \text{ kgr}}{17.1 \text{ kgr/ft}^3} = $ 151 ft^3 Amberlite IR-120 or equal	$\dfrac{2592 \text{ kgr}}{8.2 \text{ kgr/ft}^3} = $ 316 ft^3 Dowex SBR-P or equal
$\dfrac{151 \text{ ft}^3}{63 \text{ ft}^2} = 2.4$ ft deep bed	$\dfrac{316 \text{ ft}^3}{63 \text{ ft}^2} = 5.0$ ft deep bed

The shell dimensions are as follows:

Cation bed:	2.4 ft
Anion bed:	5.0 ″
	7.4 ft
Freeboard, 100%:	7.4
Shell height:	14.8 in straight height

Use two units 9 ft 0 in. in diameter and 15 ft 0 in. in height.

Acid: 5 lb $\times$ 151 ft^3 = 755 lb:

$$\frac{755 \text{ lb}}{2160M \text{ gal}} = 0.4 \text{ lb acid per 1000 gal}$$

Caustic soda: 6 lb $\times$ 316 ft^3 = 1896 lb:

$$\frac{1896 \text{ lb}}{2160M \text{ gal}} = 0.9 \text{ lb caustic soda per 1000 gal}$$

d. Regeneration Schedule for Secondary Mixed Beds

Simultaneous regeneration of the cation and anion resin parts of each mixed bed can take place safely, because there will be little, if any, calcium on the cation resin. Therefore, there will be no danger that calcium carbonate precipitates will clog the screening of the interface distributors (previously discussed).

The calculations of each step in the simultaneous regeneration are as follows.

(1) Backwashing: The backwash rate is usually limited to about 3 gal/min/ft^2 at 70°F, to avoid washing out the lighter anion resin. A 15 min period is used.

9 ft 0 in. diameter = 63.5 ft^2 $\times$ 3 gal/min/ft^2 = 190 gal/min
190 gal/min $\times$ 15 min = 2850 gal

Clean water should be used, to avoid clogging the screened underdrain.

(2) Simultaneous acid and caustic soda flow: Use a single step of 4% acid and 4% caustic soda, at 120°F. Since only sodium is being eluted, there is no danger of fouling of the cation bed with calcium sulfate and, therefore, no need of several steps of acid strength.

For the acid:

4% sulfuric acid contains 0.34 lb H_2SO_4 per gal
66°Bé sulfuric acid contains 15.3 lb H_2SO_4 per gal
Acid: 755 lb

4% acid: $\dfrac{755 \text{ lb}}{0.34 \text{ lb/gal}} = 2220 \text{ gal}$

Strong acid: $\dfrac{755 \text{ lb}}{15.3 \text{ lb/gal}} = \underline{\quad 49 \quad}''$

Dilution water: 2171 gal

For the caustic soda:

4% caustic soda contains 0.348 lb NaOH per gal
50% caustic soda contains 6.364 lb NaOH per gal
NaOH: 1896 lb

4% NaOH: $\dfrac{1896 \text{ lb}}{0.348 \text{ lb/gal}} = 5480 \text{ gal}$

50% NaOH: $\dfrac{1896 \text{ lb}}{6.364 \text{ lb/gal}} = \underline{\quad 298 \quad ''}$

Dilution water: 5182 gal

With a 60 min contact time:

Dilution rate: $\dfrac{5182 \text{ gal}}{60 \text{ min}} = 86 \text{ gal/min for NaOH}$

Dilution rate: $\dfrac{2171 \text{ gal}}{60 \text{ min}} = 36 \text{ gal/min for acid}$

(3) Displacement: Continue with same dilution rates as those used in Step 2. The total volume for the anion resin is as follows:

Voids: 316 ft^3 × 40% × 7.5 =   948 gal

6 in. space above bed = 63.5 ft^2 × 0.5 ft × 7.5 = $\underline{\quad 240 \quad ''}$

Total: 1188 gal

Time: $\dfrac{1188 \text{ gal}}{86 \text{ gal/min}} = 13.8 \text{ min}$

(4) Drain and air mix: Draining to the top of the bed takes 15 to 30 min. For air mix use about 10 std. ft^3/min per square foot of area with enough pressure to overcome the height of the water and of the resin (usu. ∼ 10 psi).

Air mix: 63.5 ft^2 × 10 std. ft^3/min = 635 std. ft^3/min

(5) Refill in two or three steps, as shown in Table 9.3.

(6) Final rinse: Use about 25 gal/ft^3 of both resins at 6 gal/min/ft^2, or 6 gal/min/ft^2 × 63.5 ft^2 = 380 gal/min

Cation resin: 151 ft^3

Anion resin: $\underline{316 \quad ''}$

467 ft^3

467 ft^3 × 25 gal/ft^3 = 11,700 gal

Time: $\dfrac{11,700 \text{ gal}}{380 \text{ gal/min}} = 31 \text{ min}$

Table 9.3 is a summary of these steps.

e. Design of Primary Units

Since the secondary mixed beds are regenerated only once in three days, as assumed above, their outage period for regeneration can be selected when none of the primary units are being regenerated. Consequently, the primary units need not be enlarged in area to provide backwash or rinse rates for the mixed beds. Further, the total water for these infrequent regenerations may be neglected in calculations of the primary-stage capacities. The capacity of the primary cation units should include the regeneration water required for

Table 9.3

CASE 2: SUMMARY OF SECONDARY MIXED-BED REGENERATION SCHEDULE[a]

Step (Cation)	Flow, gal/min	Duration, min	Total flow, gal	Step	Flow, gal/min	Duration, min	Total flow, gal
							Anion
(1) Backwash (see anion)				(1) Backwash	190	15.0	2850
(2) Acid in 4% dilution water	36	60	2171	(2) NaOH in 4% (120°F) dilution	86	60.0	5182
(3) Displacement	36	13.8	495	(3) Displacement	86	13.8	1188
(4) Air mix (see anion)				(4) Air mix			
				drain	gravity	15.0	
				partial refill	190	2.0	380
				air mix	635 ft³/min	10.0	
				drain	gravity	5.0	
				air mix	635 ft³/min	5.0	
(5) Fill (see anion)				(5) Fill			
				slow	40	10.0	400
				fast	320	10.0	3200
				slow	40	5.0	200
(6) Final rinse				(6) Final rinse for both resins	380	31.0	11,700
		TOTAL:	2666			TOTAL: 181.8	25,100

[a] Two units, 9 ft diam. × 15 ft ht, each with 151 ft³ of cation resin, 755 lb of acid, and each with 316 ft³ of anion resin, 1896 lb of caustic soda.

the primary anion units. For this purpose 100–130 gal per cubic foot of primary anion resin may be assumed.

PRIMARY UNITS

Anion units	Cation units
Use a flow rate of 10 gal/min/ft^2 with two units on, while the third is being regenerated:	Also use 10 gal/min/ft^2.

$$\frac{1000 \text{ gal/min}}{10 \text{ gal/min/ft}^2} = 100 \text{ ft}^2$$

Anion units	Cation units
Use three units, each 8 ft 0 in. in diameter (50 ft^2).	Use three units, each 8 ft 0 in. in diameter (50 ft^2).

Use 12 hr runs with the average water (255 ppm TEA), so that the length of the run with the maximum-analysis (393 ppm TEA) will be as follows:

$$\frac{255 \text{ ppm}}{393 \text{ ppm}} \times 12 \text{ hr} = 7.8 \text{ hr}$$

This will not be too short, because an anion regeneration takes 3 hr. The run length must exceed the number of units, less 1, multiplied by the number of hours:

$$(3 \text{ units} - 1) \times 3 \text{ hr} = 6 \text{ hr}$$

Therefore a 7.8 hr run with the maximum analysis water is not too short.

Run: $\dfrac{60,000 \text{ gal} \times 12 \text{ hr}}{3 \text{ units}} = 240,000 \text{ gal}$

240M gal $\times$ 14.9 gr/gal = 3580 kgr

$\dfrac{3580 \text{ kgr}}{9.5 \text{ kgr/ft}^3} = $ 377 ft^3 Amberlite IRA-402 or equal

$\dfrac{377 \text{ ft}^3}{50 \text{ ft}^2} = $ 7.5 ft

Freeboard (100%): 7.5 „
Total height: 15.0 ft

Use three units, each 8 ft 0 in. in diameter and 15 ft 0 in. in height, each with 377 ft^3 of Amberlite IRA-402, Dowex SBR-P, or equal.

NaOH = 4 lb $\times$ 377 ft^3 = 1508 lb:

$\dfrac{1508 \text{ lb}}{240M \text{ gal}} = 6.3 \text{ lb NaOH per 1000 gal}$

Cation units (right column):

Service: 240,000 gal
Anion regen.:
377 ft^3 $\times$ 130 gal = 49,000 gal
Total: 289,000 gal

289M gal $\times$ 15.4 gr/gal = 4450 kgr

$\dfrac{4450 \text{ kgr}}{11.0 \text{ kgr/ft}^3} = 405 \text{ ft}^3$ IR-120 or equal

$\dfrac{405 \text{ ft}^3}{50 \text{ ft}^2} = 8.1 \text{ ft}$

Freeboard (75%): 6.0 ft
Total height: 14.1 ft

Use three units, each 8 ft 0 in. in diameter and 14 ft 0 in. in height, each with 405 ft^3 of Amberlite IR-120, Dowex HCR-W, or equal.

Acid: 4.0 lb $\times$ 405 ft^3 = 1620 lb:

$\dfrac{1620 \text{ lb}}{240M \text{ gal}} = 6.7 \text{ lb acid per 1000 gal}$ of net output.

f. Design of the Vacuum Deaerator and Transfer Pumps

If the vacuum deaerator were omitted, the TEA for the primary anion units would be increased nearly 20% because of the free carbon dioxide present in the cation effluent. This would increase the operating cost for the extra caustic soda required by about 5¢ per 1000 gal, or $26,000 per year. Therefore the use of the vacuum deaerator is economical. It will reduce 44 ppm of CO_2 to 5 ppm (as CO_2) and decrease the dissolved oxygen to a fraction of 1 ppm.

The flow through the vacuum deaerator and the transfer pumps is as follows:

$$
\begin{array}{rl}
\text{Service flow:} & = 1000 \text{ gal/min} \\
\text{Primary anion-unit rinse} & \\
\text{at } 50 \text{ ft}^2 \times 6 \text{ gal/min/ft}^2: & = \underline{300 \quad \text{''}} \\
\text{Total:} & 1300 \text{ gal/min}
\end{array}
$$

The deaerator is a rubber-lined shell 7 ft 0 in. in diameter and 12 ft 0 in. in height, with Raschig-ring fill and an evacuator (preferably of the steam-jet ejector type).

The transfer pumps should be in duplicate (one being a spare or stand-by unit) made of stainless steel. Each pump should have a capacity of 1300 gal/min; alternatively, three half-sized pumps, each with a capacity of 650 gal/min, may be used. The dynamic head of the pumps must be sufficient to overcome the loss of head through the primary anion units and secondary mixed beds and still provide a final effluent pressure high enough for the effluent to reach the final deaerating heater.

g. Summary of Plant Design

Three primary cation exchange units, each 8 ft 0 in. in diameter and 14 ft 0 in. in height, and each with 405 ft^3 of strong-acid cation resin.

One vacuum deaerator, 7 ft 0 in. in diameter and 12 ft 0 in. in height.

Two transfer pumps, 1300 gal/min each.

Three primary anion exchange units, each 8 ft 0 in. in diameter and 15 ft 0 in. in height, and each with 377 ft^3 of strong-base anion resin.

Two secondary mixed beds, each 9 ft 0 in. in diameter and 15 ft 0 in. in height, and each with 151 ft^3 of strong-acid cation resin and 316 ft^3 of strong-base anion resin.

h. Regenerant Cost

Assume the cost of acid to be 1¢ per pound and that of caustic soda to be 3¢ per pound (both on 100% basis):

	Pounds per 1000 gal	Cents per 1000 gal
Primary acid:	6.7	
Secondary acid:	0.4	
Total acid:	7.1 at 1¢/lb	= 7.1
Primary caustic soda:	6.3	
Secondary caustic soda:	0.9	
Total caustic soda:	7.2 at 3¢/lb	= 21.6
		28.7 per 1000 gal

4. DESIGN OF PRETREATMENT PLANT

The pretreatment plant is designed in the same way as in Case 1; therefore calculations for this design are not included here.

C. Case 3: Prechlorination and Coagulation Pretreatment Followed by Primary Three-Bed and Secondary Mixed-Bed Demineralization without Vacuum Deaeration

1. DESIGN DATA

The design data are the same as those of Case 2.

2. MODIFICATION OF WATER ANALYSIS AFTER ADDITION OF PRETREATMENT CHEMICALS

The modification of the water analysis after the addition of pretreatment chemicals is the same as in Case 2; see Table 9.2.

3. DESIGN CALCULATIONS

a. Determination of Demineralizer System

A three-bed primary system is used for reducing the amount of caustic soda needed for regeneration. The vacuum deaerator is omitted, because the strong-base anion primary units will have excess capacities, so that they can remove the free carbon dioxide economically. The primary weak-base and strong-base exchangers are regenerated at the same time, when the effluent of the weak-base unit shows a conductivity breakthrough. The caustic soda passes countercurrent, first through the strong-base resin and then through the weak-base anion resin.

b. Selection of Resins, Capacities, and Regenerant Levels

The primary cation units are the same as in Case 2. The resin is strong-acid cation resin, Amberlite IR-120, Dowex HCR-W, or equal, with an acid level of 4 lb/ft^3 and a capacity of 11.0 kgr/ft^3.

The caustic levels and resin capacities for the primary weak-base and strong-base exchanger are calculated as follows:

Weak-base anion resin	*Strong-base anion resin*
TMA:	TEA (without vac. deaer.):
SO_4: 135 ppm Cl: 97 „ TMA: 232 ppm	CO_2: 44 ppm $\times$ 1.13 = 51 ppm SiO_2: 20 ppm $\times$ 0.83 = 17 „ Cat. leak.: 20 „ TEA: 88 ppm
$TMA = \dfrac{232\ ppm}{17.1} = 13.6\ gr/gal$ $\%\ Cl:\ \dfrac{97\ ppm}{232\ ppm} = 42\%$	$TEA = \dfrac{88}{17.1} = 5.2\ gr/gal$ $\%\ weak\ acids:\ \dfrac{68}{88} = 78\%$
Use weak-base resin Duolite A30-B, Amberlite IRA-93, or equal.	$\%\ SiO_2:\ \dfrac{17\ ppm}{88\ ppm} = 20\%$
Use 4 lb/ft^3, NaOH/resin, and 19 kgr/ft^3 capacity.	$\%\ Cl:\ \dfrac{10\ ppm}{88\ ppm} = 11.4\%$
	Use strong-base resin Dowex SBR-P, Amberlite IRA-402, or equal. From Table 7.17, for 0.10 ppm SiO_2 leakage, use 5 lb/ft^3 NaOH/resin and 13.5 kgr/ft^3 capacity.

Note that the cation leakage of 20 ppm is included in the TEA for the primary strong-base resin; this is done because the strong-base resin converts the salts (of the cation leakage) to sodium hydroxide.

The resins, regenerant levels, and resin capacities for the secondary mixed beds are the same as in Case 2.

c. Design of Mixed Beds

For the design of the secondary mixed beds see Case 2.

d. Design of Primary Units

The cation units are the same as in Case 2. Use three units, each 8 ft 0 in. in diameter and 14 ft 0 in. in height, and each with 405 ft^3 of Amberlite IR-120 or Dowex HCR-W or equal. Use 4 lb/ft^3, acid/resin, or 1620 lb of acid per unit, or 6.7 lb of acid per 1000 gal.

The weak-base anion units are calculated as follows:

Use a flow rate of 10 gal/min/ft^2 with one unit out for regeneration:

$$\frac{1000\ gal/min}{10\ gal/min/ft^2} = 100\ ft^2$$

Use three units each 8 ft 0 in. in diameter (50 ft^2 each).

Use 12 hr runs based on the average water (column D, Table 9.2), as in Case 2:

$$\frac{60,000 \text{ gal/hr} \times 12 \text{ hr}}{3 \text{ units}} = 240,000 \text{ gal}$$

The TMA is as follows:

Sulfates: 135 ppm
Chlorides: 97 „

TMA: 232 ppm;   then $\frac{232 \text{ ppm}}{17.1} = 13.6 \text{ gr/gal}$

$240M$ gal $\times$ 13.6 = 3270 kgr (approx.)

Use a resin capacity of 19 kgr/ft^3:

$$\frac{3270 \text{ kgr}}{19 \text{ kgr/ft}^3} = 172 \text{ ft}^3 \text{ Duolite A30-B, Amberlite IRA-93, or equal}$$

$$\frac{172 \text{ ft}^3}{50 \text{ ft}^2} = \quad 3.5 \text{ ft bed}$$

If IRA-93, add 20%:   0.7 ft for swelling
                        4.2 ft bed (swollen)
Freeboard, 100%:   4.2 ft
Straight shell height: 8.4 ft

Use three units, each 8 ft 0 in. in diameter and 8 ft 6 in. in height, and each with 172 ft^3 of Duolite A30-B, Amberlite IRA-93, or their equivalent.

Use 4 lb/ft^3, NaOH/resin:

$$4 \text{ lb} \times 172 \text{ ft}^3 = 688 \text{ lb NaOH}$$

To this must be added the kilograin equivalent of the caustic soda consumed by the strong-base anion resin. The caustic soda passing through the strong-base resin is converted to sodium silicate and sodium carbonate. Although these weaker alkalis can also regenerate the weak-base resin, it is conservative to assume that the caustic soda taken up by the strong-base resin should be included in the total caustic soda used for the countercurrent regeneration.

The strong-base anion resin units are calculated as follows:

$$240M \text{ gal} \times 5.2 \text{ gr/gal TEA} = 1248 \text{ kgr}$$

$$\frac{1248 \text{ kgr}}{13.5 \text{ kgr/ft}^3} = 92 \text{ ft}^3; \quad \text{but } \frac{92 \text{ ft}^3}{50 \text{ ft}^2} = 1.8 \text{ ft bed}$$

This is too shallow; use a minimum of 2.5 ft depth:

50 ft^2 × 2.5 = 125 ft^3 Amberlite IRA-402 or Dowex SBR-P or equal

Use three strong-base anion units, each 8 ft 0 in. in diameter and 5 ft 0 in. in height.

The strong-base resin will be only 73% exhausted at the end of the run.

$$\text{NaOH equivalent of 1248 kgr:} \frac{1248}{7} \times 0.8 = 143 \text{ lb}$$

NaOH for weak-base resin: 688 „

Total NaOH: 831 lb

These 831 lb must provide 5 lb per cubic foot of strong-base resin, as required above:

$$\frac{831 \text{ lb NaOH}}{125 \text{ ft}^3 \text{ resin}} = 6.6 \text{ lb/ft}^3 \text{ NaOH/resin}$$

This is well above the 5.0 lb/ft^3 required; the total caustic soda therefore is as follows:

$$\frac{831 \text{ lb}}{240M \text{ gal}} = 3.5 \text{ lb per 1000 gal}$$

e. Summary of Plant Design

Three primary cation exchange units, each 8 ft 0 in. in diameter and 14 ft 0 in. in height, and each with 405 ft^3 of strong-acid cation resin.

Three primary weak-base anion units, each 8 ft 0 in. in diameter and 8 ft 6 in. in height, and each with 172 ft^3 of weak-base anion resin.

Three primary strong-base anion units, each 8 ft 0 in. in diameter and 5 ft 0 in. in height, and each with 125 ft^3 of strong-base anion resin.

Two secondary mixed beds, each 9 ft 0 in. in diameter and 15 ft 0 in. in height, and each with 151 ft^3 of strong-acid cation resin and with 316 ft^3 of strong-base anion resin.

f. Regenerant Cost

Assuming the cost of acid to be 1¢ per pound and that of caustic soda to be 3¢ per pound (both on 100% basis), the regenerant cost is as calculated below:

	Pounds per 1000 gal	Cents per 1000 gal
Primary acid:	6.7	
Secondary acid:	0.4	
Total acid: (	7.1 at 1¢/lb	= 7.1
Primary caustic soda:	3.5	
Secondary caustic soda:	0.9	
Total caustic soda:	4.4 at 3¢/lb	= 13.2
		20.3¢ per 1000 gal

g. Comparison of Regenerant Costs of Cases 2 and 3

A comparison of the costs of regenerants in Cases 2 and 3 may be made as follows:

	Cents per 1000 gal
Regenerant cost, Case 2:	28.7
Regenerant cost, Case 3:	20.3
Saving in regenerant cost:	8.4 per 1000 gal

This saving is due to using the three-bed system, instead of the two-bed, in the primary stage and obtains even though the vacuum deaerator is omitted in Case 3.

h. Checking Equivalence of Excess Acid and Excess Caustic Soda in Waste Regenerant

Before one may assume that in Case 3 the saving in regenerant cost specified above can be realized, the equivalence of the excess acid to the excess caustic soda in Case 3 should be checked.

Excess acid:

Total acid per unit regeneration: 1620 lb

$$\text{Subtract:} \frac{\text{kgr (primary cation)}}{7} \text{ or } \frac{4450 \text{ kgr}}{7} = \underline{636 \text{ ''}}$$

Excess acid: 984 lb

Excess caustic soda:

Total caustic soda per unit regeneration: 831 lb

$$\text{Expressing this as } CaCO_3: \qquad \frac{831}{0.8} = 1040 \text{ ''}$$

$$\text{Subtract:} \frac{\text{kgr (weak-base anion)}}{7} = \frac{3270 \text{ kgr}}{7} = \underline{467 \text{ ''}}$$

Excess soda, as $CaCO_3$:   573 lb

Excess acid:	984 lb
Excess NaOH:	573 ,,
Net excess acid:	411 lb

Unless the net excess acid of 411 lb can be used for treating the water for a cooling tower or for some other similar application, it would have to be neutralized by adding equivalent alkali in the neutralizing system. Therefore the apparent saving of caustic soda in using the three-bed primary system would not be realized.

Instead of using the three-bed primary system in this case, then, it would be more economical to use a two-bed primary system with both weak-base and strong-base resin layers in the same units (double-layer design). This would save one battery of anion units and reduce the capital investment accordingly.

The double-layer primary anion units would each contain about 170 ft^3 of weak-base resin and 125 ft^3 of strong-base resin.

The three anion units would each be 8 ft 0 in. in diameter and 14 ft 0 in. in height. The amount of caustic soda would be 1160 lb per unit regeneration, or 4.8 lb per 1000 gal. The operating cost is as follows:

	Pounds per 1000 gal	Cents per 1000 gal
Primary acid:	6.7	
Secondary acid:	0.4	
	7.1 at 1¢/lb = 7.1	
Primary caustic soda:	4.8	
Secondary caustic soda:	0.9	
	5.7 at 3¢/lb = 17.1	
		24.2¢ per 1000 gal

This is about halfway between the 28.7¢ per 1000 gal of Case 2 and the 20.3¢ per 1000 gal of Case 3, but there is no imbalance of excess acid and excess caustic, because the total caustic soda of 1160 lb given above is 330 lb more than the 831 lb used in Case 3. The extra 330 lb of caustic soda (as NaOH) is equal to 411 lb (as $CaCO_3$). This equals the 411 lb of net excess acid calculated above for the three-bed primary system. Therefore, the excess acid now equals the excess caustic soda, and the waste regenerants are in balance. In these double-layer weak-base and strong-base anion resin units it is advisable to backwash a second time after regeneration, because Amberlite IRA-93 and Amberlite IRA-402 have a greater difference in density between them in the regenerated form than in the unregenerated. The second backwash thus stratifies the resin bed more completely, bringing the weak-base resin to the top and the strong-base resin to the bottom. This allows the weak-base resin to remove the strong sulfuric and hydrochloric acids, and it utilizes the strong-base resin for removing the weak carbonic and silicic acids, as in a three-bed system. The technique of the double-layer of weak-base and strong-base resins is quite new and is going into operation at this writing (Chapter 6, *23, 24*).

D. Case 4: Two-Bed Demineralization with Decarbonation, with Weak-Acid and Strong-Acid Resin Layers in One Double-layer Unit

1. DESIGN DATA

The total flow is 300 gal/min and 260,000 gal per 20 hr.

The effluent quality required, TDS 16 ppm, conductivity 80 μmhos and silica 0.4 ppm (as SiO_2).

The influent is from a well (see column A, Table 9.4), requiring no pre-treatment. This two-bed system is to be an extension of a similar demineralizer. However, the existing plant uses strong-acid cation exchanger alone,

Table 9.4
CASE 4: OPERATING RESULTS[a]

	Impurities ppm as $CaCO_3$ (except[b])		
	A	B	C
Ca	40	0	0
Mg	20	0	0
Na	253	16	16
H	0	55	0
TC	313	71	16
HCO_3	242	0	0
CO_3	0	0	0
OH	0	0	16
SO_4	11	11	0
Cl	60	60	trace
TA	313	71	16
CO_2[b] (as CO_2)	3	5	0
SiO_2[b] (as SiO_2)	18	18	0.4
Water temp.[b]	79°F		

[a] The columns are as follows:
    A, raw well water.
    B, after decarbonator.
    C, after anion unit.

and there is a large net excess of acid in the regeneration waste water. The net excess acid requires the addition of equivalent alkali in the waste neutralizer. Therefore this new demineralizer must be so designed that its regeneration will provide a net excess caustic soda that will neutralize the net excess acid from the existing demineralizer.

2. DESIGN CALCULATIONS

a. Determination of Demineralizer System

A two-bed system with strong-base anion resin is adequate to supply the effluent quality specified above, but to reduce the acid regenerant level to a minimum, the cation unit should have a layer of weak-acid cation resin above a layer of strong-acid cation resin in the double-layer design. The decarbonator is justified because the free carbon dioxide in the cation effluent is 88 % of 242 ppm (HCO_3), or 213 ppm plus 3 ppm present in the raw well water, or 216 ppm total. The decarbonator should be designed to decrease this 216 ppm to 5 ppm, to reduce the amount of anion resin and save caustic soda regenerant.

b. Selection of Resins, Capacities, and Regenerant Levels

Weak-Acid Cation Exchanger (Upper Layer)

To remove the cations associated with the HCO_3 alkalinity (242 ppm), use Amberlite IRC-84 carboxylic weak-acid cation exchanger or equal.

From Table 7.11, for a ratio of hardness to alkalinity of 60/242 = 25 %, a TMA of 71 ppm, and a temperature of 79°F the rated capacity is 14 to 15 kgr/ft^3, but, as the footnote to the table indicates, when the weak-acid cation resin is used in a double-layer unit with the strong-acid resin below it, the capacity rating of the weak-acid resin can be increased appreciably. In this case laboratory tests have shown that a rating of 19 kgr/ft^3 can be used.

Strong-Acid Cation Exchanger (Lower Layer)

To remove the cations associated with the TMA (sulfates plus chlorides) of 71 ppm, use strong-acid Dowex HDR-W, Amberlite IR-124, or equal because their densities are higher than those of Dowex HCR-W or Amberlite IR-120. The heavier material stays below the lighter weak-acid resin more completely.

The cation leakage of 16 ppm required is 23 % of the TMA (71 ppm). Since most of the run will result in low alkalinity and nearly 100 % sodium present in the effluent of the weak-acid cation layer, an acid level somewhat over 7.5 lb/ft^3, acid/resin, would ensure this cation leakage of below 16 ppm (see Table 7.4). The cation leakage for Amberlite IR-124 or Dowex HDR-W or equal is about the same as for Amberlite IR-120 as given in that table. To be safe, use 10 lb of acid per cubic foot. This can be obtained readily by passing the acid upward, first through the strong-acid resin layer and then through the weak-acid resin layer as calculated below. The capacity of the Amberlite IR-124 will be slightly lower than for the Amberlite IR-120, which is given as 20 kgr/ft^3 (Table 7.4). Use 10 % less, or 18 kgr/ft^3.

Strong-Base Anion Exchanger

The TEA is as follows:

		ppm as $CaCO_3$
Free CO_2 after decarbonator:	5 ppm $\times$ 1.13 =	6
SiO_2:	18 ppm $\times$ 0.83 =	15
TMA:		71
	TEA:	92 ppm

$$TEA = \frac{92\,ppm}{17.1} = 5.4\,gr/gal$$

$$\%\ weak\ acids: \frac{21\,ppm}{92\,ppm} = 23\%$$

$$\%\ SiO_2: \qquad \frac{15\,ppm}{92\,ppm} = 16\%$$

The silica leakage of 0.4 ppm specified can be obtained with 5 lb of caustic soda per cubic foot of resin with porous Dowex SBR-P or Amberlite IRA-402 strong-base anion resin, or their equivalent. From Table 7.17 the capacity is 11.7 kgr/ft^3 with 5 lb of caustic soda per cubic foot of resin.

c. Design of Demineralizer

Anion Unit

Capacity: 260M gal $\times$ 5.4 gr/gal (TEA) = 1410 kgr

$$Anion\ resin\ volume: \qquad \frac{1410\,kgr}{11.7\,kgr/ft^3} = 121\,ft^3$$

For 300 gal/min and a flow rate of 8 gal/min/ft^2:

$$\frac{300\,gal/min}{8\,gal/min/ft^2} = 37.4\,ft^2; \qquad use\ diameter\ of\ 7\ ft\ 0\ in.$$

$$\frac{121\,ft^3}{38\,ft^2} = 3.2\,ft\ bed$$

Bed depth:	3.2 ft
Freeboard (100%):	3.2 ″
Straight height:	6.4 ft, or one unit 7 ft 0 in. diam. $\times$ 7 ft 0 in. ht.

Caustic soda: 5 lb $\times$ 121 ft^3 = 605 lb as NaOH.
Regeneration waste water with anion rinse recycling: ca. 50 gal/ft^3.
Then: 50 gal/ft^3 $\times$ 121 ft^3 = 6050 gal.

Decarbonator

For a flow of 300 gal/min and for reducing the free CO_2 from 216 ppm to 5 ppm, use a wood tower 4 ft 0 in. in diameter 11 ft 0 in. in height, with

Raschig rings 5 ft 0 in. in depth and a blower 1000 std. ft^3/min in capacity, at 4 in. of pressure.

Cation Unit

Weak-acid cation layer

Anion outlet capacity:	260,000 gal
Anion waste water:	6050 „
1/2 of anion recycling water:	3025 „
Total:	269,075 gal

Alkalinity: 242 ppm = 14.1 gr/gal

Capacity: 269.1 M gal × 14.1 gr/gal = 3800 kgr

Vol. of Amberlite IRC-84: $\dfrac{3800 \text{ kgr}}{19 \text{ kgr/ft}^3} = 200 \text{ ft}^3$

Acid: 120% of theoretical = 120% × $\dfrac{3800 \text{ kgr}}{7}$ = 650 lb

Strong-acid cation layer

TMA: 71 ppm; $\dfrac{71 \text{ ppm}}{17.1}$ = 4.2 gr/gal

Capacity: 269.1 M gal × 4.2 gr/gal = 1130 kgr

Vol. resin: $\dfrac{1130 \text{ kgr}}{18 \text{ kgr/ft}^3} = 63 \text{ ft}^3$

This would be too shallow. Therefore use a minimum of 18 in. for the height of the resin layer; that makes 75 ft^3 in a unit 8 ft 0 in. in diameter. This diameter is selected so as to avoid too deep a resin bed.

The straight height of the cation unit shell required is calculated as follows:

Strong-acid resin:	75 ft^3:	75 ft^3/50 ft^2 =	1.5 ft
Weak-acid resin:	200 ft^3:	200 ft^3/50 ft^2 =	4.0 ft
20% of swelling:			0.8 ft
		Total bed in swollen state:	6.3 ft

75% freeboard:	4.8
Add for anthracite subfill:	1.4
Straight height:	12.5 ft

Use one cation unit 8 ft 0 in. in diameter and 13 ft 0 in. in height. The anthracite subfill is included to aid in the distribution of the upward flow of the acid.

The total acid required for both the weak- and strong-acid resins is calculated as follows:

Acid required for the weak-acid resin: 650 lb
Add 120% equivalent of kgr
removed by the strong-acid resin, or

$$\frac{1130 \text{ kgr}}{7} \times 1.2 = \underline{194 \text{ "}}$$

Total acid: 844 lb

These 844 lb of acid are equal to 844/75, or more than 11 lb per cubic foot of the strong-acid resin, so that the cation leakage will be reduced to a minimum (below the 16 ppm required).

d. Regeneration Schedules

The acid and caustic soda regenerations take place at the same time. In this system the acid can be injected in a single dose of 3% strength, because there is so little calcium in the well water. For other waters, higher in calcium content, two steps of acid strength may be advisable, the first at 1 to 2%, and the second at 3 to 4%, for the prevention of calcium sulfate precipitates, which may foul the resins. The caustic soda is injected in a single dose at 4% strength at 120°F. The simultaneous cation and anion regeneration schedule will be similar to that given for Case 1, and anion rinse recycling should be included. The total regeneration period for simultaneous regeneration is less than 3 hr.

e. Checking Equivalence of Excess Acid and Excess Caustic Soda in Waste Regenerant

Total acid: 844 lb

Weak cation: $\dfrac{3800 \text{ kgr}}{7} = 545$ lb

Strong cation: $\dfrac{1130 \text{ kgr}}{7} = 162$ "

707 lb =   707 "

Excess acid: 137 lb

Total caustic soda: 605 lb as NaOH

$$\frac{605 \text{ lb}}{0.8} = 758 \text{ " as } CaCO_3$$

Less anion: $\dfrac{1410 \text{ kgr}}{7} = 201$ "

Excess caustic soda: 557 lb
Less excess acid: 137 "
Net excess caustic soda: 420 lb

This net excess caustic soda is available for neutralizing the net excess acid from the existing demineralizer, mentioned in the design data. Moreover, this double-layer weak-acid and strong-acid cation exchange column uses about 1000 lb of acid a day less than does a single layer of strong-acid resin. This saving amounts to $10 a day, if acid costs 1¢ a pound.

f. Summary of Plant Design

One cation exchange unit 8 ft 0 in. in diameter and 13 ft 0 in. in height, with 200 ft^3 of Amberlite IRC-84 and 75 ft^3 of Dowex HDR-W, Amberlite IR-124, or equal.

One decarbonator 4 ft 0 in. in diameter and 11 ft 0 in. in height.

Two stainless-steel pumps, 300 gal/min each.

One anion exchange unit, 7 ft 0 in. in diameter and 7 ft 0 in. in height, with 121 ft^3 of Dowex SBR-P, Amberlite IRA-402, or their equivalent.

10

Condensate Purification for High-Pressure Utility and Industrial Boilers

Before the advent of once-through drumless boilers, which were installed in this country in electrical utility power stations in the nineteen-fifties, the condensate had not been demineralized; only the makeup (about 1 % of the total feed) had been purified, and supplementary chemicals for coping with impurities introduced by corrosion and condenser leakage had been injected into the boilers.

I. Turbine and Boiler Deposits before Advent of Condensate Demineralization

The policy of not demineralizing the condensate and treating only the makeup worked fairly well for drum-type boilers of less than 1500 psi pressure, but when higher pressures were adopted, troublesome boiler and turbine deposits occurred in increasing amounts. In 1957 a turbine manufacturer reported that six stations, operating in the 1800 to 2400 psi pressure range, suffered a loss of efficiency of 1 %, due to deposits in the turbine (1). This loss was evaluated at $34,000 per annum for a 200,000 kw unit; for the entire utility industry, on the basis of 600,000,000,000 kw-hr generated in 1956, the loss was estimated at $20,000,000 per annum. It was becoming apparent that a change in water-treating policy was needed, so that the condensate in addition to the makeup would be purified (2).

The boiler manufacturers observed that high-pressure drum boilers also suffered from increasing deposits that resulted in costly outages. The deposits were attributed to the solids introduced into the condensate by corrosion in the preboiler cycle and by condenser leakage. It was estimated

261

that, even if the iron content of the condensate, due to such corrosion, were increased by only 10 ppb, 175 lb of iron would be deposited annually in a boiler generating 2,000,000 lb of steam per hour (3). When the deposits formed in areas of high heat-transfer, they caused boiler-tube failures.

Table 10.1
SOLIDS ADDED TO CONDENSATE BY CONDENSER LEAKAGE[a]

Condenser leakage, % of feedwater	Condenser water leakage, lb/hr	Solids added to condensate	
		lb/hr	lb/yr
0.005	50	0.015	131
0.025	250	0.075	655
0.050	500	0.150	1310
0.500	5000	1.500	13,100

[a] The figures are based on a condensate flow of 1,000,000 lb/hr and on a condenser cooling-water total solids content of 300 ppm.

Condenser leakage introduced large amounts of solids. Table 10.1 gives figures for the solids added by various condenser leaks when the condenser cooling water contains only 300 ppm of total solids (TS). If the condenser cooling water is brackish (1000 to 5000 ppm TS) or consists of seawater (30,000 to 35,000 ppm TS), the amount of solids introduced by condenser leakage increases proportionately.

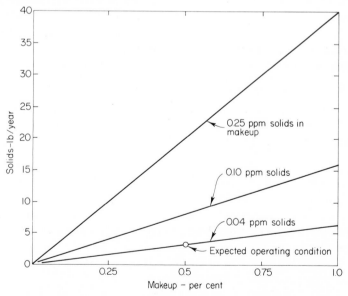

Fig. 10.1. Solids added from the makeup (at 1,825,000 lbs/hr feedwater flow). [From Ulmer (3).]

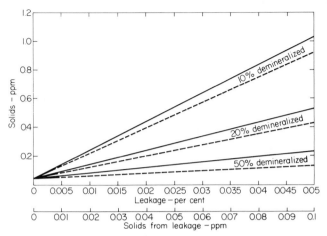

Fig. 10.2. Effect of demineralizing condensate on solids in condensate and feedwater.
(——) Condensate, (- - -) Feedwater
(at equilibrium, ppm solids in feedwater equals ppm solids in condensate minus ppm solids from leakage). Based on: (1) 200 ppm solids in condenser cooling water, (2) no solids deposit in system, (3) 0.04 ppm solids in demineralizer effluent. [From Ulmer (3).]

Figure 10.1 shows the effect of improved makeup quality in reducing the pounds of solids introduced per year. Figure 10.2 also estimates the reduction of the solids, in parts per million, introduced when 10 to 50% of the condensate is demineralized.

A report by a boiler manufacturer discussed the tube failures that occurred in drum-type boilers of over 2000 psi pressure when the makeup alone had been purified (4). A total of 79 boilers was studied; fresh condenser cooling water was used by 57 of these units (or 72%), and salty cooling water was used by 22 units (or 28%). There were 11 tube failures caused by deposits resulting from solids introduced by condenser leakage; 9 units (82% of the 11 cases) failed with the salty condenser cooling water, and only 2 units (18% of the 11 cases) failed with the fresh cooling water. The effect of condenser leakage on boiler-tube failures was quite apparent. As a result, the boiler manufacturer made a recommendation for tolerances of impurities in the feedwater for drum boilers of over 2000 psi pressure (4); these are given in Table 10.2.

II. Advent of Once-Through Drumless Boilers and Condensate Demineralizers

As steam pressures were made still greater for the purpose of reducing the cost of generating electricity, the boiler drum became thicker and its cost excessive. It constituted more than 25% of the metal weight of the whole

Table 10.2

FEEDWATER AND BOILER WATER QUALITY RECOMMENDED BY
THE BABCOCK & WILCOX COMPANY FOR DRUM BOILERS
OF OVER 2000 PSI[a]

Feedwater		Boiler water	
Impurity	Max. toler., ppm	Impurity	Max. toler., ppm
Oxygen	0.007	Total solids	15
Iron	0.010	Na_3PO_4	3 to 10
Copper	0.005	OH	1
Hardness	0	pH	9.0 to 10.0
CO_2	0	SiO_2	Varies with pressure
Organics	0		
pH	8.5 to 9.2		

[a] This table is based on data in a paper by Lux (4).

boiler. The foundations and structural steel for supporting the drum also added to the cost. When the drumless type was designed abroad and developed further in the United States, a considerable saving in capital investment resulted. The Babcock & Wilcox Company called their once-through design Universal Pressure Boiler, built for pressures over 1800 psi (5), and Combustion Engineering, Inc. used the name Monotube Steam Generator (6); Foster Wheeler Corp. and Riley Stoker Corp. also developed once-through boiler designs.

All these designs were drumless, for supercritical pressures (over 3206 psia). At these pressures the water and steam are of equal density, and they cannot be separated in a drum. The feedwater enters at one end, and the "steam" comes out at the other end, of a continuous boiler-tube circuit. There is no latent heat at supercritical pressures and no boiling; instead, there is a gradual change in fluid properties, only a single phase existing at one time. The absence of a drum permits neither concentration nor boiler blowoff; therefore any salts present in the feedwater either crystallize out and deposit in the boiler or go over in the steam to deposit in the turbine. The boiler manufacturers then set the feedwater quality tolerance at only 50 ppb total solids, corresponding to about 10,000,000 ohm-cm specific resistance, or 0.1 μmho conductivity. This definitely called for mixed-bed demineralization of the condensate or main feedwater stream. Table 10.3 gives The Babcock & Wilcox Company limits of feedwater impurities for their Universal Pressure Boilers.

Table 10.3

FEEDWATER QUALITY RECOMMENDED BY THE
BABCOCK & WILCOX COMPANY FOR THE
UNIVERSAL PRESSURE BOILER

Impurity	Max. tolerance	
	ppm	ppb
Tot. diss. solids	0.05	50
Diss. oxygen	0.007	7
Silica	0.02	20
Iron	0.01	10
Copper	0.002	2
Hardness	0	0
CO_2	0	0
Organics	0	0
pH	8.5 to 9.2	

Combustion Engineering, Inc., built their once-through boilers of subcritical pressure (under 3206 psia) with a separator drum. The water drained from this drum could be mixed with the makeup and the mixture treated by an evaporator or demineralizer. The feedwater quality recommended by Combustion Engineering, Inc., for these subcritical boilers, called for a total solids of less than 500 ppb, but for their drumless supercritical-pressure boilers they specified the purer feedwater quality given in Table 10.4 (6).

Table 10.4

FEEDWATER QUALITY RECOMMENDED BY COMBUSTION ENGINEERING, INC.,
FOR MONOTUBE STEAM GENERATOR SUPERCRITICAL-PRESSURE BOILERS

Impurity	Maximum Tolerance, ppb			
	Copper-free system		Copper alloy condenser tubes	
	Startup[a]	Normal	Startup[a]	Normal
Total solids	250	50	250	50
Iron	10	10	50	10
Copper	—	—	20	2
Silica	30	20	30	20
Oxygen	10	5	10	5
pH	9.5 to 9.7	9.5 to 9.7	8.8 to 9.1	8.8 to 9.1

[a] Short time duration.

Condensate purification by demineralization was adopted generally and it was called condensate "polishing," "scavenging," or "cleanup." Figure 10.3 shows a flow diagram of typical early purification systems.

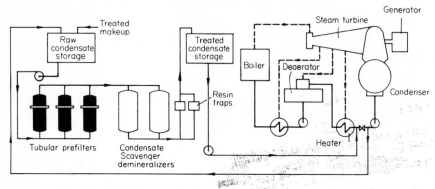

Fig. 10.3. Flow diagram of typical early condensate-purification system.

III. Condensate-Purification Equipment at the Philo Station

The first once-through boiler in a United States utility power plant was designed for the Philo Station in 1953 (7). It was built for 4500 psi pressure, to generate only 125 MW. The size was small, to permit study of the design and the metallurgy involved with minimal risk. It became a prototype for the larger stations to follow. The design was based on experimental work with a pilot test plant at Alliance, Ohio.

The test work at Alliance showed that it was important to limit the iron crud picked up by corrosion, because this formed objectionable boiler deposits (7). The pilot plant contained the usual makeup demineralizer but, in addition, it included for the first time a mixed-bed demineralizer for purifying about 30 % of the condensate. Prefilters for removing the crud and so protecting the ion exchange resin were installed ahead of the mixed bed. The full-scale prefilters at Philo were later enlarged to handle 60 % of full condensate flow. The prefilters were of the tubular-element design then in use with diatomite filter aid, but since the latter was siliceous and caused silica pickup, a cellulose filter aid (Solka-Floc) was selected. The filter flow rates were 4 gal/min/ft^2.

The condensate-demineralizer flow rate adopted was the same as that in use at the time for makeup demineralizers, about 10 gal/min/ft^2. Later, as discussed below, this rate was increased at other stations to 50 gal/min/ft^2. The Philo demineralizer was designed for only 30 % of full load condensate stream, because during startups, when the impurities are highest in amount, the flow is usually only 25 to 33 % of the full-load stream. Later, however.

other stations decided to design demineralizers for 100 % of full-load flow, to obtain complete protection at all times (*8*).

IV. Prefilter Design

Although currently prefilters are being omitted by most modern utility stations, as discussed below, until fairly recently they were included for protecting the demineralizer resin from fouling by the crud. Some still favor their inclusion (*9*).

Two types of prefilters, tubular and leaf, were used.

A. Tubular Type of Prefilter

A number of tubular filter designs were in commercial use with diatomite filter aid. They were adopted for condensate prefiltration with cellulose aid. The filter elements still used are of the vertical tubular type, several inches in diameter and only a few feet long, hanging from a horizontal tube sheet in a flanged joint of a pressure shell. The elements may be made of a number of materials: porous stone of alumina crystals vitrified together, rigid porous carbon, and stainless-steel well-screen (Johnson type) with a helically wound wedge wire welded to vertical support rods. The wedge wire is trapezoidal in shape rather than round, to reduce fouling.

Above the tube sheet, in the upper head, an air dome may be created. When the pressure loss through the filter-aid cake during the service run increases to 25–35 psi, the filter is cleaned. This is done by rapidly opening the bottom drain valve, the quickly decreasing pressure in the air dome causing a sudden high reverse flow of water, which backwashes the spent cake from the elements. Figure 10.4 shows the three steps in the operation of a tubular filter, and Fig. 10.5 shows a close-up of the elements during these steps.

This method of backwashing works efficiently when brittle diatomite is used as filter aid, but since the cellulose used for preventing silica pickup is more compressible and tends to adhere to the wire of the elements, clogging or fouling the fine openings, another method was adopted. A mixture of air and water, instead of backwash water alone proved more successful. The air rate is 0.5 to 1.0 std. ft^3/min per square foot of filter area at 60 psi pressure. The backwash-water flow rate (mixed with the air) is 2 to 3 gal/min per square foot.

Uniform precoating of the elements is essential to the reduction of fouling. If any part of an element is not properly coated, it becomes clogged. The crud must be caught by the filter-aid coating and not by the bare wire of the elements. If the bare wire catches it, the crud gets embedded between the wires and cannot be easily dislodged. For uniform precoating the precoat pump should have ample capacity (2 to 2.5 gal/min per square foot of filter area).

During precoating the effluent is recycled (see Fig. 10.4), until it becomes clear.

After precoating a rinse to waste is required; this washes off the organic impurities present in the new cellulose coat and so avoids their entering the demineralizer and the feedwater. After this some of the first filter effluent should be recycled back to the main condenser, to become rid of dissolved oxygen introduced by precoating, before the start of the next service run.

"Holding" pumps, low-flow recycling pumps, one for each filter unit, are desirable, since they prevent the cake from falling off the elements. The pumps should have a capacity of 0.25 to 0.5 gal/min per square foot of filter area and should be started automatically by a contactor on a flow indicator,

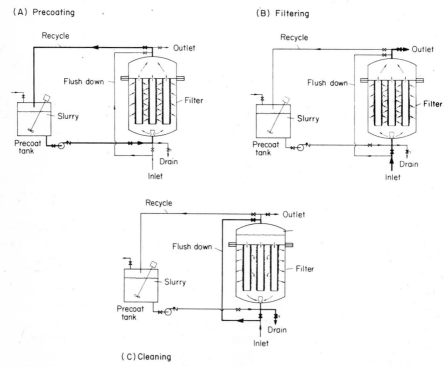

Fig. 10.4. Three steps in operation of tubular filters. (*A*) Precoat inlet and recycle outlet valves are opened, and precoat pump is started. Cellulose slurry forms coat on outside of filter elements. Recycling continues until effluent is crystal-clear, showing that coat is well formed. (*B*) After precoating is finished, inlet and outlet valves are opened, and filter is placed in service. This continues until pressure-loss buildup becomes excessive. (*C*) Clogged coat is completely removed by high-rate backwash, obtained by explosive expansion of air dome in top head, which pushes water ahead of it in reverse flow. Downflushing follows, sluicing dirty cake to drain.

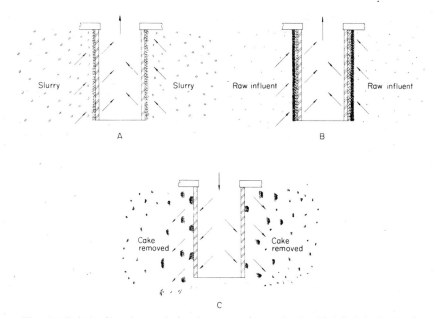

Fig. 10.5. Tubular filter element during three steps of operation (see Fig. 10.4). (*A*) Precoating: filter-aid coat covers outer surface of filter element. During precoating filtrate is recycled back to precoat tank. (*B*) Suspended matter in influent is filtered out by filter-aid coat and builds up on outside of coat. (*C*) High-rate backwash (reverse flow) cracks dirty coat off filter element.

whenever the flow drops below these figures. The pumps recycle the effluent back to the inlet, until the flow increases again.

In an attempt at coping with the problem of cleaning the filters one of the later tubular designs constructed elements with internal orificed tubes, which improved the distribution of the mixture of air and wash water (*9*). The elements have been made as long as 9 ft; the length reduces the diameter of the filter shell and its cost for high operating pressures. Figure 10.6 is a schematic diagram of this design and includes the various valve operations for the wash steps in an automatic filter system.

Despite strenuous air–water washing the filter elements in time get fouled. Periodically the upper flanged joint on the shell must be opened and the assembly of elements removed for external mechanical cleaning with a wire brush. High-pressure compressed air also has been used for periodical cleaning "in place" (without removing the elements), the air hose being introduced into the top of each element after the top head is opened. Another means is chemical in-place cleaning. Various chemicals can partially dissolve and loosen the cellulose from the wire. Strong sulfuric acid will accomplish this, but handling of the acid is difficult. Cupric ammonium hydroxide

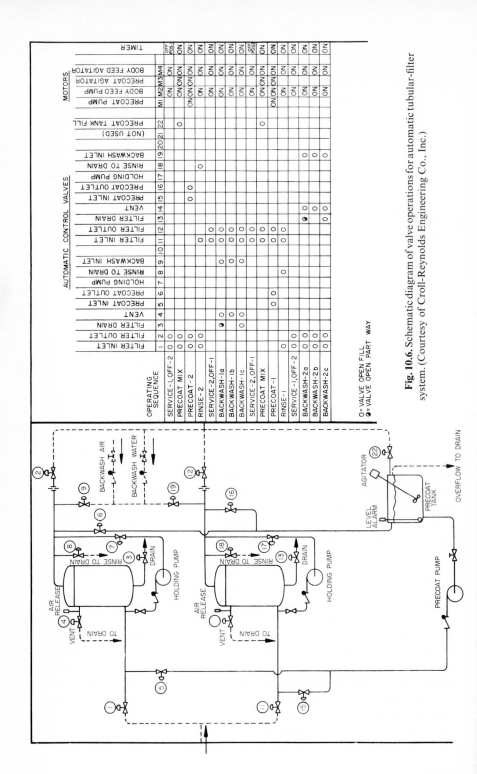

Fig. 10.6. Schematic diagram of valve operations for automatic tubular-filter system. (Courtesy of Croll-Reynolds Engineering Co., Inc.)

(Schweitzer's Reagent), circulated through the filter, can dissolve the cellulose rapidly. This solution is prepared by making 58 % NH_4OH and copper powder or drillings react for several days, and the product is then diluted to a 1:1 strength. Wackenhuth, Senior Engineer of Public Service Electric and Gas Co., and Cox of their Maplewood Laboratory, who developed this chemical treatment, found that 740 gal of the solution dissolved 5.6 lb of cellulose in several hours. Another cleaning chemical that has been used is citric acid.

B. Leaf Prefilter Designs

The elements of leaf filters are flat circular sheets of stainless-steel wire screening, mounted close together on a shaft in a cylindrical pressure shell. Although in some designs the leaves are horizontal, so as to avoid falloff of the cake, in most of them they are vertical. Table 10.5 gives three leaf-filter designs that provide automatic cleaning.

Table 10.5
THREE LEAF PREFILTER DESIGNS FOR AUTOMATIC CLEANING

Manufacturer	Trade name
Davis Filtration Company	Graver-Davis
(marketed by Graver Water Conditioning Co.)	Clearflow
Hercules Filter Corp.	Roto-Jet
(Division of De Laval Separator Co.)	
United States Filter Corp.	Auto-Jet

The operation of leaf filters is similar to that of the tubular filters described above, except that the washing is done with water alone. The water, in the form of fan-shaped jets, impinges on the cake and peels it off the outer leaf surface. The three leaf-filter designs differ in washing method. The Davis leaves during washing remain stationary, mounted on the bottom effluent header. There is a space in the center of the leaves, within which the wash header (with jet nozzles) slowly revolves. This rotates the fan-tailed jets a full 360°, in washing off the cake. In the other two designs the leaves are not stationary; they rotate, mounted on a central hollow revolving shaft, which acts as the effluent header. The wash inlet header (with nozzles), mounted above the leaves, remains stationary during the washing process, but the jets hit the leaves at the periphery rather than in the center (as in Davis). See Fig. 10.7 for the Hercules design. Peripheral jets are effective, because more of the cake is located near the periphery. As the effluent header is located in the center, it aids in the uniform precoating and effluent collection from both sides of each leaf. Since the leaves are 48 in. in diameter in large filters, uniformity of precoating requires good distribution.

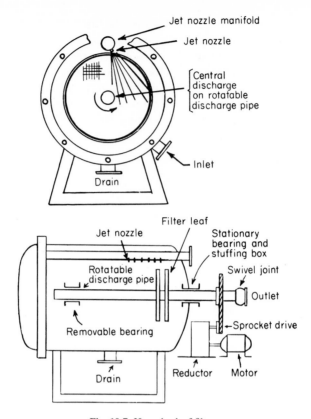

Fig. 10.7. Hercules leaf filter.

V. Development of High-Rate Mixed-Bed Condensate Demineralizers

The early condensate demineralizers were designed for the same flow rates that were used at that time for makeup demineralizers, that is, 10 to 15 gal/min/ft^2; see Table 10.6. Later research, however, with pilot mixed-bed units showed that, as the total solids in the influent decreased to the amounts present in the usual untreated condensate, the required time of contact in the resin bed could be substantially reduced and still there could be produced a very pure effluent. High flow rates, therefore, were justified. For example, Fig. 10.8 shows the effect of increasing flow rate on the time to breakthrough (or the exchange capacity) for waters of different amounts of solids. Other research work has confirmed the feasibility of rates of over 50 gal/min/ft^2 for condensate demineralizers (13); Dresden (a nuclear station) adopted such rates in 1960 (14–16) and Sewaren, a fossil-fuel station, adopted them in 1961 (17).

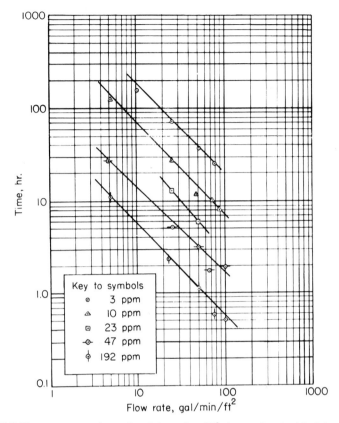

Fig. 10.8. Flow rate versus time to breakthrough at 10^6 ohm-cm in mixed-bed demineralizers with waters of various solids contents. [From Caddell and Moison (*12*) with permission of the Am. Inst. of Chem. Engrs.]

The higher flow rate called for more uniform resin beads of maximal toughness, to withstand the pressure losses involved, and the demineralizer had to be designed with special internal systems for distributing the high flows uniformly without channeling or gouging of the resin bed.

VI. External Regeneration System

The early condensate mixed-bed demineralizers (see Table 10.6) used in-place regeneration; that is, the acid and caustic soda were brought to the main shells, where the regeneration was conducted. After about 1960, however, all new condensate-demineralizer projects adopted external regeneration. In this system the resins after exhaustion are hydraulically sluiced out of the main shells and transferred into external vessels for regeneration. The

Table 10.6

PARTIAL LIST OF UTILITY CONDENSATE-PURIFICATION PLANTS:
FOSSIL-FUEL ONCE-THROUGH BOILERS, AS OF SPRING, 1966[a]

No.	Utility	Steam press., psig	Turbine rating, mw	Condensate, gal/min	Prefilt., %[e]	Filt.[b]	Condens. demind., %	Demin. rate, gal/min/ft²	Regen.	Start-up date[d]
1	Ohio Power Co. Philo No. 6	4500	125	1030	60	T	20	10 to 11	I	1957
2	Clev. Elec. Ill. Co. Avon No. 8	3500	215	2500	100	T	50 to 100	7.5 to 15	I	1959
3	Phila. Elec. Eddystone No. 1	5000	325	2450	25 to 50	L	25 to 50	7.5 to 20	I	1959
4	Eddystone No. 2	3500	450	3750	100	T	35	10 to 12	I	1960
5	Ohio Power Sporn No. 5	3500	450	3750	100	T	35	10 to 12	I	1960
6	Ind. Mich. El. Co. Breed No. 1	3500	450	3750	100	T	35	10 to 12	I	1960
	Sou. Cal. Edison.									
7	Hunt. Beach No. 3	2400	210	2900	50	L	50	30 to 45	E	1961
8	Hunt. Beach No. 4	2400	210	2900	50	L	50	10 to 15	I	1961
9	Balt. Gas & Elec. Crane No. 1	2400	191	1860	100	L	100	25 to 50	E	1961
10	Pub. Ser. El. & Gas Sewaren No. 5	2400	342	4800	100	T	100	25 to 50	E	1962
11	T. V. A. Colbert No. 5	2400	500	4900	100	T	100	31	E	1962
	T. V. A.									
12	Paradise No. 1	2400	650	6900	100	L	100	30	E	1963
13	Paradise No. 2	2400	650	6900	100	L	100	30	E	1963
14	Pub. Serv. El. & G. Hudson No. 1	3500	400	5100	0	None	100	50	E	1964
	Indiana-Mich. Elec.									
15	Tanners Creek No. 4	3500	580	6900	100	T	35	25	E	1964
	Potomac Elec. Pow.									
16	Chalk Point No. 1	3500	335	3625	100	T	100	37	E	1964
17	Chalk Point No. 2	3500	335	3625	100	T	100	37	E	1965
	Hartford Elec. Light									
18	Middletown No. 3	2400	225	2800	0	None	100	50	E	1965
	Boston Edison Co.									
19	New Boston No. 1	2400	380	3400	0	None	100	50	E	1965
20	T. V. A. Bull Run No. 1	3500	900	8750	33	T	100	50	E	1965
21	Cent. Ill. Pub. Serv. Coffeen No. 1	2400	335	4500	0	None	100	50	E	1965
22	Union Elec. Co. Sioux Station No. 1	3500	472	5660	100	L	100	50	E	1966
23	Sioux Station No. 2	3500	472	5660	100	L	100	50	E	A
	Balt. Gas & Elec.									
24	Wagner No. 3	3500	320	3200	100	L, P	100	40	E	1966

Table 10.6 (*continued*)

No.	Utility	Steam press., psig	Turbine rating, mw	Condensate, gal/min	Prefilt., %[e]	Filt.[b]	Condens. demind., %	Demin. rate, gal/min/ft^2	Regen.	Start-up date[d]
25	Pac. G. & E. Co. Moss Landing No. 6	3500	702	9000	0	None	100	50	E	1966
26	Moss Landing No. 7	3500	702	9000	0	None	100	50	E	A
27	Sou. Cal. Edison Alamitos No. 5	3500	475	5200	0	None	100	50	E	1966
28	Alamitos Station No. 6	3500	475	5200	0	None	100	50	E	A
29	Ohio Power Co. Cardinal No. 1	3500	590	6400	100	T	25	25 to 50	E	A
30	Cardinal Station No. 2	3500	590	6400	100	T	25		E	A
31	Common. Ed. Kincaid No. 1	2400	580	6400	0	None	100	50	E	A
32	Kincaid Station No. 2	2400	580	6400	0	None	100	50	E	A
33	Sou. Cal. Ed. Redondo No. 7	3500	477	5200	0	None	100	50	E	A
34	Redondo No. 8	3500	477	5200	0	None	100	50	E	A
35	Consumers Power Campbell No. 2	3500	375	4825	100	P				A
36	T. V. A. Paradise No. 3	3500	1150	11,000	0	P				A
37	Boston Edison Co. New Boston No. 2	2400	390	3400	0	None	100	50	E	A
38	Keystone Util. Grp. No. 1	3675	865	9200	100	L	100	50	E	A
39	Keystone Util. Grp. No. 2	3675	865	9200	100	L	100	50	E	A
40	Allegheny Power Fort Martin No. 1	3500	540	6000	100	P	50	50	E	A
41	Fort Martin No. 2	3500	540	6000	100	P	50	50	E	A
42	Miss. P. & L. Co. Baxter Wilson No. 1	3500	518	6000	0	None	100	50	E	A
43	Arkansas P. & L. R. E. Ritchie	3500	518	6000	0	None	100	50	E	A
44	Dallas P. & L. Co. Mt. Creek No. 8	3334	531	6400	0	None	100	50	E	A
45	Houston L. & P. Parrish No. 4	3334	531		100	P	0		E	A
46	Penna. P. & L. Co. Brunner No. 3	3500	715	9000	0	None	100	50	E	A
47	City of Jacksonville Southside Station No. 1	2400	276	3000	0	None	100	45	E	A
48	Dairyland Power Coop Genoa No. 3	3500	350	3500	0	None	100	50	E	A
49	New Orleans P. Serv Michoud No. 3	3500	531	6390	0	None	100	50	E	A
50	La. P. & L. Co. Nine Mile No. 4	3500	531	6390	0	None	100	50	E	A
51	Pub. Serv. E. & Gas Hudson No. 2	3500	600	7400	0	None	100	50	E	A
52	Northern States P. Allen King No. 1	3500	559		100	P				A

Table 10.6 (*continued*)

No.	Utility	Steam press., psig	Turbine rating, mw	Condensate, gal/min	Prefilt., %[e]	Filt.[b]	Condens. demind., %[e]	Demin. rate, gal/min/ft²	Regen.	Start-up date[d]
53	North. Ind. P. Serv. Bailey No. 8	3675	380	4400	100	P				A
54	New Eng. G. & E. Canal No. 1	3500	542	5300	0	None	100	50	E	A
55	Texas P. & L. Co. Valley No. 2	3334	531	6800	0	None	100	50	E	A
56	Georgia Power Co. Harlee Branch 3	3500	481	5000	0	None	100	50	E	A
57	Pub. Serv. of New Hamp.- Merrim. No. 2	2400	327	4200	0	None	100	50	E	A

[a] See Applebaum and Zahn (*10*), Calise and Dallman (*11*).
[b] Filter: T, tubular; L, leaf; P, powdered resin.
[c] Regeneration: I, in-place; E, external.
[d] Date: A, after 1966.
[e] % of the total condensate flow, filtered or demineralized.

regenerated resins then are transported hydraulically to an external storage vessel. An extra resin charge, a spare bed, kept in this vessel, replaces the exhausted resin in the main shell, the operation taking about 30 min, considerably less than the several hours needed for regeneration. Figure 10.9 is a simplified flow diagram of a modern condensate demineralizer with an external regeneration system.

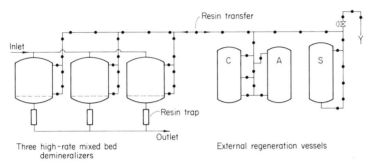

Fig. 10.9. Condensate demineralizer with external regeneration system. C, resin separation; A, anion regeneration; S, resin storage.

A. Procedure for Resin Transfer and External Regeneration

The transfer of exhausted resin from a main demineralizer shell to an external separation vessel usually is controlled by remote manual operation of the valves, but in some cases it is fully automatic. The main demineralizer unit that has become exhausted is removed from service by closing its inlet and outlet valves. Then its vent and drain valves are opened, and the shell is partially drained. The vent and drain valves then are closed, and the sluice-water inlet valve is opened, so that the resin bed is fluidized. For hydraulic transport of the exhausted resin to the external separation vessel the following valves are opened: resin outlet valve at the main shell and the resin inlet, and vent and drain valves at the separation vessel.

Soon thereafter the main demineralizer shell, just emptied, is refilled pneumatically with the regenerated resin held in reserve in the storage vessel. The main shell thus refilled is placed in service or held on standby. Pneumatic, rather than hydraulic, transfer avoids separation of the cation and anion resins as the regenerated mixed resin falls into place in the empty main shell; hydraulic transfer would cause a separation, because the excess transfer water would accumulate in the main shell, and the heavier cation resin beads, falling through this layer of water, would go to the bottom while the lighter anion resin beads would remain above. In that case an additional air mix would be required to remix the separated resins. The pneumatic propulsion of the regenerated mixed resin from the external storage vessel to the empty main shell makes the extra air mix less necessary. The resin bed in the storage vessel, however, must have water in the voids between the resin beads, when the transfer air is applied.

The regeneration of the exhausted resins in the external vessels is automatically controlled, initiated by pushbutton. The exhausted resin is first backwashed in the external separation vessel, the cation and anion beads being thus separated. This is done by opening the backwash inlet and backwash outlet valves. After the beads are separated, these valves are closed, and the anion resin is sluiced out to the external anion regeneration vessel. A sluice-water inlet distributor is provided for this purpose, located just above the top of the cation resin layer. The sluice-water inlet valve is opened, so that the anion resin layer is fluidized. For hydraulic transport of the fluidized anion resin to the external anion resin vessel the following valves are opened: the anion resin outlet valve at the separation vessel, and the vent and drain valves at the anion regeneration vessel.

The cation resin left in the separation vessel is air-scrubbed, backwashed, and regenerated with acid. The crud on the cation resin is thus removed. The anion resin is cleaned similarly and regenerated with caustic soda in the anion regeneration vessel.

After regeneration both the cation and the anion resins may be transferred hydraulically to the resin storage vessel for a final rinse and air mix, but in some systems the regenerated anion resin is first transferred back to the separation vessel for rinse and air mix. This permits checking the conductivity of the rinse effluent for proper quality, which would indicate that the regeneration had been carried out correctly. If the rinse effluent conductivity remains too high, an alarm is sounded, and the operator can initiate a second regeneration, repeating the steps given above before the properly regenerated resin is transferred to the resin storage vessel.

B. *Advantages of External Regeneration*

External regeneration not only reduces the outage time for regeneration, but it eliminates the danger of regenerants' entering the boiler, because the acid and caustic soda are not connected to the main shells. Furthermore, the external piping, valve nests, and internal distributors of the main shells are simplified, because no flow of regenerants takes place in these shells. Moreover, the air-scrubbing and higher cation-resin backwash water rates used in the external separation vessel (after the anion resin is transferred away) accomplish a more thorough cleaning of the cation resins than was possible with in-place systems. Most of the crud is present on the cation resin. The ability of external regeneration to remove the crud from the resin was one of the important factors that led to the omission of the prefilters.

VII. Omission of Prefilters

Dresden omitted prefilters, because their pilot-plant tests with high-rate demineralizers without prefilters showed that the resin could combine filtration and demineralization successfully (*14*).

Sewaren included prefilters, but a paper later reported (*17*): "Subsequent experience with condensate polishing during the start-up of the number 5 unit at Sewaren Generating Station indicated that filters were not necessary to satisfactorily remove suspended materials from the condensate. Therefore filters were omitted from the condensate purification system for Hudson No. 1 unit." Figures 10.10 and 10.11 show the satisfactory removal of iron and of silica during the initial startup of the Hudson No. 1 unit by the demineralizer without prefilters.

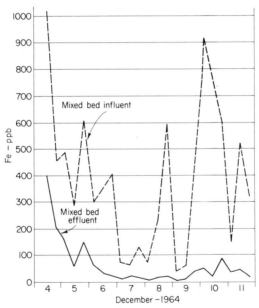

Fig. 10.10. Iron removal during initial startup of Hudson No. 1 unit [from (*17*)].

The filtering capacity of the demineralizer resins was the subject of a research study reported in 1964 (*18*). This work was done with a pilot high-rate mixed-bed demineralizer without prefilters, operating on condensate to which various amounts of metal oxides had been added. The oxides were equal in particle size and composition to the corrosion products normally in condensate. The pilot bed removed the metal oxides successfully. The oxides accumulated "in depth" rather than on top of the bed. The pressure loss did

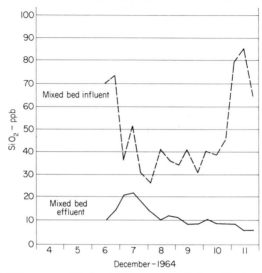

Fig. 10.11. Silica removal during initial startup of Hudson No. 1 unit [from (*17*)].

not increase excessively during the runs. The resin bed had a definite capacity for crud-removal up to the breakthrough, when the oxides came through.

Omission of the prefilters is mainly dictated by economic considerations. The volume of resin in the modern high-rate demineralizers is only about 20 % of the resin in the early low-rate units, and the cost of a complete resin replacement is only about 15 % of the cost of the prefilters. Even if a resin bed has to be completely replaced after the first year, owing to omission of the filters, it would still be economical to use demineralizers alone. Nevertheless, experience shows that a complete replacement normally is not required when the prefilters are omitted; besides, eliminating the prefilters saves 25 to 35 psi pressure loss.

For all these reasons most utilities now are installing condensate mixed beds, which do both the filtering and the demineralizing. This trend is clearly indicated in Table 10.6, a partial list of condensate-purification systems in utility fossil-fuel once-through boiler plants as of the spring of 1966. By October, 1966, more than forty-five utility stations, including once-through and drum boilers and including nuclear plants, adopted standard mixed-bed units without prefilters (*19*). This list of stations is continuing to grow rapidly.

VIII. Condensate-Demineralizer Design

A. Demineralizer Shell

The demineralizer shell and piping are built for operating pressures dictated by the pumping system that transfers the condensate from the condenser to the deaerating heater or the boiler. Depending on the pressure in the deaerating heater, when that is used, the condensate-pump discharge pressures may range from 250 to 600 psi. The shell and piping of the demineralizer must be designed for such pressures, unless a booster pumping station is interposed downstream from the demineralizer. In the latter case the shell and piping may be designed for only 100 to 150 psi. A comparison of cost of the booster pumps and the extra cost of the higher-pressure demineralizers forms a basis for deciding on the final design. For high pressures demineralizer shells have been made spherical, instead of cylindrical, to save costs.

The demineralizer shell may be unlined, since no acid enters it when external regeneration is employed, but most demineralizer shells have either polyvinyl chloride plastic lining (80 mils thick) or the usual sheet-rubber lining (3/16 in. thick). The piping and valves are not lined.

1. INTERNAL DISTRIBUTORS IN MAIN SHELLS

The upper inlet distributor must be designed for high flow rates, 50 gal/min/ft^2. The same umbrella-head design shown in Fig. 8.1 is used, but the radial arms and umbrella heads must be in sufficient number for the exit velocities to be low enough to avoid the gouging out of cavities in the resin bed. The distributor is made of stainless steel.

There is no regenerant distributor, because the regenerants do not enter the main shells. This is one of the savings resulting from external regeneration.

The underdrain distributor is made of stainless steel and consists of either a Neva-Clog screen or a header–lateral system with a stainless-steel Johnson well-screen type of lateral. The Neva-Clog screen contains two stainless-steel thin plates, tack-welded together but with a controlled fine space between them. The small orifices in the upper plate are not directly over those in the lower one. This prevents resin escape. Neva-Clog plates come in sections that may be rolled up to be put through the manhole. The sections are supported by a rubber-covered peripheral angle and, in the center, by a plastic-covered "subway grating," to which they are bolted. The grating in turn is supported by rubber-covered channels welded into the lower head. Good workmanship and design will ensure that the supports are level and that the bolts are well enough gasketed to prevent leakage of resin. The Neva-Clog screen aids in complete resin transfer out of the shell, because it is flat and offers no obstructions on which resin can lodge. However, since underdrains often are designed conservatively for a pressure loss of over 100 psi, the supports are costly; the trend is therefore toward the header–lateral underdrain system.

An internal flat bottom may be used for supporting the header–lateral underdrain system (as in Fig. 8.1), but the supports under this bottom likewise are costly, and the header and laterals interfere with complete emptying of the resin to the external vessels. Therefore a header–lateral system submerged in the resin in the lower head is generally used. Here the resin outlet is at the bottom of the head. Extra resin is added below the header–lateral system to fill the lower head. It must supplement the active bed of resin above the underdrain system. Special stainless laterals located close to the lower head will minimize the amount of this extra resin.

B. External Regeneration Vessels

If the main shells are of low-pressure design (under 150 psi), the external vessels often are made for the same pressure, but if they are built for higher pressures, the vessels are designed for 75 to 100 psi. Pressure-relief valves in the resin-transfer piping, as indicated in Fig. 10.9, prevent the higher main-shell pressure from being applied to the external vessels.

The vessels are rubber-lined (lining 3/16 in. thick). The internal distributors are of stainless steel and consist of the usual inlet and underdrain systems. The separation vessel has a sluice-water inlet distributor, mentioned above, for fluidizing the anion resin for its transfer to the anion regeneration vessel. The storage vessel has no regenerant distributor. The height of the vessels is usually 10 or 12 ft, because the resin transferred from the main shells forms beds 5 or 6 ft deep. Since the resin beds in the main shells are only 3 or 4 ft deep, the diameter of the external vessels is less than that of the main shells.

C. External Piping and Valves

Unlined valves and piping are used on the main shells. The valves are of the ball type, when the diameter of the piping is 6 in. or less. When the diameters are larger and the pressures in the main shells are high (over 150 psi), motor-operated gate valves are preferred.

The external piping and valves on the external vessels are rubber-lined. The valves are usually of the Saunders type with pneumatic diaphragm operators. The resin-transfer piping may be unlined, but usually it is rubber-lined, so that it will reduce friction and avoid corrosion that might foul the resins.

D. Instrumentation, Automatic Controls, Panel, and Postfilters or Resin Traps

The service runs of condensate demineralizers usually end on conductivity breakthrough. Occasionally silica breaks through before the conductivity, if the influent contains more than the amount usual in condensate. The premature breakthrough may be avoided by having a greater proportion of anion resin than the normal one third of the mixed bed. Effluent silica-monitoring by frequent testing during the run or by silica analyzers is essential.

Individual orifice flowmeters on the inlet of each main shell are included. Loss of head through each main unit is measured by differential-pressure meters. Loss of head across the battery is also monitored, and when this pressure loss becomes excessive, a contactor on the differential-pressure meter automatically opens a main bypass valve.

Since the valves on the main units are generally remote-manually controlled, selector switches on the panel are used for actuating them. Resin-transfer valves, described above, are usually remote-manually controlled too. The regeneration in the external vessels is automatically controlled after initiation by pushbutton. The types of timer, program-sequence controllers, and stepping switches for this automatic regeneration are the same as for the makeup demineralizers, as described in Chapter 8, Section VII. The regenerant dilution and injection controls are of the closed in-line type. The panel for the condensate demineralizer is often combined with that for the makeup plant.

To prevent resin that might leak through the demineralizer underdrain from entering the feedwater, it has become standard practice to use either a postfilter or a resin trap (strainer) in the outlet of each main unit. The earliest condensate demineralizers had cartridge postfilters. These consist of pressure shells containing a number of cotton cartridges mounted on stainless-steel perforated cores. The cores are fitted into a fixed, lower tube sheet. Each cartridge is about 2.5 in. in diameter and 10 in. high and has an outer surface area of about 0.5 ft^2. A number of cartridges are mounted above each other in tiers or columns. Each cartridge is made of a continuously wrapped, single cotton thread, like a bobbin. The cotton layer thus formed is sufficiently thick so that even fine resin beads cannot pass through. Pressure loss is measured, and when it increases excessively, it indicates a resin leak and sounds an alarm. The cause of the leak is then determined, repairs are made, and the cartridges are replaced. To facilitate cartridge replacement some designs include a cage that holds all the tiers of cartridges. The cage is lifted out after the top flanged head is unbolted.

The high cost of these cartridge postfilters for the large flows and high pressures involved led to the development of the resin trap. This consists of a cylindrical strainer held in a pressure-steel shell. The strainer is of the Johnson well-screen type, described previously in connection with the tubular prefilters. The openings between any two turns of the helically wound wedge wire are made small enough to retain fine resin. The trap should be designed to be strong enough to withstand pressure losses of over 100 psi. The total screen area is made sufficient to keep the pressure loss, when the trap is clean, under 2 to 5 psi. Rates of several hundred gallons per minute per square foot have been used successfully. Pressure-differential indicators with alarm contactors tell when the screen has become fouled by resin. To backflush the screen, the main influent valve is closed, and the rinse outlet valve is opened; water then backs up from the outlet header through the open effluent valve and washes the screen, then going to waste.

E. Resin Beds in Condensate Demineralizers

The resin beds in the demineralizers are usually 36 in. deep, with a cation-to-anion resin ratio of 2:1. The preponderance of the cation resin is necessary for the removal of ammonia and a better removal of iron oxide crud. Ammonia is the major cation in the condensate.

The removal of ammonia is not desired but is incidental to the removal of all the other ions present. The amount of ammonia present varies with the pH value maintained in the condensate for the prevention of corrosion in the preboiler cycle. With pH values of 8.8 to 9.2, which were standard when copper alloy tubing was used in the extraction heaters, the amount of ammonia was less than 500 ppb (as NH_3). The capacity of the cation resin for removing ammonia is fortunately quite high, 20 to 25 kgr (as $CaCO_3$) per cubic foot of resin; therefore, at a flow rate of 50 gal/min/ft^2 and with 24 in. of cation resin the service runs to an ammonia or conductivity break-through usually last more than a week. The steel tubing used today for the extraction heaters and the high pH values required for the prevention of iron pickup from these tubes have caused shorter service runs and led to ammonia-tion of the resin, as discussed below.

The other reason for using a 2:1 ratio rather than a lower one has been the more complete removal of iron oxide. The removal is accomplished by both filtration and ion exchange. The iron is present in both dissolved and suspended forms. Dissolved iron, being a cation, is removed by the cation exchanger. Even the colloidal and suspended forms of iron appear to be removed mostly by the cation resin, as was found in an examination of resins after use. The better removal of iron crud through the use of a higher ratio of cation resin to anion resin was reported in pilot demineralizer tests (20); when the crud level was 500 ppb, it was found that with a cation-to-anion resin ratio of only 1:2 the removal of the crud was poor, but when the ratio was made 2:1, it increased to 90%.

The types of resin that have been used in many condensate demineralizers are Dowex HCR-W and HGR-W cation resin and SBR-P anion resins and the Amberlite IR-120, IR-122, and IR-200 cation resins and IRA-400 anion resins. Equivalent competitive resins are also in use. The fines in these resins (finer than 40 mesh) should be kept to a minimum (only a few percent), so as to keep the pressure loss through the resin at high flow rates to a minimum. The elimination of fines reduces the loss at 50 gal/min/ft^2 to under 25 to 30 psi, when the resin is clean. When the pressure loss through the whole battery from inlet to outlet reaches 50 psi, the resin should be cleaned, even if not regenerated. The more crosslinked (10%) cation resins have the advantage of slightly greater density than the standard resins (8% crosslinked). The higher density aids in more complete separation of the cation and anion resins by backwashing before regeneration.

If the condenser cooling water is brackish or consists of seawater, condenser leakage will introduce considerable amounts of sodium chloride. The condensate demineralizer has the important function of removing these chlorides, to keep the boiler on the line long enough for the leaky condenser tube to be located, the compartment in the condenser isolated, and the tube plugged or replaced. Since the chlorides are removed by the anion resin, the ratio of cation resin to anion resin for salty condenser cooling water has been reduced from 2:1 to 60:40 or even 55:45. The total bed depth also has been increased from the usual 36 in. to 42 or even 48 in., so as to increase the amount of anion resin used.

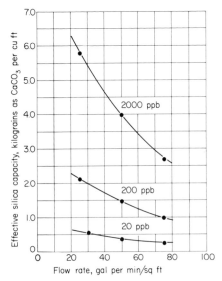

Fig. 10.12. Capacity of high-rate mixed beds for silica removal. [From Pocock and Stewart (*18*).]

Another reason for using resin beds deeper and richer in anion resin is to avoid premature silica breakthrough. Figure 10.12 shows that the silica-removal capacity of the anion resin in mixed beds (cation-to-anion ratio of 2:1) decreases as the flow rate increases and the influent silica decreases. With the usual influent silica of about 20 ppb the capacity is slightly under 0.5 kgr/ft^3 at 50 gal/min/ft^2. For the prevention of a premature silica breakthrough and for a better chloride removal it may be advisable to use 42 or 48 in. for the depth of the resin beds and a lower ratio of cation resin to anion resin.

The acid and caustic soda regenerant levels should be enough to give the longest service runs possible while producing the ultrapure effluent quality desired, 10,000,000 ohms-cm specific resistance (0.1 μmho conductivity), at all times. Good conservative practice therefore calls for acid and caustic levels of 7.5 to 10.0 lb/ft^3. Even higher doses may be desirable for protection against condenser leakage, when the condenser cooling water is salty.

Table 10.7 gives data on a typical utility condensate purification plant,

Table 10.7

DATA ON A TYPICAL CONDENSATE PURIFICATION PLANT

Normal condensate flow	6400 gal/min	Normal pressure	266 psig
Flow during startups	2200 gal/min	Design pressure	375 psi

Influent composition, ppb

	Normal	Startup	Condenser leak.
TDS (less NH$_3$)	50 to 500	500 to 2000	200 to 1500
Ammonia	200 to 2000	200 to 2000	200 to 2000
Total susp. solids	10 to 40	100 to 2000	200
Soluble silica	20	500	20
pH	9.2 to 9.6	9.2 to 9.6	9.2 to 9.6
Temp., °F	75 to 125	75 to 125	75 to 125

Performance

Effluent quality required, ppb: normal periods

Total iron:	8	Total copper:	2
Diss. silica:	5	Total susp. solids:	10
Total diss. solids:	20	Conduct. at 25°C,	0.1 μmho

Effluent quality required: startups
Influent susp. solids to be reduced 90% or to 15 ppb
Influent diss. solids to be reduced 95% or to 20 ppb

Effluent compn. required: condenser leakage lasting 8 hours with 14 gal/min river-water leakage
Effluent diss. solids,   50 ppb (exclusive of NH$_3$)
Influent iron and copper to be reduced 90% or to 10 ppb

Pressure loss
35 psi from demineralizer inlet to outlet, when resin clean

Annual resin losses, %, for 3 years

	By attrition	Capacity loss
Cation resin	6	6
Anion resin	10	10

Regenerants, per unit regeneration, lb
H$_2$SO$_4$,   1005   NaOH,   502 (100% basis)

Table 10.7 (*continued*)

Vessel specifications

Demineralizer units
Three main shells, for 375 psi, rubber-lined, each for 3200 gal/min at 50 gal/min/ft^2; 9 ft 0 in. diam. × 4 ft 6 in. ht., each with 24 in. cation resin and 12 in. anion resin and resin traps.

External vessels
Separation and cation regeneration vessel, 6 ft 6 in. diam. × 12 ft 0 in. ht
Anion regeneration vessel, 4 ft 0 in. diam. × 11 ft 0 in. ht
Resin-storage vessel, 6 ft 6 in. diam. × 9 ft 0 in. ht with spare charge of resin
All external vessels rubber-lined and for 75 psi pressure

Instrumentation for conductivity, flow, differential pressure across resin traps, analyzers for SiO$_2$ and suspended solids.

including sizes of demineralizer units and external vessels, the resins used, and the performance expected.

IX. Ammoniation of Cation Resin

The first supercritical once-through boiler utility stations experienced copper deposits in the turbine, which caused losses of efficiency of as much as 14 % (*21*). Later stations then adopted steel tubes for the extraction heaters, to eliminate copper from the preboiler cycle (*22, 23*). The pH value could then be raised, so that the steel would not be corroded and iron picked up, without any danger of copper pickup.

The pH value is determined by the amount of ammonia added. The pH value that will avoid excessive iron pickup has been reported to be above 9.6 (*23*); however, in a study of this at several stations it was concluded that a value of 9.3 to 9.4 appeared sufficient (*24*). It is important, through good "housekeeping," to maintain low amounts of dissolved oxygen in the condensate in addition to a high enough pH value.

The higher the pH value selected and the higher the consequent amount of ammonia added, the shorter the demineralizer runs to an ammonia or conductivity breakthrough; this is shown in Table 10.8. When the pH is 9.6, the length of the run is reduced to less than 2 days, and the regenerations are then quite frequent.

Ammoniation of the cation resin after acid regeneration converts the resin from the hydrogen form to the ammonium form. The latter form does not remove the ammonia in the condensate and the length of the service runs is therefore increased until other ions break through.

Some question remained, whether ammonium cation resin mixed with hydroxide anion resin would satisfactorily remove the silica, sodium, and

Table 10.8

EFFECT OF pH VALUE IN THE CONDENSATE
ON THE LENGTH OF DEMINERALIZER SERVICE RUNS[a]

pH at 25°C	As NH_3, ppb	As $CaCO_3$, ppb	As $CaCO_3$, gr/gal	Length of service run, days
9.0	260	765	0.045	15.5
9.2	490	1440	0.084	8.3
9.4	1000	2940	0.172	4.1
9.6	2250	6600	0.386	1.8
9.7	3300	9700	0.568	1.2

[a] This table is based on using 50 gal/min/ft^2 and 24 in. of cation resin and a capacity of the cation resin for NH_3 removal of 25 kgr of NH_3 (as $CaCO_3$) per cubic foot of cation resin.

chloride introduced by condenser leakage. A research study therefore was undertaken with a pilot mixed-bed demineralizer (without prefilter) (25). As a simulant of condenser leakage, sodium chloride was injected, and silica also was added. Ammonia was injected, to raise the pH value to 9.7. The cation resin was ammoniated after its acid regeneration, and the tests were made at 50 gal/min/ft^2. The results proved successful. The runs lasted more than 30 days without any breakthrough, because the ammonia in the condensate was not removed. The iron crud was reduced by about 90%. Large amounts of sodium, chloride, and silica likewise were eliminated. The results of this study were confirmed by others (26). A utility is now using ammoniation with service runs lasting 30 to 90 days (27).

Several other utility demineralizers now have been equipped with facilities for ammoniation (27). Figure 10.13 is a flow diagram of a feedwater and steam cycle in a utility and shows a condensate demineralizer (ammoniated) located near the hotwell. It also shows Filterex cation resin units for the removal of iron from heater drains. These units are discussed below.

The ammoniation may be carried out either in the separation and cation regeneration vessel or in the resin-storage tank. It is important, however, during sluicing of the anion resin from the separation vessel to the anion regeneration vessel, to avoid entraining cation resin, because the caustic soda regeneration of the anion resin will place sodium on the entrained cation resin, and this sodium will then leak off into the treated condensate.

Special regeneration techniques for avoiding sodium leakage have been developed.*

* Patent application by Cochrane Division, Crane Co., pending.

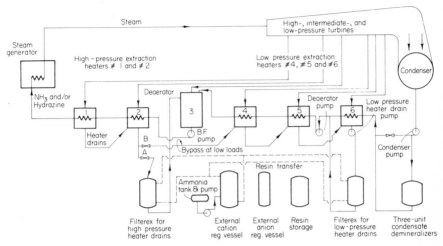

Fig. 10.13. Flow diagram of feedwater and steam cycle in utility, with condensate de-mineralizer (ammoniated) and Filterex cation resin units for removing iron from heater drains. B.F. pump, boiler-feed pump.

X. Condensate-Purification for Industrial High-Pressure Boilers

The operating pressures of industrial power boilers have also been elevated with the aim of lessening the cost of generating electricity. The pressures in the latest plants have gone above 2000 psi, making the boilers more costly and complex and requiring purer feedwater, as in the utility field.

The steam used for processing in these plants forms a condensate, which picks up iron and copper by corrosion from the condensate return system. Supplementary chemicals, such as amines, have been added to the boiler cycle for the purpose of inhibiting the corrosion, but they have not been successful in keeping the metal pickup sufficiently low.

The feedwater quality requirements have called for iron not to exceed 20 ppb. Condensate that contained more than that therefore needed to be purified before it could be recovered and used for boiler-feed purposes. The industrial condensate was usually fairly hot (150 to 300°F), and its recovery was therefore desirable as a saver of heat. Cation resin in the sodium cycle (regenerated with salt) could withstand the temperatures, and it could remove dissolved iron, copper, and hardness by ion exchange; however, the metal picked up was also in suspended form, so that filtration was necessary.

Consideration was given to filters operating with cellulose filter aid ahead of the cation exchanger, but their cost was high and their operation troublesome. Therefore cation exchangers alone, without prefilters, were tried out at an industrial plant in the eastern United States and found to be practical

(28). A large-scale plant was installed there. The cation exchange system, without prefilters, was given the trademark Filterex* (it was a combination of filtration and ion exchange). To remove accumulated suspended iron from the resin in this plant, provision was made for occasional cleaning with hydrochloric acid in an external vessel. This acid wash was required less than

Table 10.9
OPERATING RESULTS OF FILTEREX
CONDENSATE SODIUM CATION EXCHANGERS

	Avg. influent, ppb	Max. influent, ppb	Effluent
Iron, as Fe	230	400	(Fe + Cu)
Copper, as Cu	140	300	< 20
Hardness, as CaCO$_3$	1700	10,000	< 500

twice a year. The operating chemical results are given in Table 10.9 (28). A large chemical plant in the midwest installed similar condensate cation exchangers, which also have operated successfully, although with more frequent hydrochloric acid treatments (29).

At a paper mill in the southern United States a condensate cation exchanger plant has been operated without any hydrochloric acid cleaning treatments (30). Instead, a weak reducing agent, sodium sulfite, is used with the sodium chloride for in-place regeneration; the sulfite prevents ferrous iron, which may be eluted during regeneration, from being oxidized to the ferric form and precipitated on the resin. In addition, after a number of regenerations a stronger reducing agent, sodium hydrosulfite, is used with the brine; this reduces any ferric iron present to the ferrous form and keeps the resin clean and unfouled. Regenerations take place once or twice a week.

The operating cost of Filterex systems is low, reported (31) to be about 0.3¢ per 1000 gal. The first cost also is low, because the units are unlined and small, since they are operated at 20 to 30 gal/min/ft^2.

Figure 10.14 is a schematic diagram of the cation exchange plant at the paper mill (30), it is typical. A considerable number of such systems are operating satisfactorily in industrial plants.

XI. Ammoniated Cation Resin for Removing Iron from Utility High-Pressure Heater Drains

Sodium cation exchangers regenerated by brine are successful in removing metals from industrial condensate, as described above, but if any appreciable

* Property of Cochrane Division, Crane Company.

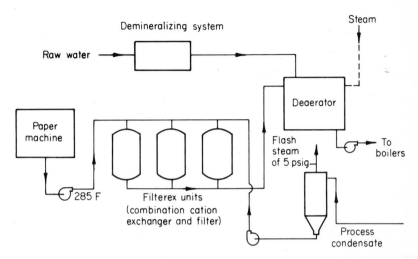

Fig. 10.14. Schematic diagram of typical cation exchange plant for purification of industrial condensate. Condensate-treating system designed to utilize all process condensate as supplement to demineralized makeup water. Some flash steam is obtained from condensate (*30*).

cation exchange occurs, the amount of sodium in the effluent is a few parts per million more than in the influent. The amount may be objectionable in the utility field, because it may lead to turbine difficulties (*21*). Therefore, the use of ammoniated cation resin instead of sodium cation resin was indicated for utility applications.

It was reported that in utility cycles iron was picked up by corrosion mainly from the shell side of the high-pressure extraction-heater tubing (*23, 24*). The conclusion was reached because the iron increase was found in the heater drains introduced into the deaerator storage tank located upstream of the high-pressure heaters. The temperature of the heater drains exceeds 300°F, which was the limit assigned for the usual sodium cation exchangers used in Filterex industrial condensate-polishing systems. Therefore it was necessary to investigate various cation exchange resins in the ammonium form, in order to select those capable of standing the higher temperatures.

Tests were made with a pilot plant filtering high-pressure heater drains in a utility power station (*32*). The resin degradation was determined by passing the influent and effluent through hydrogen cation exchange columns (which removed the ammonia present) and measuring their conductivities. If the conductivity was higher in the effluent than in the influent, the increase was a measure of resin degradation. It was found in these tests that the standard sulfonic strong-acid cation resin, 8 % crosslinked, did not pass this sensitive deterioration test but that certain other, stabler, resins were capable of resisting degradation at temperatures ranging from 300 to 360°F. The tests also demonstrated that the ammoniated resin did reduce the iron from a 25 to 50 ppb down to 5 ppb.

Figure 10.13 shows how ammoniated cation resin would be applied in a utility power plant to treat both high-pressure and low-pressure heater drains; the resin would supplement a standard high-rate mixed-bed condensate-demineralizer plant located at the hotwell. This arrangement is patented (33). The cation resin would be transported (dashed lines) to the external cation regeneration vessel of the demineralizer for acid regeneration followed by ammoniation.

For example, the two cation resin units could be designed for a flow of 1000 gal/min, and the demineralizer for 3000 gal/min. If the cation resin units were omitted and the high-pressure heater drains were cascaded all the way back to the condenser, so that the demineralizer could remove the iron, the demineralizer would have had to handle about 33% more flow, or 4000 gal/min. The expense saved by making the demineralizers smaller would more than pay for the cation resin units included for removing the iron from the heater drains. Furthermore, if the high-pressure heater drains had been cascaded to the condenser, there would have been an appreciable heat loss, 20 Btu/kw, or more than 2%. If the high-pressure heater drains had been passed into the deaerator or pumped into the feedwater stream after the low-pressure heaters, so as to avoid this thermal loss, and if the cation resin units had been omitted, the iron oxide would have deposited in the boiler. Thus the use of the cation resin units for removing the iron at high temperatures would prevent both the boiler deposits and the thermal loss. This application of ammoniated cation resin is a new development and further experience on a large scale is needed for its evaluation.

XII. Disposable, Nonregenerated Powdered Resin

Powdered resin* (mixture of cation and anion exchangers) as a filter aid (instead of, or combined with, cellulose) was introduced in 1962 (34), and patents on its use were granted in 1966 (35). Of extremely fine particle size (90% finer than 325 mesh), it is applied as a thin (1/8 to 1/2 in.) precoat to the outside of cartridge elements in a pressure shell. It is not regenerated but is discarded to waste on exhaustion or on high-pressure drop.

The filter design is similar to that of the cartridge filters previously used as postfilters after demineralizers for catching resin leakage. The cartridges originally were made of cotton but later were made of nylon. They are about 2.5 in. in diameter and 10 in. in height and have a surface area of 0.5 ft². They

* Marketed, under the trademark, "Powdex," by the Graver Water Conditioning Company, Union, N.J.

are stacked up in tiers or columns of four or more cartridges, one above the other. The tiers are spaced several inches apart. An example of a large filter would be a shell 6 ft 0 in. in diameter by 6 ft 4 in. in straight height with nylon 300 stacked elements 5 ft 0 in. high, each 2.64 ft^2 in area, giving a total area of 800 ft^2. The flow rates are 4 gal/min/ft^2, so that this filter would handle 3200 gal/min.

The allowable maximum of condensate temperature is usually 250°F, although higher figures have been mentioned (*19*). The pressure loss is 2 to 5 psi, when the resin is clean, and 25 to 30 psi, when it is dirty. The method of precoating and cleaning follows the general practice for the tubular filters (Section IV A).

The advantages claimed (*19, 34, 36, 37*) for this process are as follows:

(a) Regenerants and regeneration waste water are saved. However, about 12 gal of water are used per square foot of filter area for precoating the filter and washing the cartridges. Precoating takes about 60 to 90 min.

(b) The greater surface area due to the fine particle size of the resin is said to accomplish the removal of colloidal silica, iron, and copper, but the economics of the removal has been questioned by one user (*38*).

(c) The fine resin is claimed to have greater capacity than standard 20 to 50 mesh resin. However, the silica-removal capacity, calculated from the test illustrated in Fig. 7 of Grant *et al.* (*36*), is only 0.3 kgr/ft^3, which is no higher than that given in Fig. 10.12 for the standard bead size.

(d) The pressure loss is low when the resin is clean, because electrostatic forces cause the mixture of fine cation and anion particles to clump and become more permeable.

(e) The filter units may be located downstream of the low-pressure heaters (where condensate temperatures are less than 250°F). They can then remove iron picked up through corrosion of the inside of the steel tubing now used in these heaters. However, the major pickup of iron occurs on the shell side of the high-pressure heaters (*23, 24*).

(f) The ratio of cation resin to anion resin in the precoat may be varied according to the function of the filters. For the removal of metals alone a high ratio, 9:1, may be used; for the removal of silica and other anions lower ratios are favored. High ratios reduce the cost, because anion resin is several times as expensive as cation resin, but with 9:1 ratios the amount of anion resin may be inadequate for the removal of any appreciable amount of anions.

The reported disadvantages of the system are as follows:

(a) The first cost is about as high as that of standard high-rate mixed-bed demineralizers without prefilters (*19*).

(b) The annual cost of the precoats varies with the ratio of cation resin to anion resin and with the average length of the service runs to the 25 to 30 psi pressure loss. Run lengths of a few hours or less are to be expected during startups, when the crud level is high. The cost of the precoats during a five-week startup of a subcritical pressure boiler was reported to run to a five-digit sum (9). With normal condensate, when crud levels are low, run lengths of several weeks may be expected (37).

(c) The life of the cartridges is in question. Cartridges, as used in postfilters in the past, were not backwashed when clogged but were replaced (8, 39). Strenuous air and water wash may prolong their life to some extent. A cartridge life of about nine months was estimated at one installation (40). Another user stated (41): "Each of three treatment units consists of a tank with 208 filter elements, coated with powdered resin. Total design capacity is 3.5 million lb/hr. However, the system is operated at 1.8 million lb/hr maximum to prolong element life." Cartridge replacement is costly in both material and labor and in the outages required. Spare filter units should be provided, to allow for the outages.

(d) The anion resin inventory with standard mixed beds running at 50 gal/min/ft^2 and having 36 in. of resin depth is about ten times as great as that with powdered-resin filters running at 4 gal/min/ft^2 and having 0.3 in. of resin. This is with the same ratio of anion resin to cation resin, of 1:2. If the ratio in the powdered-resin filter is 1:9 instead of 1:2, the inventory of the anion resin in the standard units is forty-five times as great. Therefore the lower capacity of the powdered-resin system for removing silica, chlorides, and other dissolved salts resulting from condenser leakage or weepage must be recognized.

The suggestion has been made that the virtues of the regenerable mixed-bed demineralizers and those of the powdered-resin filters could be combined by using them both in utility power plant cycles (19). The filters would be operated upstream of the demineralizers during startups and downstream (at the outlet of low-pressure heaters) during normal operation. These alternate operations would be controlled by suitable valves and piping. The filtering coat would be of cellulose during startups, so as to reduce operating cost, and of powdered resin only during the normal operating periods, when the service runs are longer.

REFERENCES

1. J. Angelo and K. C. Cotton, Observed effects of deposits on steam turbine efficiency. *Am. Soc. Mech. Engrs. Paper 57-A-116, ASME Ann. Meeting, New York, December 1957.*
2. S. B. Applebaum, Condensate demineralizers – combat deposits for potential 1 % heat rate gain. *Power* (May 1958).
3. R. C. Ulmer, Water treatment for natural and controlled circulation subcritical and supercritical pressure once-through boilers. *Pennsylvania Elec. Assoc. Prime Movers Comm. Meeting, October 1956.*
4. J. A. Lux, Boiler water quality control in high pressure steam power plants. *National Power Conf., Baltimore, Maryland, September 1962.*

5. E. G. Kispert, The Universal Pressure boiler for operation at pressures as low as 1800 PSI. *Southeastern Elec. Exchange Conf.*, at *Clearwater, Florida, April 1959.*

6. H. A. Klein, J. J. Kurpen, and W. G. Schuetzenduebel, Cycle clean-up for supercritical pressure units. *Proc. Amer. Power Conf.* **27** (April 1965).

7. W. H. Rowand and A. M. Frendberg, First commercial supercritical pressure steam generator for Philo Plant. ASME Paper No. 55-A-135, *ASME Ann. Meeting, Chicago, November 1955.*

8. H. J. Vyhnalek and C. D. Banks, Water treatment experience during the start-up and initial operation of the Avon supercritical unit. *Proc. Ann. Water Conf., Engrs. Soc. West Penn. 21st Ann. Conf.* (1960).

9. J. J. Quinlan, Condensate polishing using the proven approach – prefiltration and demineralization. *Southeastern Elec. Exchange Conf., Atlanta, Georgia, October 1966.*

10. S. B. Applebaum and W. Zahn, Standard utility condensate mixed bed demineralizers without prefilters (combining filtration and ion exchange), *Southeastern Elec. Exchange Conf., Atlanta, Georgia, October 1966.*

11. V. J. Calise and C. Dallman, Ultrapure water for power plants. *Mech. Eng.* **86** (1964).

12. J. R. Caddell and R. L. Moison, Mixed bed deionization at high flow rates. *Chem. Eng. Progr. Symp. Ser.* **50**, No. 14 (1954).

13. I. B. Dick and P. L. Silliman, Experiences with the high rate of flow demineralization. *Proc. Ann. Water Conf., Engrs. Soc. West Penn., 19th Ann. Conf.* (1958).

14. A. B. Sisson, R. C. Reid, and H. W. Frazer, High flow rate demineralization of condensate for boiling water reactors. *Proc. Am. Power Conf.* **20**, 709–719 (1958).

15. A. B. Sisson, R. C. Reid, and H. W. Frazer, Operating experience with high flow rate condensate polishing equipment at Dresden. *Proc. Am. Power Conf.* **23** (1961).

16. H. W. Frazer, Operating data on high flow rate condensate polishing without filters. *Proc. Ann. Intern. Water Conf., 22nd, Pittsburgh, Pennsylvania, October 1961.*

17. R. I. Smith and H. D. Reppin, A combination arrangement for high flow condensate polishing and make-up demineralization at Hudson Generating Station. *Proc. Am. Power Conf.* **28** (1966).

18. F. J. Pocock and J. F. Stewart, Research on high flow rate condensate polishing. *Proc. Am. Power Conf.* **26** (1964).

19. D. M. Spillane and L. Limon, Factors in selection of condensate purification equipment. *Southeastern Electric Exchange Conf., Atlanta, Georgia, October 1966.*

20. H. J. Vyhnalek, Discussion. *Proc. Ann. Water Conf., 22nd, Pittsburgh, Pennsylvania, October 1961*, p. 94.

21. H. J. Vyhnalek, A review of water treatment experience after five years of operation in the supercritical range. *Proc. Am. Power Conf.* **27**, 774 (1965).

22. T. C. Hoppe, Basic design and operation results of two copper-free boiler turbine systems. *Proc. Am. Power Conf.* **26** (1964).

23. W. L. Riedel, The control of metal pick-up in cycles with steel tube feedwater heaters. *Proc. Am. Power Conf.* **26** (1964).

24. F. J. Pocock, J. A. Lux, and R. V. Seibel, Control of iron pick-up in steel feedwater cycles. *Proc. Am. Power Conf.* **28** (1966).

25. S. B. Applebaum and G. J. Crits, The use of ammoniated cation resin in high rate mixed bed demineralizers for condensate purification. *Proc. Intern. Water Conf., Engrs. Soc. West Penn., September 1964.*

26. J. J. Kurpen, Demineralizer operation and filtration in a supercritical steam cycle. *Proc. Am. Power Conf.* **28** (1966).

27. C. M. Kennedy, P. S. Meyers, and G. J. Crits, Experience with high rate ammoniated mixed beds for condensate polishing at CIPSCO Coffeen Station. *Proc. Intern. Water Conf., Engrs. Soc. West Penn., December 1967.*

28. S. B. Applebaum, High purity steam at Eastman Kodak Company, *Power* (August 1966).
29. P. H. Caskey, A large industrial installation of hot condensate cation exchange. *Proc. Am. Power Conf.* **24**, 736 (1962).
30. S. B. Applebaum and Y. T. Allen, New regenerable process up-grades condensate for boiler feed. *Power* (March 1964).
31. S. B. Applebaum and G. J. Crits, Cleaning up condensate, *Ind. Water Eng.* (November 1965). From lecture at *Liberty Bell Corrosion Course of Natl. Assoc. Corrosion Engrs., Drexel-Inst. of Technol., Philadelphia, 1965.*
32. S. B. Applebaum and G. J. Crits, Use of ammoniated cation resin to remove iron from heater drains. *Proc. Intern. Water Conf., October 1965.*
33. S. B. Applebaum and G. J. Crits, U.S. Patent 3,336,747 (1967).
34. J. H. Duff and J. A. Levendusky, Powdex – a new approach in condensate purification. *Proc. Am. Power Conf.* **24** (1962).
35. J. A. Levendusky, U.S. Patents 3,250,702–3,250,705 (1966).
36. J. S. Grant, E. C. Novak, J. A. Levendusky, and D. M. Spillane, Progress report on Powdex – Bay Shore Station, Toledo Edison Co. *Proc. Am. Power Conf.* **25** (1963).
37. J. A. Levendusky and B. J. Peters, Jr., Application of Powdex process for the purification of utility power plant condensate. *Southeastern Elec. Exchange Conf., Tampa, Florida, October 1963.*
38. I. B. Dick, Discussion of paper by K. A. Kun and R. Kunin entitled Amberlite XE-238 – A macroreticular anion exchange resin for removing colloidal silica and hydrous oxides from water. *Proc. Intern. Water Conf., November 1966.*
39. P. F. Santaro, Survey of high temperature demineralization for dual-purpose BWR plants. Prepared for Oak Ridge Natl. Lab. by Allis-Chalmers Mfg. Co., August 1965.
40. J. S. Grant and R. P. Crouse, The history of Powdex condensate polishing equipment at Bay Shore Station, Toledo Edison Co. *Proc. Am. Power Conf.* **28** (1966).
41. J. S. Peri and G. J. Bogin, Water quality is checked at every step. *Power* **110**, 53 (1966).

II

Demineralizing Water Treatment in Nuclear (Atomic) Power Plants

In modern nonnuclear high-pressure power stations ultrapure water is needed for preventing deposits in the boiler and turbine. The nuclear station calls for equally pure water for this and a number of other purposes.

I. Functions of Demineralizers in Nuclear Stations

Water is used as a coolant and moderator in many types of nuclear plant. Impurities in the water become radioactive as the coolant passes through the radiation field of the nuclear-reactor core, and when the water passes to other parts of the system, it forms radioactive deposits there. The deposits interfere with the accessibility and safe maintenance of the many components involved. Demineralizers therefore are used for treating the coolant water so as to remove the long-lived impurities and thus reduce the buildup of radioactive deposits in the circulating system.

Impurities in the coolant water also reduce the efficiency of the reactor by absorbing neutrons that sustain the fission reactions. They form insulating scale on the fuel elements, increasing their surface temperature. This diminishes the efficiency of the heat transfer and increases corrosion of the elements. The scale also plugs up spaces between the elements and interferes with the flow of coolant through them.

Radiation induces chemical reactions that are not normal in nonnuclear plants, such as dissociation of the water into hydrogen and oxygen. This increases the corrosiveness of the water and requires the addition of inhibiting chemicals. Despite these additives some corrosion products are formed, so it is necessary that the reactor water be scavenged continuously by demineralizers.

Stainless steel, which is the metal most widely used in nuclear plants, is subject to stress corrosion in the presence of appreciable amounts of chlorides in the water, and demineralizers are used for removing them.

Certain chemical poisons, such as boric acid, supplement the control rods, to absorb neutrons, when the nuclear reactions must be dampened or stopped. On restarts these poisons are removed by ion exchange.

Makeup water of demineralized quality is needed for flushing and filling the entire reactor system and for replacing losses by leakage and blowdown.

Radioactive impurities in the waste waters from nuclear plants require special precautions for their safe and economical disposal. Ion exchangers play a significant role in solving these disposal problems.

Spent fuel elements are unloaded into pits or canals, where they are quenched with cooling water and stored for a period, before they are returned for reprocessing. The canals provide a neutron shield that facilitates refueling. The cooling water in the canals is demineralized continuously so as to be free from radioactivity.

Typical water-treatment plants in nuclear stations are described below to illustrate how these nuclear requirements are fulfilled. The two main types of nuclear power plant in the United States are the pressurized-water reactor and the boiling-water reactor (commonly abbreviated to PWR and BWR, respectively).

II. Pressurized-Water Reactor Systems

In the pressurized system the radioactivity is confined to the reactor and primary loops. The turbine, condenser, and secondary loop are not exposed to radioactivity and so are of conventional unshielded design; see Fig. 11.1.

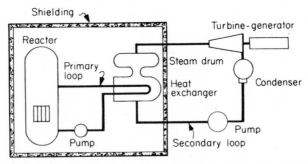

Fig. 11.1. Simplified flow diagram of pressurized-water system. [From Homer (1). Reproduced with permission of *Power Engineering*.]

The heat-exchanger boilers act as a wall between the radioactive primary loops and the nonradioactive secondary equipment. The primary loops are pressurized at a pressure high enough that the coolant is not heated to the boiling point and no steam is formed. The exclusion of radioactivity from the secondary loop made this pressurized design acceptable for use in the *Nautilus* and later nuclear submarines and in the nuclear merchant ship *Savannah*. The first utility nuclear-power station (Shippingport) also adopted this design (2); the Westinghouse Electric Company pioneered in the development of the pressurized-reactor system (3).

A. The Shippingport Atomic-Power Station

Figure 11.2 shows a schematic drawing of the plant at the Shippingport atomic-power station. The station consists of a 100,000 kw turbogenerator and four heat-exchanger boilers, each generating 329,000 lb of steam per

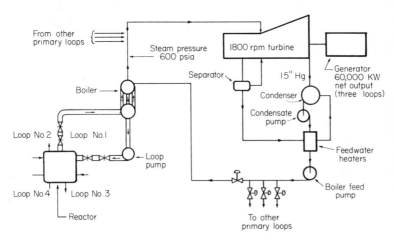

Fig. 11.2. Schematic diagram of pressurized-water reactor at Shippingport station. [Reproduced from Whirl and Tash (4) with permission of ASTM (STP 235 Radioactivity Ind. Water and Ind. Waste Water).]

hour at 600 psi and 486°F. A single pressurized reactor supplies the heat. High-purity (light) water serves as a neutron moderator and core coolant. The coolant flow is 58,000 gal/min at a pressure of 1945 psi; it enters the bottom of the reactor at 510°F and leaves the top at 540°F. The warm water flows through the tubing in the heat-exchanger boilers and is recycled by pump back to the reactor. Each of the four boilers has a separate primary loop. The steam from the heat-exchanger boilers passes to the turbine and condenser. The condensate then flows through water heaters and is recycled by pumps through the secondary loop back to the heat-exchanger boilers.

The use of four separate primary loops provides flexibility, because any of the loops may be shut down and repaired without the others' being shut down.

1. MAKEUP TREATMENT

The Shippingport makeup water (60 gal/min) comes from the Ohio River and is coagulated, filtered, softened, demineralized, and deaerated. The treated makeup is stored in two steam-sealed 50,000 gal storage tanks for the primary and secondary systems. The primary storage is of type 304 stainless steel, and the secondary tank is of steel.

2. INHIBITION OF PRIMARY-REACTOR COOLANT CORROSION

The dissociation of water into oxygen and hydrogen is inhibited by the addition of hydrogen gas, which scavenges the oxygen in the system. The amount of hydrogen maintained in the coolant is 25 to 35 cm^3 per kilogram of water. The hydrogen also reacts with any free nitrogen present, which comes from the original air in the system, to form ammonia. The ammonia increases the pH value and prevents the formation of nitric acid from the original nitrogen present. The pH of the reactor coolant is increased to 9.5 to 10.5 by the addition of lithium hydroxide.

3. PRIMARY-LOOP TREATMENT

The addition of hydrogen and lithium hydroxide is supplemented by an internal cleaning up, the system for which consists of mixed-bed demineralizers with lithium cation resin and hydroxide anion resin. About 80 gal/min are continuously withdrawn from the discharge of the recirculation pumps, cooled, demineralized, and returned to the suction side of the pumps. Two demineralizer systems are used for the four boilers.

The lithium cation resin exchanges lithium for other cations, and the hydroxide anion resin exchanges hydroxides for other anions. The soluble impurities thus are replaced by lithium hydroxide. The demineralizer resin also acts as a filter, removing suspended impurities. The demineralizer is not regenerated, and the resin, when exhausted, is sluiced out to underground waste-disposal storage tanks. New nuclear resin is then sluiced into the demineralizers. All the sluicing operations are done by remote manual control, to avoid the hazards of handling radioactive hot resin.

The purity of the primary loop is maintained at 1 to 2 ppm total dissolved solids with a specific resistivity of 2,000,000 to 4,000,000 ohms-cm. The resin is considered exhausted when the effluent specific resistance drops below 1,000,000 ohms-cm and is then replaced.

4. SECONDARY-LOOP TREATMENT

Treated makeup from the steel storage tank was used in the secondary loop and boiler. The boiler water was further treated with phosphate, to prevent the formation of scale, and with sodium sulfite, to scavenge the oxygen and prevent corrosion. After some period of operation, however, cracks in the heat exchanger boilers were discovered which were attributed to stress corrosion in the presence of excessive amounts of chlorides. More rigid control measures were then adopted and the following limits in parts per million were set (5) for the concentrated boiler water:

Sulfite (SO_3),	25 to 100	Silica (SiO_2),	25
Phosphate (PO_4),	100 to 300	Hydroxide (OH),	0
Chloride (Cl),	0.3	pH value,	10 to 11.0

The pH value was thus kept a few tenths below the Whirl-Purcell coordinated phosphate pH-control curve, so that caustic soda would not form. Three measures were taken to control the chlorides: the boiler blowoff was more carefully regulated so as to avoid excessive chloride concentration in the boiler, the condenser leakage was monitored to prevent chloride in-leakage, and about 5% of the secondary-loop water was withdrawn and demineralized continuously to scavenge the chlorides. As a result of these measures the chlorides were kept below 0.3 ppm in the boiler water at all times.

5. RADIOACTIVE-WASTE DISPOSAL

Wastes are disposed of by storage, concentration, natural decay, and dilution. Figure 11.3 shows a diagram of the Shippingport disposal system. The radioactive liquid wastes are discharged to underground stainless-steel storage tanks, where the radioactivity decays; after storage they are purified

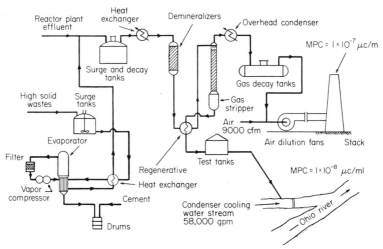

Fig. 11.3. Liquid and gaseous waste-disposal process at Shippingport station. [From Whirl and Tash (4) with permission of ASTM.]

by mixed-bed demineralizers. Dissolved fission gases are removed by a steam stripper, and the stripped gas is compressed and stored for decay; then the gas is diluted with air and released to the atmosphere. Highly concentrated liquid wastes are passed into an evaporator, and the distillate formed is stored in surge tanks; the concentrate may be mixed with cement in drums and then discharged into the ocean or buried.

Exhausted radioactive resin from the primary-loop and waste-disposal demineralizers is sluiced in a slurry to underground storage of watertight concrete. The settled water from the slurry is decanted to reactor-plant effluent tanks for further processing. The use of resin for capturing and concentrating radioactivity in a compact volume is efficient. Regeneration is not warranted, because the regenerant waste water would occupy twenty to thirty times the volume of the resin itself and thus intensify the disposal problem. The capacity of the resins is great enough for their replacement to be infrequent and inexpensive.

6. NUCLEAR-QUALITY RESINS

Since the resins are used directly in the form produced by the resin manufacturer, without subsequent washing and regenerating at the site, a special nuclear grade of resin was developed (6) that would not introduce undesirable impurities into the primary loops. This resin must meet three requirements: small amount of leachables, uniform bead size, and high degree of conversion to the desired ionic form.

The organic leachables are trapped in the interstices of the beads during synthesis and are washed out by solvents in the resin factory. The bead size is controlled so that the amount of fines, passing 50 mesh, are kept under 0.3%. This avoids high-pressure drop and resin leakage. For adequate exchange capacity however, the size of the cation beads is kept below 0.45 mm; that of the anion, below 0.6 mm. A high degree of conversion to the desired ionic form is accomplished by using sufficient doses of acid and alkali regenerants in the resin factory. More than 80% of the anion resin as shipped is in the hydroxide form, less than 15% in the carbonate form, and less than 5% in the chloride form.

The cation and anion resins are mixed in the factory before shipment. The ratio of anion resin to cation resin is 1.5 to 1.0, so that the total capacities of the two exchangers are about equal. The rates of flow through these non-regenerated nuclear-resin mixed-bed demineralizers range from 5 to 20 gal/min/ft^2.

Mixed beds have a much higher decontamination factor than separate cation and anion beds. The factor is defined as the ratio of the influent radioactivity to the effluent radioactivity. A two-bed demineralizer was reported (7) to have a factor of 1400, contrasted with 17,000 of a mixed bed; a cation resin bed alone had a factor of only 10 to 15. Mixed beds therefore are used universally for decontamination. However, cation units may precede the mixed beds, as was the case, for example, at the Indian Point nuclear station; in such position they act as filters and reduce the exchange load on the mixed beds. Since cation resin is much less expensive than anion resin, the operating cost for replacement is thereby reduced (8).

B. The Indian Point Nuclear Power Station (Unit No. 1)

Figure 11.4 gives a simplified flow diagram of the primary coolant and other purification systems installed in the Indian Point nuclear power station (electrical capacity, 275,000 kw). The primary coolant flow is

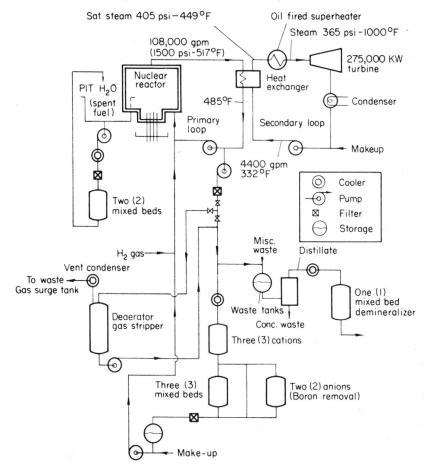

Fig. 11.4. Simplified flow diagram of Indian Point nuclear station: primary coolant and other purification systems. [From Applebaum (9).]

108,000 gal/min, operating at 1500 psi pressure and 517°F outlet tempera-ture. Heat from the primary loop is transferred to the secondary loop in a heat-exchanger boiler, which generates 2,200,000 lb of saturated steam per hour at 405 psi and 449°F. A secondary oil-fired superheater raises the steam temperature to 1000°F, ahead of the turbine. This nuclear station went critical and started up in 1962.

The water-treatment processes and equipment for makeup, primary-loop cleanup, spent-fuel pit cooling water, and liquid-waste-disposal treatment selected for this station, as described by Muller (*10*),* are summarized below.

1. MAKEUP WATER PURIFICATION

The raw water is taken from the New York City Supply and is purified for makeup purposes by evaporators. They produce a distillate of the following quality: conductivity less than 1 μmho, TDS 0.25 ppm, and silica 0.03 ppm. This distillate then is polished by four mixed-bed demineralizers, which reduce the TDS to 0.05 ppm and the silica to 0.01 ppm.

As pretreatment for protection of the evaporators four hydrogen cation exchangers are provided; they soften and dealkalize the feedwater. The softened water is passed through a decarbonator, which removes the free carbon dioxide, and then caustic soda is added to the decarbonated water, raising its pH value to 8.5. Then, before the final demineralized distilled water is discharged to storage, its pH value is increased to 8.8 or 9.0 by the addition of cyclohexylamine, and its dissolved-oxygen content is lowered by the addition of a scavenger, Hydrazine.

2. PRIMARY-LOOP CLEANUP SYSTEM

Despite the high purity of the treated makeup water filling primary-loop system the demineralizer (in Fig. 11.4) was provided for the removal of radio-active impurities picked up by corrosion and, thus, cleaning up the primary system. The capacity of this bypass cleanup demineralizer is 300 gal/min, or 0.3% of the primary recirculation rate of 108,000 gal/min.

The bypassed water is cooled and passed first through three cation ex-change units each 4 ft 6 in. in diameter and containing 63 ft³ of cation resin. The cation units act as filters, reducing the exchange load on the three mixed-bed units that follow them. The normal path of flow from the cation units is through these three mixed-bed demineralizers, each of which is 4 ft 6 in. in diameter and contains 63 ft³ of mixed resin. There are, besides, two anion units, each of which is 4 ft 0 in. in diameter and contains 60 ft³ of nuclear

---

* Muller's paper (*10*) described the planned method of operation. After the plant was operated for some time, however, changes were made, particularly in the use of the boric acid and its removal (described below). Also, the method of disposal of exhausted resin in concrete drums (also described below) was not always used. (See also Section C for Unit No. 2.)

Type I Amberlite IRA-400 anion resin; these operate at startup instead of the mixed beds, to remove boric acid previously added. Boric acid serves as a chemical poison that absorbs neutrons and thus supplements the control rods that dampen or stop the nuclear reactions. It was reported that for this purpose boric acid, made up as a 19 % solution at 200°F, would be added, to maintain a boric acid concentration of about 200 to 300 ppm (*10*). On re-starting after a shutdown the boric acid must be removed in order that the reactor may come to its full power level. The cation units then reduce the soluble cations to 1 ppm, and the anion units reduce the borate anion in the cation effluent to 1 ppm. After the startup the anion units are bypassed, and the normal operation through the cation units and the mixed-bed units is resumed. The purity of the primary coolant is kept to less than 1 ppm TDS, so that the primary loop and reactor remain clean and deposits on the fuel elements are at a minimum. Hydrogen, added to the primary-loop water, maintains a concentration of 40 cm^3 of hydrogen per liter of water; this inhibits the dissociation of water and scavenges the oxygen.

All the ion exchange units are located in a shielded pit, and no access to the pit for their operation is permitted. The exchanger shells are of stainless steel, and the stainless piping comes out of the top head of the units, as shown in Fig. 11.5. One of the design problems was how to load the new resin from a

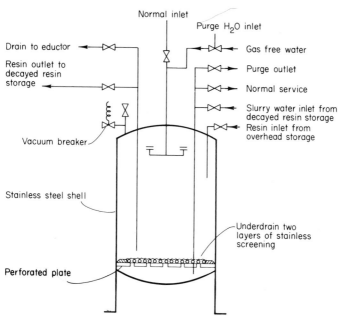

Fig. 11.5. Diagram of typical demineralizer unit at Indian Point nuclear station.

hopper into the units without separating the cation resin from the anion resin; the use of compressed air after loading for the remixing of the resins was not desired. A research pilot plant was put into operation to simulate the loading conditions. After loading the resin layers in the pilot unit were tested for segregation of the resins. The solution of this problem of avoiding separation and stratification of the two resins consisted of reducing the amount of excess water in the resin slurry to a minimum for transporting the resin. Without excess water, in which the heavier cation resin can settle during the filling of a unit, segregation does not occur. However, during the filling, complete draining should be avoided, so that air does not accumulate in the resin bed.

3. SPENT-FUEL COOLING-WATER DEMINERALIZERS

As Fig. 11.4 shows, two mixed-bed demineralizers, each of 50 gal/min capacity, are provided for purifying the pit water. Each is 3 ft 6 in. in diameter and contains 38 ft^3 of mixed resins. These units reduce the amount of radio-active corrosion and fission products in the cooling pit water to less than 1 ppm. When the reactor fuel elements are spent, they are unloaded into the pit and quenched with the cooling water. This water contains boric acid (about 1.2%), which inhibits the spread of radioactivity from the spent elements. The demineralizer must avoid removal of this boric acid, but it must remove all the other anions. This is accomplished by borating the anion resin and operating it in the borate form.

4. EQUIPMENT FOR LOADING AND UNLOADING OF RESIN

A hopper 5 ft 0 in. in diameter is mounted over the shielded pit containing the ten ion exchange units; it delivers by gravity the mixed resin in slurry form to any unit. In the pilot-plant research work described above a certain minimum slope in the conical bottom of the hopper was found necessary, to give a gravity flow without resin segregation. The hopper, being movable, on a track, may be placed over any one of the ten ion exchange tanks and will thus keep the loading lines as short as possible. The valves are located above the pit for controlling the unit that is being loaded.

Four tanks 6 ft 0 in. in diameter store the exhausted or spent resin and allow the radioactivity in the resin to decay before disposal. The spent resin is sluiced out of the ion exchange vessels by water recirculating into the bottom below the underdrain plate of the exchange unit. This fluidizes the resin bed and forces it out of the vessel into the storage tanks. The resin settles into the conical bottom of the tanks, and the water recirculates back to the exchange vessel; this avoids increasing the amount of waste water to the waste-disposal system. A water-cooling pipe coil is included in the storage tanks for removing heat generated during the decay of radioactivity in the resin. A storage time of approximately a year was assumed for the decay to be completed, so that the resins later could be dealt with safely during their final disposal. The plan for disposal was the mixing of the resin with cement and loading of the resulting concrete into drums for ultimate burial. For satisfactory concrete the decayed resin had to be dewatered before entering the concrete mixer. A specially designed dewatering tank squeezed the excess water from the resin slurry through screens to waste.

5. EQUIPMENT FOR WASTE-DISPOSAL TREATMENT

As Fig. 11.4 indicates, the liquid wastes pass into an evaporator, and the distillate formed is purified by a mixed-bed demineralizer. This system was designed to remove the large amounts of solids that might enter the primary loop during emergencies, such as a fuel-element rupture. The contaminated loop water is first passed to filters, then to coolers, then to waste tanks, and finally to the evaporator, which concentrates the waste products. The mixed bed then polishes the evaporator distillate for complete removal of the solids.

The primary-loop water may be passed first through a gas-stripper deaerator. In the event of fuel-element failure the decomposition of the uranium will generate highly radioactive gases, such as xenon and krypton. The stripper is designed to reduce these gases to less than 0.2 cm^3 per million gallons. The hydrogen is incidentally reduced to less than 0.005 cm^3 per liter at the same time. Since removal of the hydrogen is normally not desired, this stripper was to be used only in the event of fuel-element failure; at other times it was to be bypassed.

The deaerator stripper is a four-stage system made of special stainless steel. Steam is supplied to an evaporator coil in the storage section. Gas is vented through a direct-contact condenser to special facilities for handling radioactive gases.

C. Indian Point Unit No. 2

Westinghouse Electric Corporation is supplying the pressurized water reactor system for Unit No. 2 on a turnkey basis. Its net electrical output will be 873,000 kw and the steam entering the turbine will be 11,650,000 lb/hr at 690 psia and 500°F.

In a recent paper, Haga (10a) described the so-called "chemical and volume control system" and its operation as follows: "This system is used to control the concentration of boric acid (chemical shim) in the reactor coolant system and to add certain chemicals to the reactor coolant for corrosion control. The system also supplies the high pressure injection water for the reactor coolant pump shaft seals and purifies the reactor coolant. The system automatically regulates the water level in the pressurizer as a function of load and automatically dissolves hydrogen in the reactor coolant to suppress the generation of free oxygen by the dissociation of water as the coolant passes through the core."

Boric acid (the chemical shim), dissolved in the reactor coolant, supplements the control rods for reactivity control. The core is operable with the control rods almost entirely withdrawn. Boric acid is removed from the reactor coolant by dilution with demineralized water. In earlier pressurized water systems, the water removed from the coolant system was processed to concentrate the boric acid which was ultimately mixed with concrete for disposal. In the Indian Point Unit No. 2, the boric acid is reconcentrated and stored for further reuse in the coolant and recycled.

During power operation, the reactor coolant is purified (after pressure and temperature reduction) by a mixed bed demineralizer and filter. Makeup to the reactor coolant system consists of the proper blend of demineralized water and 12% boric acid solution, based on daily reactor coolant sample analyses. The addition of the boric acid, which compensates for fission product (Xenon) decay after shutdown or for plant cooldown, also results in diversion of letdown flow to the holdup tanks, from which it is processed for further use or disposal.

In earlier plants, the coolant in the holdup tanks was passed through a gas stripper and then to an evaporator where the boric acid was concentrated for disposal. During the last 10 to 15% of core life, boric acid concentration was reduced by deborating ion exchangers operating in series with the mixed bed demineralizer that polished the evaporator "overheads." The deborated water was returned to the coolant system.

In the Indian Point Unit No. 2, the system has been modified to reuse the boric acid after concentration in the evaporator. Ion exchangers have also been added ahead of the gas stripper to remove lithium (previously added for corrosion control) and cesium (originating from fission products leaking from the fuel rods).

It is estimated that the new recycle system will reduce waste production to 375 drums of solid wastes per core cycle, of which 300 drums will be for disposal of deborating exchanger regenerant chemicals and the remainder for resin disposal and other solid wastes. Without the new recycle system, the total number of drums would have been 975 drums per core cycle, and of this, the additional 600 drums would have been required for the disposal of boric acid.

In conclusion, Haga says, "Improvement in the Indian Point Unit No. 2 nuclear steam supply system is the result of: (1) improvements in core design, (2) improvements in capital cost due to lower unit costs on larger components, and (3) improvements in operating cost."

III. Boiling-Water Reactor System

In boiling-water reactor plants the steam for the turbine is generated directly in the nuclear reactor, and the heat-exchanger boilers of the pressurized-water reactor systems are omitted. When the General Electric Company received in 1955 the contract to build the first boiling-water reactor at the Dresden Station only the operating experiences from the pressurized-water nuclear plants were available. A joint research program was therefore initiated for study of the possible unique problems that might arise. Pilot plants were established at Vallecitos, California, and at Joliet, Illinois, for this purpose.

A. Objectives of the Pilot Plant Studies

The technical questions investigated were as follows.

The steam entering the turbine would contain the hydrogen and oxygen gases formed by radiolytic water decomposition. These gases could accelerate corrosion. The corrosion products then formed would become irradiated when transported through the circulating system and reactor, and they could foul the refined control mechanisms. The products could also deposit in the turbine itself and affect accessibility for safe maintenance of the turbine.

Since the primary steam would be generated directly in the reactor, the solids in the feedwater would concentrate as in any drum boiler. The accumulated solids could deposit on the heat-transfer surfaces of the reactor core and cause hot spots. Shorter life and failure of the fuel elements might result, increasing maintenance problems and operating cost.

A cleanup nonregenerated demineralizer, handling only a small bypassed percentage of the primary circulating stream, as in the pressurized-water reactor plants, might not suffice for the boiling-water reactor system. A much larger cleanup demineralizer might be required because of the greater load of corrosion products to be scavenged. Without regeneration the resin replacement costs then might be excessive. Moreover, the amount of spent, radioactive resin to be discharged to the waste-disposal system would increase excessively. Therefore the removal of the corrosion products from the total condensate before it enters the reactor appeared to be necessary in order to supplement the cleanup demineralizer. The latter could then be kept reasonably small in size. It was decided that a mixed-bed demineralizer should be included in the pilot plant at Joliet to handle 100% of the condensate flow, and designed for external regeneration. To reduce capital costs, it was also decided that the operation of this demineralizer at high rates ($50 \, gal/min/ft^2$) and without prefilters should be investigated.

B. Test Results at the Vallecitos Pilot Plant

The results of the Vallecitos tests (*11*) are summarized in Table 11.1.

Table 11.1 compares the water quality desired for the Dresden plant with the actual Vallecitos results. The latter were satisfactory except with respect to copper and total solids. The copper content was traced to certain copper fittings and the total solids to accidental contamination. Because the latter

Table 11.1

COMPARISON OF WATER QUALITY DESIRED FOR DRESDEN AND
TEST RESULTS FOR VALLECITOS PILOT-PLANT

	Dresden	Vallecitos
Reactor water:		
Additives	none	none
pH	7.2 ± 0.2	7.0 ± 0.2
Resistivity, Mohm-cm	1	>1
Total solids, ppm	0.6	1 to 12
Feedwater:		
Resistivity, Mohm-cm	10	10 ± 1
Copper, ppm	0.002	0.01 ± 0.01
Iron, ppm	0.002	0.002 ± 0.001
Chloride, ppm	0.01	0.005 ± 0.005

were mostly non-ionic and suspended it was recommended that suspended solids be monitored in addition to the conductivity, which indicates the dissolved solids only. It was apparent that the main condensate demineralizer would have to act as a combined filter and ion exchanger.

The effect on corrosion of using the coolant in a neutral pH range was studied. The results were encouraging. They appeared to indicate that the oxygen and hydrogen in the feedwater of the boiling-water reactor would cause very little corrosion. An excess of hydrogen, as maintained in the pressurized-water reactor systems, for eliminating the oxygen due to radiolytic dissociation could not be used in this design because the steam passes directly to the turbine. The study indicated that the amount of oxygen present (without hydrogen inhibition) was reduced by the higher operating pressure maintained. It was felt therefore that the metals to be used in the Dresden plant would resist corrosion satisfactorily.

The amount of fission and nonvolatile corrosion products carried over in the steam from the reactor to the turbine was found to be minimal.

C. Test Results at the Joliet Pilot Plant

The results of the Joliet tests (*12*) are summarized as follows.

The demineralizer had a resin bed 36 in. deep, consisting of 24 in. of cation resin and 12 in. of anion resin. It operated for nine to ten days between regenerations at a rate of up to 69 gal/min/ft^2, and the pressure losses ranged from 30 to 48 psi, without any prefilters.

The chemical results showed a reduction of influent iron plus copper of 15 to 50 ppb to less than 5 ppb and a reduction of conductivity of 3 to 4 μmhos to less than 0.1 μmho. Some resin-bead breakage occurred, so that particles larger than 30 mesh in size were reduced to mesh size of 40 to 50. The breakage, however, was not excessive in amount.

These satisfactory results caused the adoption of regenerated high-rate demineralizers (50 gal/min/ft^2) operating without prefilters and handling 100% of the condensate stream at the large Dresden Station.

IV. Two Boiling-Water Reactor Installations

Two stations are described that illustrate the water-purification systems for boiling-water reactors: the Dresden station and the Oyster Creek station.

A. The Dresden Station

1. UNIT NO. 1

Unit No. 1 has a capacity of 180,000 kw and consists of a "dual cycle" (see Fig. 11.6 for the flow diagram). The primary cycle included the reactor,

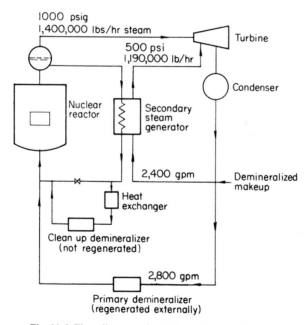

Fig. 11.6. Flow diagram of Dresden station, Unit No. 1.

which generated 1,400,000 lb of saturated steam per hour at 1000 psi. The steam–water mixture from the reactor core flows to a separator drum, and the steam from this drum passes directly to the turbine. The water separated in the drum provides the heat for the secondary cycle.

The secondary cycle involves a heat-exchanger boiler generating 1,190,000 lb of steam per hour at 500 psi. The steam is introduced into an intermediate-pressure stage of the turbine so that its capacity will be increased. The secondary steam is mixed in the turbine with the primary steam, after the latter has passed through the high-pressure turbine stages.

The condensate from the turbine condenser is returned partly (2400 gal/min) to the secondary heat-exchanger boiler and partly (2800 gal/min) back to the reactor. Extraction heaters (not shown in the figure) are included in the feed cycle, as in conventional power plants.

The full-scale Dresden condensate demineralizer plant includes three units, each 6 ft 6 in. in diameter. The resin beds are 36 in. deep (24 in. of cation, and 12 in. of anion, resin). Two of the units handle the full condensate flow of 3200 gal/min at a rate of 50 gal/min/ft^2; the third is a spare, or standby, unit. An external regeneration system consists of a separation and cation-regeneration vessel, an anion regeneration vessel, and a resin-storage vessel. A fourth or spare charge of resin is contained in the storage vessel. These external vessels have open tops, and ejectors are used for resin transfer (other stations later adopted closed pressure vessels operating without ejectors).

The station went critical in October, 1959, produced power in April, and reached full power in June, 1960. The operating results (*13*) are summarized as follows.

Table 11.2

AVERAGE TOTAL IRON AND AVERAGE TOTAL COPPER
BEFORE AND AFTER DEMINERALIZERS AT DRESDEN

	Iron, ppb		Copper, ppb	
	In	Out	In	Out
April 15 to 21	1086	498	313	137
April 22 to May 1	163	49	59	15
June 20 to 30	184	17	61	7
July 1 to 4	32	8	31	3

During the initial startup and 50% power run in April the first influent contained 6 ppm iron and more than 100 ppm turbidity. The suspended matter was removed in one hour's recirculation through the demineralizers. The later iron and copper removal are shown in the first two lines of Table 11.2. The reactor water had the following analysis:

Conductivity, μmho:	0.76 to 7.9	averaging 2.5
pH value	5.1 to 6.5	averaging 5.7
Chloride, ppb	10 to 169	averaging 70

During the first full-power run, from June 20 to July 4, the iron and copper removal were as given in the last two lines of Table 11.2.

After the full-power run the station operated normally for various periods from July 16 to November 14. During the runs the total iron was reduced from an average of 44 ppb (influent) to 15 ppb (effluent). The average total copper was reduced from 22 ppb to 7 ppb. The conductivity averaged 0.5 μmho in the influent and 0.2 μmho in the effluent.

Individual demineralizer runs were terminated when the pressure loss across the system reached 40 psi. During 1960 each of the four resin charges made eight round-trips to the external vessels for cleaning.

Frazer (13) gives the following conclusion: "Removal of suspended and dissolved solids from condensate by high flow rate, externally regenerated demineralizers operating directly in the cycle has proved to be a satisfactory method of providing high quality reactor feedwater."

In November, 1962, the station was shut down for refuelling, and resin samples were collected and analyzed; the results were reported in a 1963 paper (14). There were four charges of resin in the system, each containing 80 ft^3 of cation resin and 40 ft^3 of anion resin, or a total of 480 ft^3. The volume of resin was measured and found to be reduced by 11 to 14% owing to losses through attrition. About 1,900,000,000 gal of water had been treated in the three years of operation, including many startups with high crud levels. This amounts to about 15,000,000 gal of water treated per cubic foot of resin.

The resin samples were cleaned and analyzed. The cation resin had normal moisture content and total capacity. Few of the cation resin beads were fractured, and they were of normal size. The anion resin had a normal moisture content but its salt-splitting capacity, or basicity, was 17% below normal. Many anion resin beads were fractured, and screen tests showed a shift to the finer fractions. Frazer and Young (14) suggest adding new cation resin at the rate of 5% per year and anion resin at 5 to 20% per year; this would involve reasonably low resin-replacement costs.

2. UNIT NO. 2

A second nuclear unit is being installed at Dresden for 715,000 kw. The design is simpler than that of Unit No. 1, using a single cycle and omitting both the secondary heat exchangers and the separator drum. Unit No. 2 has, instead, an internal separator and dryer in the reactor; see Fig. 11.7 for the flow diagram. The result of these improvements is that the space requirements are only 20% greater for more than three times the kilowatt capacity. The cost of generating power is expected to be far less than for Unit No. 1 and even 5 to 10% less than for fossil-fuel power stations in the same general area.

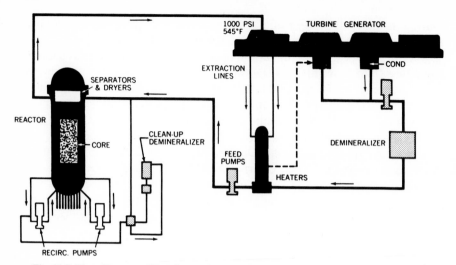

Fig. 11.7. Flow diagram of Dresden station, Unit No. 2. The boiling-water reactor is depicted as a simplified single-cycle system. The nuclear-fueled core boils water, generating a supersaturated steam, which goes through water separators and dryers, then directly to the turbine. Condensers provide deaeration, followed by a full-flow demineralizer, which removes corrosion products and protects the reactor against condenser tube leaks and other sources of impurities. External recirculation loops to the reactor control transfer of heat. [From Elliott (*15*).]

B. The Oyster Creek Station

The improvements made at the Dresden Unit No. 2 were incorporated at Oyster Creek (*16*). Figure 11.8 shows the full heat cycle. The turbogenerator capacity is 640,000 kw. The reactor system, single cycle, is designed to generate 7,000,000 lb of steam per hour. The estimated power cost is under 4 mills/kw-hr and the heat rate is 10,600 Btu/kw-hr, both of which are lower than for fossil-fuel plants in the eastern United States (*17*).

1. REGENERATED MAIN-CONDENSATE DEMINERALIZER

The capacity of the main-condensate demineralizer at Oyster Creek is 15,300 gal/min; it is designed for a 310 psi operating pressure and consists of seven units, each 8 ft 0 in. in diameter. Six units are planned to handle the full load at 51 gal/min/ft^2; a seventh unit is a spare. Each unit has its own effluent resin trap.

The resin beds are 36 in. deep (two thirds cation), and there are eight charges, one of which is a spare in the resin-storage vessel. The usual external regeneration vessels are included: the separation and cation regeneration vessel, 6 ft 0 in. in diameter, the anion regeneration vessel, 3 ft 6 in. in diameter, and the resin-storage vessel, 6 ft 0 in. in diameter. The specified performance of the condensate demineralizer is given in Table 11.3.

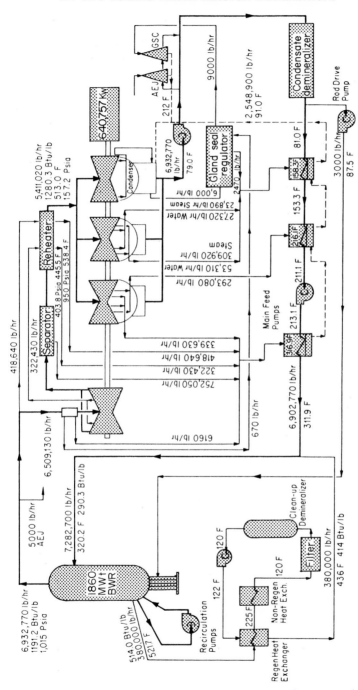

Fig. 11.8. Flow diagram of Oyster Creek station.

Table 11.3
EXPECTED PERFORMANCE OF
OYSTER CREEK MAIN-CONDENSATE DEMINERALIZER PLANT

	Impurities, ppb	
	Normal	Startup
Contaminant in influent:		
Dissolved solids (soluble)		
Iron	5	40
Copper	5	50
Nickel	5	30
Chloride	5	100
Silica	10	500
Suspended solids (insoluble)		
Iron	20	1000
Copper	10	500
Nickel	5	100
Total solids	60	60 to 3000
Effluent quality:		
Iron	2 to 10	20 to 500
Copper	2 to 8	25 to 250
Nickel	2 to 5	15 to 50
Chloride	2 to 10	10 to 50
Silica	2 to 10	10 to 250
Dissolved solids	25	35 to 350
Suspended solids	10	80 to 800

Pressure drop: At a unit flow rate of 51 gal/min/ft^2 the pressure drop when the resin is clean will not exceed 35 psi from inlet header to outlet header. The pressure drop when the resin is dirty, particularly at startup, will depend upon the amount of crud present and the flow rate, but the maximum pressure loss is to be under 85 psi at any time.

2. NONREGENERATED DEMINERALIZERS

As Fig. 11.8 indicates, in addition to the regenerated main-condensate demineralizer, described above, there is included a nonregenerated cleanup demineralizer for a capacity of 380,000 lb/hr. This operates on a bypassed stream (5 % of the main condensate). It consists of a stainless-steel unit 78 in. in diameter and containing 100 ft^3 of mixed resin (two thirds cation).

In the system are two other nonregenerated rubber-lined demineralizers: a radwaste unit 78 in. in diameter, for 332 gal/min capacity, and a fuel-pool demineralizer 90 in. in diameter, for 442 gal/min capacity.

3. MAKEUP PRETREATMENT PLANT AND DEMINERALIZER

The makeup pretreatment plant is designed for 100 gal/min capacity, and treats either a well or a creek supply high in organic content. It includes the following:

(a) A solids-contact Reactor coagulator, 13 ft 0 in. in diameter and 12 ft 6 in. in height, holding 120,000 gal.

(b) Chemical feeds for alum, soda ash, coagulant aid, and sodium hypochlorite.

(c) Two Syphomatic gravity, valveless, self-washing filters, 5 ft 0 in. in diameter, with a clearwell (6450 gal) located below the coagulator.

(d) Three pressure-activated carbon filters 3 ft 6 in. in diameter.

The demineralizer includes two pairs of cation–anion two-bed demineralizers, each 3 ft 6 in. in diameter. The two cation units each contain 25 ft^3 of resin, and the two anion units each contain 28 ft^3 of porous type I strong-base resin. These are followed by one mixed-bed polisher 3 ft 0 in. in diameter with 16 ft^3 of cation resin and 16 ft^3 of anion resin and with a capacity of 400,000 gal in four days.

The specified quality (in parts per million) of the demineralizer effluent is as follows: TDS, 0.2; silica, 0.01; chlorides, 0.05. The specific conductivity specified is 0.5 μmho-cm.

REFERENCES

1. W. A. Homer, Ultra-pure water – prime requisite for nuclear plants. *Power Eng.* (August 1958).
2. Shippingport Station – A pioneering project in atomic power. *Westinghouse Eng.* **18**, No. 2 (1958).
3. W. E. Shoup, Physics of nuclear power. *Westinghouse Engr.* Reprint 5240; also J. W. Simpson and M. Shaw, PWR power plant. *Westinghouse Engr.* Reprint 5240.
4. S. F. Whirl and J. A. Tash, Radioactive waste processing control – Shippingport Atomic Power Station. *ASTM Ann. Meeting, Boston, Massachusetts, June 1958.*
5. W. J. Singley, I. H. Welinsky, and S. F. Whirl, Stress corrosion of stainless steel and boiler water treatment – Shippingport Atomic Power Station. *Proc. Am. Power Conf.* **21** (1959).
6. C. T. Dickert, R. Hetherington, and C. F. Raines, Radioactive water poses new problems. *Power* Pt. I (Sept. 1958); Pt. II (April 1959).
7. H. G. Swope, Mixed bed ion exchange for the removal of radioactivity. *J. Am. Water Works Assoc.* (August 1957).
8. J. Thompson and A. C. Reents, Water treatment processes for nuclear power plants. *Am. Chem. Soc. Natl. Meeting, 135th, Boston, Massachusetts, April 1959.*
9. S. B. Applebaum, Modern water treatment developments for boiler and nuclear plants. *ASME Sectional Meeting, Youngstown, Ohio, March 1959.*
10. A. C. Muller, Proposed water treatment at the Indian Point Nuclear Power Plant of Cons Edison Co. of N.Y. *Am. Chem. Soc. Natl. Meeting, 135th, Boston, Massachusetts, April 1959.*
10a. P. B. Haga, Indian Point Unit No. 2 nuclear steam supply system. *Proc. Am. Power Conf.* (April 1967).

11. F. J. Brutschy, H. S. Dreyer, and W. L. Pearl, Coolant technology in the VBWR. *Am. Chem. Soc. Natl. Meeting, Boston, Massachusetts, April 1959.*

12. A. B. Sisson, R. C. Reid, and H. W. Frazer, High flow rate demineralization of condensate for boiling water reactors. *Proc. Am. Power Conf.* **20**, 709 (1958).

13. H. W. Frazer, Operating data on high flow rate condensate polishing without filters. *Proc. Intern. Water Conf. October 1961*, p. 87.

14. H. W. Frazer and J. M. Young, Operating experiences with high flow rate polishing of condensate. *Proc. Am. Power Conf.* **25**, 647 (1963).

15. V. A. Elliott, Boiling water reactor. *Mech. Eng.* (January 1967).

16. V. A. Elliott and W. R. Kanne, The Oyster Creek nuclear boiler design. *Proc. Am. Power Conf.* (April 1966).

17. D. H. Kregg, L. C. Koke, and D. R. Rees, Oyster Creek BWR sets 4 mill target. *Electrical World* (June 14, 1965).

12

Comparison of Evaporators and Demineralizers and New Demineralizer Processes for Desalination

Until about 1950 it was standard practice in utility power stations to install evaporators only for purifying their boiler-feed makeup water but then silica-removing demineralizers became available and began to challenge the evaporator.

I. Advantages of Evaporators

Although demineralizers are preferred today by many utilities, the evaporator still finds advocates, who continue to install them in some power plants. The advantages claimed for the evaporator are as follows: they are mechanical in nature rather than chemical, requiring less operating skill, and are less likely to get out of order, and they are more economical to operate with many waters, particularly those containing large amounts of dissolved solids. The recent drought has accentuated the latter advantage (1).

II. Operating Problems with Evaporators

Despite the reluctance of some engineers to adopt a chemical process, pioneer installations of demineralizers were made by a number of power stations in the midwestern United States (2). Many of the stations had had experience with submerged-coil evaporators and found them subject to the following operating problems.

The evaporator coils became encrusted with insulating scale owing to the hardness of the water. In some designs attempts were made to crack off this scale by thermal coil contraction, by introducing cold water into the coils but this was only partially successful with hard, brittle scales, softer scales not responding well to the treatment. Other methods therefore were necessary, including acid cleaning. Sodium zeolite softeners subsequently were installed for pretreating the evaporator feedwater.

The steam vapor formed by the evaporator contained carbon dioxide gas resulting from decomposition of the feedwater alkalinity. This caused corrosion of the distillate piping, so that iron was picked up, forming deposits in the high-pressure boilers. Sodium zeolite cation exchangers for softening the evaporator feedwater therefore did not suffice. The pretreatment plants had to remove the alkalinity besides the hardness, using split-stream hydrogen and sodium cation exchangers, the blended effluent of which was passed through a decarbonator for removal of the carbon dioxide. This increased the capital and operating costs of the pretreatment plants so much that it was more economical to adopt demineralization and omit the evaporators.

The evaporator distillate was often not pure enough to prevent scale in the high-pressure boilers. It was reported at Waukegan, Illinois, for instance, that the total solids in the distillate ranged from 2 to 6 ppm (3, 4). This formed sludge deposits in the boilers, and these entailed appreciable outages for chemical cleaning. When the Waukegan station needed to be expanded, a comparison was made between demineralizers and new evaporators pretreated by cold or hot lime–soda or by split-stream hydrogen and sodium cation exchangers. Demineralization was adopted, because it could "produce an adequate quantity of high quality water at an operating cost low enough to more than justify its investment and because plant maintenance and labor costs would be reduced." Actual operating experience confirmed these predictions (3, 4): the boilers were cleaner, the boiler blowoff was reduced, and the overall operating cost was lower.

The evaporators suffered from carryover, resulting in a poor quality of vapor. Evaporator shells are similar to boiler drums, and vapor purity is decreased by the same three factors that influence boiler-steam quality. These are as follows: excessive steam-disengaging velocity, caused by the small shell area, high water level, and too great a concentration of dissolved solids in the evaporator water. Some engineers recognized these causes of poor distillate quality and recommended larger evaporator shells, more conservatively designed to reduce carryover with changes of load (5). They also favored adequate pretreatment of the feedwater going to the evaporator, so that scale and corrosion would be avoided. These changes, however, were found to increase the equipment costs excessively.

The evaporator output varies with the turbine load. At low loads the required output may not be maintained. Demineralizers, operating on cold water and requiring no steam, are independent of turbine load and therefore provide greater flexibility when a power station must change its heat balance. For example, a central station, to increase efficiency, may decide to sell extraction steam to industrial plants in the area, but evaporators, which are tied to a definite heat balance for maximum thermal efficiency, interfere with making such changes. An example of this was reported by a utility station in the midwestern United States, which had to abandon its evaporators when extraction steam was sold to industrial plants near-by (6). The existing split-stream pretreatment plant was converted to a demineralizer, replacing the evaporators.

Evaporator-coil replacement and other maintenance repairs may be costly. A large automobile manufacturer found it advisable to abandon an old evaporator rather than make the repairs (7). Instead, a demineralizer was installed, to operate on the precooled effluent of an existing hot lime–zeolite plant. The demineralizer also permitted a change in the heat balance when it was decided to use turbine-extraction steam instead of operating existing low-pressure boilers.

The startup and restarts of a power plant require large amounts of pure water for cleaning the system and filling the boilers. Unless auxiliary steam is available, the evaporator cannot be operated to provide this water. Some stations have installed low-pressure boilers that produce the steam required by the evaporators during startups. Others have included a demineralizer that provides the pure water before the evaporator is put into operation; the demineralizer is used later on for purifying a fraction of the main-condensate stream of the station.

The evaporators operate with steam extracted from the turbine. The degradation of the pressure of this extracted steam causes a definite power loss. The cost of operating the evaporators must include the value of this loss of power.

III. Typical Economic Studies of Evaporators and Demineralizers

As demineralizers continued to be installed for purifying the boiler-feed makeup, more data on their operating costs and performance became available. This led to a number of economic studies comparing evaporators and demineralizers to determine the conditions that favored one or the other. Table 12.1 summarizes five of such economic studies (4, 8–11).

These studies include the following factors: the cost of fuel, costs of chemicals for the pretreatment before evaporator or demineralizer and of demineralizer regenerants, the cost of replacing the demineralizer resins, the cost of maintenance and operating labor, the equipment costs, including erection and the building for its housing, and the cost of the power lost through degradation of the extracted steam used for the evaporator.

Table 12.1
ECONOMIC STUDIES OF
EVAPORATION VERSUS DEMINERALIZATION[a]

Raw water	Tot. diss. solids, ppm	Alkal., %	Fuel cost, cents per 1,000,000 Btu	Cost, cents per 1000 gal	
				Evaporation	Demineralization
Ohio River	300	19	20	92	93
New England well	100	48	39	284	81
Delaware well	50	12	—	181	44
Iowa well	150	50	21	187	92
Lake Michigan	156	80	—	46	12

[a] From Applebaum and McKeown (2).

Table 12.2 gives guidelines, based on these economic studies, for choosing the demineralizer or the evaporator. The table shows that demineralizers are more economical when the fuel cost is higher and when the total dissolved solids of the feedwater are lower, especially when the alkalinity of the water is a large proportion of the total solids present, but it indicates also that the evaporators are more economical when the total solids in the raw water exceed 500 to 1000 ppm. Other economic studies have confirmed these guidelines (12, 13).

Table 12.2
GUIDELINES FOR SELECTION OF
DEMINERALIZER OR EVAPORATOR[a]

Fuel cost, cents per 1,000,000 Btu	Raw-water diss. solids, ppm	Raw-water ratio Alk. tot. diss. solids, %	Economical method
25 to 30 or more	Under 300 to 500	Over 30% to 40%	demineralizers
20 to 25 or lower	Over 300 to 500	Under 20% to 30%	evaporators

[a] From Applebaum and McKeown (2).

IV. The Flash Evaporator

The studies cited above were based on the submerged-coil type of evaporator. In 1959 the Westinghouse Electric Company recommended that their flash type of evaporator, previously used only for seawater distillation, be applied also for purifying fresh-water makeup (14). The poorer distillate quality of the older submerged-coil type was attributed to the absence of suitable separators in the steam space. A new type of wire-mesh separator, applied in the flash evaporator, permitted the production of purer distillate: 0.05 ppm total dissolved solids with fresh-water feed (15) and 0.25 ppm with seawater feed. These figures, however, were based on testing the distillate only for sodium by the flame photometer; other solids, including silica, should also be monitored.

The older submerged-coil evaporators were usually located between the second and third extraction points of the turbine (see Fig. 12.1); this caused

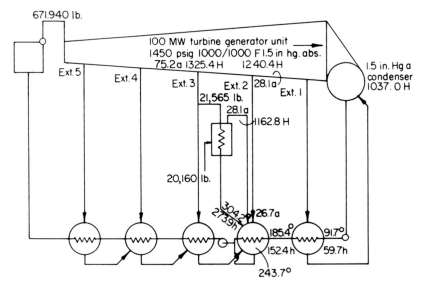

Fig. 12.1. Utility power cycle, showing usual location of submerged-coil evaporator. [From Stalcup *et al.* (*14*).]

greater power losses due to degradation of the extraction steam. The flash evaporator was located nearer the condenser and used lower-pressure steam from extraction point no. 1 (see Fig. 12.2); this reduced the power losses due to degradation. Stalcup *et al.* (*14*) and Coit (*15*) also claimed for the flash evaporator the following additional advantages: the lower operating temperature of the steam from extraction point no. 1 was likely to reduce the amount of scale formed, and good deaeration of the makeup is accomplished in the flash evaporator because the non-condensible gases are removed successively in each stage.

V. Comparison of Flash Evaporator and Demineralizer

An economic study was made comparing a flash evaporator and a demineralizer for a capacity of 20,000 lb/hr (*16*). The operating costs studied

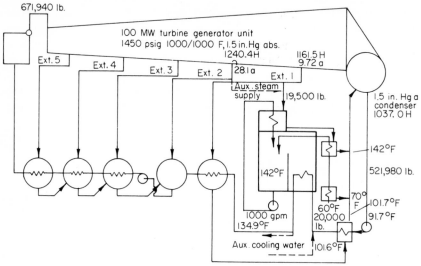

Fig. 12.2. Utility power cycle, showing location of flash evaporator. [From Stalcup *et al.* (*14*).]

included the fixed charges and the costs of labor, chemicals, and resin replacement. The conclusion reached was that the operating cost would be lower for the demineralizer if the total dissolved solids in the raw water were below 500 ppm; see Fig. 12.3. The equipment cost of the demineralizer was also found to be lower, even when the total dissolved solids in the raw water

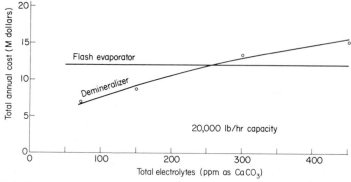

Fig. 12.3. Comparative operating costs of demineralizer and flash evaporator versus total dissolved solids in raw water. [From Gilwood and Mack (*16*).]

reached 1200 ppm; see Fig. 12.4. If the capacity had been appreciably greater than the 20,000 lb/hr used in this study, the comparison would have been still more favorable to the demineralizer, because the cost of the automatic controls included does not rise appreciably as the capacity is increased.

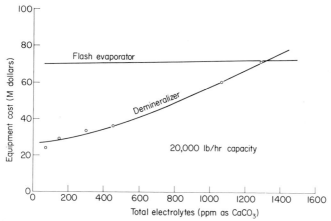

Fig. 12.4. Comparative equipment costs of demineralizer and flash evaporator versus total dissolved solids in raw water. [From Gilwood and Mack (*16*).]

VI. Experiences with Flash Evaporators

A. *The Possum Point and Brayton Point Stations*

A flash evaporator was installed at the Possum Point station (*17*), where the raw water from the Potomac River at times contained a salinity of 2000 ppm (as Cl); the total solids occasionally reached 4000 ppm. The station already had submerged-coil evaporators, which were to be used for re-evaporating the distillate from the flash evaporator, so as to ensure proper makeup-water quality at all times for the 2535 psi boilers in this station.

The flash evaporator was to be blown off enough to maintain a concentration of total dissolved solids in the evaporator water not exceeding 3000 ppm, when that in the raw water was under 1500 ppm. At higher values the total dissolved solids in the evaporator water was not to exceed double that in the raw water. No pretreatment equipment was installed. The only chemicals added to the evaporator feed were 50 to 100 ppm tannin organic dispersive and 0.5 to 1.0 ppm antifoam compound.

After one month of operation scale was found in the brine heater, necessitating an acid cleaning. The tannin was then replaced by ligninsulfonate. After two months a soft deposit again formed, which required another acid cleaning. After four acid cleanings phosphate was added with the ligninsulfonate. But nine more days of operation showed that scale again had formed. It was decided then to install an acid feed for pretreating the feedwater and so reducing its alkalinity and preventing the formation of calcium carbonate scale. The distillate was also found to contain too much iron and copper picked up by corrosion of the flash-evaporator metal surfaces. Therefore a powdered-resin filter following the evaporator was installed for cleaning up the distillate.

Another station, the Brayton station, located in New England, also installed a flash evaporator, but a zeolite softener was included as pretreatment of the evaporator feedwater for preventing scale. In addition, as a posttreatment a cartridge filter and two mixed-bed demineralizers were installed for polishing the distillate.

B. The Richmond Station

The operating pressure of the various boilers in this station ranged from 400 to 1250 psi. The operating results with a flash evaporator during the first year of operation were reported in a 1961 paper (18). The distillate contained excessive amounts of metals. Some internal changes were made, but the distillate still contained a total iron of 65 to 235 ppb and copper of 13 to 70 ppb. These figures would have been unacceptable if modern high-pressure boilers (over 2500 psi) had been in operation.

C. A Chemical Plant in Texas

In this case the boiler pressure was 1250 psi. The raw water was from the Brazos River, which at times contained a total dissolved solids of 1500 ppm, the average being 750 ppm. In an economic study a comparison was made between a demineralizer and a flash evaporator (19). The estimated equipment cost was based on the 1500 ppm; the operating cost, on the 750 ppm. The demineralizer equipment cost was found to be the lower, but the evaporator was selected because it "provided the highest return on incremental investment." Pretreatment equipment was included for coagulating and filtering the river water, and sodium cation exchangers for presoftening it.

Despite this pretreatment scale formed in the brine heater, and several acid cleanings were needed to maintain evaporator capacity. The scale was attributed to leakage of hardness from the zeolite softeners.

The hardness of the zeolite effluent was then monitored so that it was kept below 2 ppm, and a supplementary chemical was introduced into the evaporator feedwater. These measures restored the evaporator capacity to 90% of rating and inhibited further incrustation.

These experiences with flash evaporators indicate the need for proper pretreatment to avoid scale formation. For reducing iron and copper pickup noncorrodible titanium tubing has been recommended (20); the thin-wall titanium is claimed to improve heat transfer by promoting dropwise condensation.

VII. Cation Exchange Presoftening of Brackish-Water Feed for an Evaporator Desalination Plant

The United States Office of Saline Water (OSW) has installed a number of prototype desalting plants of various designs to explore their relative efficiencies. One of these plants, at Roswell, New Mexico, consisted of a vapor-compression type of evaporator for desalting a brackish well water having the following analysis (in parts per million as $CaCO_3$):

Ca	2,340	HCO_3	155
Mg	922	SO_4	3,350
Na	16,943	Cl	16,700
TC:	20,205	TA:	20,205

The scale that forms in evaporators causes a loss of thermal efficiency and a reduction in capacity. Shutdowns for its mechanical and chemical removal involve costly outages and maintenance. Therefore the Roswell water, with its high hardness, required proper presoftening for the prevention of scale.

Two types of scale form in evaporators, one caused by the carbonate hardness and the other by the noncarbonate hardness. The former results from the decomposition of the bicarbonate alkalinity to carbonates and hydroxides; this takes place in the evaporator. The carbonates combine with the calcium to precipitate calcium carbonate, $CaCO_3$, and the hydroxides combine with the magnesium to precipitate magnesium hydroxide, $Mg(OH)_2$. At operating temperatures lower than about 185°F the calcium carbonate scale predominates, and above this temperature the magnesium hydroxide scale predominates. The other type of scale, due to noncarbonate hardness, consists of calcium sulfate, $CaSO_4$. It forms when the product of the concentrations of the calcium and sulfate ions exceeds the solubility of calcium sulfate.

The formation of calcium carbonate and magnesium hydroxide is usually inhibited by sulfuric acid added to the evaporator feedwater. This reacts with the alkalinity to form calcium sulfate and free carbon dioxide. The amount of acid required is fairly low, because the alkalinity of brackish waters or seawaters is usually less than 200 ppm.

The calcium sulfate is more difficult to prevent. The solubility of calcium sulfate depends on the operating temperature and on the concentrations of calcium and sulfate ions. A typical solubility stability curve for calcium sulfate is given in Fig. 12.5. The curves show an inverse relation of solubility to temperature. Calcium sulfate is precipitated from normal seawater after 2.9 concentrations when the water is boiled at atmospheric pressure (the boiler water then contains 2.9 times as much dissolved solids as the feedwater).

Three forms of calcium sulfate precipitates may occur: gypsum, $CaSO_4 \cdot 2H_2O$, at lower temperatures, anhydrite, $CaSO_4$, at higher temperatures and α-anhydrite, $CaSO_4 \cdot 1/2H_2O$. The latter is the usual precipitate, and Fig. 12.5 is based on this form. The method of preventing the precipitation of these sulfates is the control of the concentration below the solubility value, but if the amount of calcium ions is reduced by presoftening,

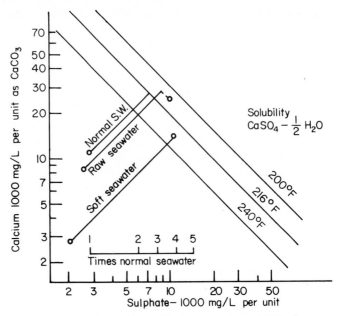

Fig. 12.5. Solubility of calcium sulfate (α-anhydrite, $CaSO_4 \cdot 1/2H_2O$) in seawater. [Reproduced from McIlhenny (*21*) with the permission of the Am. Chem. Soc.]

a greater number of concentration may be allowed before the calcium sulfate precipitates. Partial reduction of the calcium may be sufficient for this purpose.

Cation exchangers on the sodium cycle can accomplish efficiently this partial reduction of calcium in the evaporator feedwater. Furthermore, the concentrated evaporator water has a sufficient ratio of sodium to calcium to permit its use as a regenerant for the cation exchangers. This reduces or eliminates the purchasing of sodium chloride for the regeneration.

The results of research work on this scheme were published in 1962 (*21*). The test softener had external regeneration. The resin was transferred by a pump, and a resin-storage tank was used. The tests showed that removal of 64% of the calcium in the Roswell water prevented scale when the brackish water was concentrated four times in an experimental evaporator. The concentrated brine could be used successfully for regeneration.

To simplify the softener design and its cost, further research work was carried out with in-place regeneration (*22*). Table 12.3 gives the analyses of the influents, effluents, and regenerating brines used in both research projects. As a result of the second study a large cation-exchange softener plant was installed at Roswell for treating 1000 gal/min of the brackish water. About 75% of the calcium was to be removed, so that at four concentrations the calcium sulfate would not precipitate at 230°F. The concentrated evaporator brine was to be used for regenerating the cation exchanger.

The softening plant consists of six fixed-bed in-place-regenerated units, each 6 ft 6 in. in diameter and containing 141 ft^3 of Dowex HCR-W cation resin, connected up in parallel in two batteries of three units each; Figure 12.6 is a flow diagram of the plant. Each unit treats 12,000 to 14,000 gal in 46 min and is out of service during the subsequent 23 min for regeneration. Evaporator blowdown at 226 or at 339 gal/min, depending on brine concentration, is used for regeneration. This short-run fixed-bed softener plant approximates the continuous type of exchanger (Chapter 13) without moving the resin. The operation is fully automatic.

The operation involves four steps: about 25 gal of concentrated evaporator water per cubic foot of resin is passed upward* through the bed for regeneration, then one bed volume is passed downward for displacement, then the bed is rinsed downward with one more bed volume and, finally, the downward softening service run follows for the next 100 gal/ft^3, removing 75% of the calcium, reducing it from 2400 to 600 ppm, as $CaCO_3$.

The plant removes 20,000 lb of calcium, as $CaCO_3$, per day. If conventional softeners with 8 hr runs had been used, about 8800 ft^3 of resin housed in a number of large shells would have been required. By shortening the cycle (service run plus regenerating period) to about 70 min the required resin inventory was reduced more than 90%, to 846 ft^3.

After the plant was put into operation, the brackish water was found to contain 40% less dissolved solids than in the original analysis. The calcium was only 1400 ppm, as $CaCO_3$. With this new-raw water analysis the evaporator brine with three concentrations was 6.5% sodium chloride, and the hardness in the softener effluent was 400 to 500 ppm, better than the 600 ppm specified when the original 2400 ppm of hardness was to be reduced by 75%.*

VIII. New Demineralizing Processes for High-Solids Waters

In the economic studies previously cited, comparing evaporators and demineralizers, the total dissolved solids in the raw water was one of the controlling factors. When it reached 500 ppm [see Gilwood and Mack (*16*)], the operating costs for demineralizers and evaporators were about equal, when it exceeded 1000 ppm, evaporators were usually considered the more economical. Between 500 and 1000 ppm other factors would control the selection.

* Some calcium sulfate scale still formed however, requiring the use of some purchased salt to supplement the evaporator brine for regeneration. In 1965 the regeneration was changed to downflow and this reduced the calcium leakage a further 20%, solving the calcium sulfate scale problem in the evaporator, and evaporator brine (three concentrations) was used without any purchased salt for regeneration.

Table 12.3

ANALYSES OF BRACKISH WATERS AND
REGENERANTS IN ROSWELL RESEARCH STUDIES[a]

	Composition as $CaCO_3$, ppm					
	Cochrane pilot work			McIlhenny-Dow work		Recent Roswell water anal.
	Raw	Effl.[b]	Regen.	Raw	Evap. brine	
Calcium	2,400	600	2,400	2,250	2,430	1,400
Magnesium	980	520	1,700	940	2,180	650
Sodium	17,000	19,260	85,000	17,200	60,000	11,000
TOT. CATIONS:	20,380	20,380	89,100	20,390	64,610	13,050
HCO₃	180	180	0	142	35	170
Sulfate	3,100	3,100	14,500	3,000	14,600	1,800
Chloride	17,100	17,100	74,600	16,300	59,000	11,080
TOT. ANIONS:	20,380	20,380	89,100	19,442	73,635	13,050

[a] From Crits *et al.* (*22*).
[b] Average results.

Recently, however, two demineralizing processes that reduce regenerant costs have appeared. They have extended the field of application of demineralizers to include the conversion of brackish water to potable water, reducing the total dissolved solids from several thousand to several hundred parts per million. They are called the Kunin process (Rohm and Haas Company) and the SUL-biSUL Process (Nalco Chemical Company).

A. The Kunin Process (Rohm and Haas Company)

In the development of the Kunin process, which competes with evaporators or electrodialysis for the conversion of brackish waters, there were four requirements: inexpensive regenerants, reducing operating cost, high resin exchange capacity, reducing capital costs, low rinse-water requirements, avoiding exhaustion of the resin during rinsing, and low excesses of regenerant, minimizing waste-disposal problems.

The resins selected to meet these requirements were the recently developed weak-electrolyte resins Amberlite IRC-84, a weak-acid carboxylic cation resin, and Amberlite IRA-68, a weak-base anion resin. These resins could be regenerated with inexpensive chemicals and low regenerant levels, approaching the equivalent of the ions removed without appreciable excess. The former is regenerated with sulfuric acid and the latter with ammonia or lime.

The process is a reverse two-bed demineralization; that is, the anion exchange precedes the cation exchange. Mixed beds could not be used, because

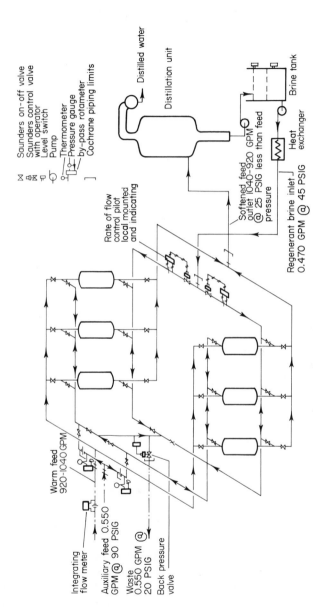

Fig. 12.6. Flow diagram of sodium cation exchange plant for softening brackish water before evaporation at Roswell, New Mexico.

the two resins are almost equal in density and therefore could not be segregated by backwashing for regeneration.

The key to the success of the process was the discovery that Amberlite IRA-68, when converted by carbon dioxide to the bicarbonate form, has a high selectivity and exchange capacity for the chlorides present in brackish water. The chloride leakage in the effluent is very low despite the high amounts of sodium cations also present.

The conversion of this resin to the bicarbonate form is called "carbonation," and the chemical reaction is given, in molecular form, by

$$[\text{R-N}] + \text{H}_2\text{O} + \text{CO}_2 \rightarrow [\text{R-NH}]\text{HCO}_3 \qquad (1)$$
$$\text{carbonation}$$

The removal of chlorides by the resin in the bicarbonate form is called "alkalization," and the chemical reaction is

$$[\text{R-NH}]\text{HCO}_3 + \text{NaCl} \rightarrow [\text{R-NH}]\text{Cl} + \text{NaHCO}_3 \qquad (2)$$
$$\text{alkalization}$$

The sodium bicarbonate thus produced is then removed by the Amberlite IRC-84 in the downstream cation exchange column. This is called "dealkalization," and the reaction is

$$\text{R---COOH} + \text{NaHCO}_3 \rightarrow \text{R---COONa} + \text{CO}_2 + \text{H}_2\text{O} \qquad (3)$$
$$\text{dealkalization}$$

The regeneration of the anion resin in the chloride form, as accomplished by ammonia, is

$$[\text{R-NH}]\text{Cl} + \text{NH}_4\text{OH} \rightarrow [\text{R-N}] + \text{NH}_4\text{Cl} + \text{H}_2\text{O} \qquad (4)$$
$$\text{ammonia regeneration}$$

If lime is used for the regeneration, the reaction is

$$2\,[\text{R-NH}]\,\text{Cl} + \text{CaO} \rightarrow [\text{R-N}] + \text{CaCl}_2 + \text{H}_2\text{O} \qquad (4a)$$
$$\text{lime regeneration}$$

The regeneration of the cation resin is accomplished by sulfuric acid:

$$2\,\text{R---COONa} + \text{H}_2\text{SO}_4 \rightarrow 2\,\text{R---COOH} + \text{Na}_2\text{SO}_4 \qquad (5)$$
$$\text{sulfuric acid regeneration}$$

Rather than use solutions of purchased carbon dioxide gas for converting the regenerated anion resin in the first exchanger column to the bicarbonate form, the Kunin process normally uses a third column of anion resin, as shown in the flow sheet of Fig. 12.7. This removes the carbon dioxide from the effluent of column 2 (see Eq. 3), and the resin is thus converted to the bicarbonate form. The third column saves the cost of carbon dioxide

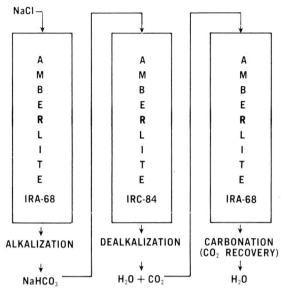

Fig. 12.7. Flow diagram of Kunin process. [From Kunin (*23*).]

purchased for this purpose, but it increases the capital costs. Therefore if waste flue gas, rich in carbon dioxide, is available, it can be scrubbed and used for the conversion, and the third column may be omitted, reducing the investment.

When the three-column system is used, the first anion column, after its exhaustion by the chlorides, is regenerated with ammonia and is placed in the third-column position. The flow is then reversed, passing through column 3, then column 2, and finally column 1. The alternate switching of columns 1 and 3 is accomplished by operating suitable valves in the piping interconnections. Some carbon dioxide is lost in the process, and about 10% of the carbon dioxide in the influent of column 3 has to be made up by introducing purchased gas for this purpose.

A large pilot plant using the Kunin process was installed in Italy for desalting a brackish water containing 2300 ppm total dissolved solids. The operating results, exchange capacities, and regenerant levels, reported by Sturla in a 1964 paper (*24*), are shown in Table 12.4. A total of 105 service runs was completed. The regeneration of the Amberlite IRA-68 was mainly done with ammonia, but a number of successful regenerations were made with lime used in slurry form. Raw water was used for the rinse and regeneration. The report concluded: "The new system is definitely capable of competing with the flash evaporator and it is far superior to a conventional ion exchange system."

Flow rate:	
Exhaustion,	1 to 2 gal/ft^3/min
Regeneration,	0.5 gal/ft^3/min
Regeneration levels:	
Amberlite IRA-68,	110% theory (4% NH$_3$ or CaO slurry)
Amberlite IRC-84,	110% theory (4% HCl or H$_2$SO$_4$)
Capacity:	
Amberlite IRC-84,	20 kgr/ft^3
Amberlite IRA-68,	18 kgr/ft^3
Effluent quality:	10 to 20 μmhos

In a later paper an estimate was given for a Kunin-process plant to de-mineralize, a flow of 1,000,000 gal/day, brackish water containing 1100 ppm total dissolved solids (25). The plant was to consist of three ion exchange units, each containing 400 ft^3 of its respective resin. The estimated total installed cost was approximately $300,000, and the operating cost was 11 to 22¢ per 1000 gal, depending on the regenerant cost. If silica was to be removed, as for high-pressure boilers, the Kunin-process columns were to be followed by a strong-base resin column regenerated with caustic soda.

B. The SUL-biSUL Process (Nalco Chemical Company)

The name SUL-biSUL process is derived from the unique sulfate–bisulfate cycle of the anion exchanger used in an otherwise conventional two-bed demineralizer. The process has been described in two papers (26, 27). Strong-acid cation exchanger (Dowex HCR or HCR-W) is used in the first step and strong-base anion exchanger (Dowex SBR) in the second step.

The chemical reactions involved in the sulfate–bisulfate cycle are shown in ionic form in the accompanying scheme, taken from one of the above-mentioned papers (27).

Sulfate–bisulfate cycle

Divalent sulfate ions on the anion resin exchange sites are converted to the monovalent bisulfate:

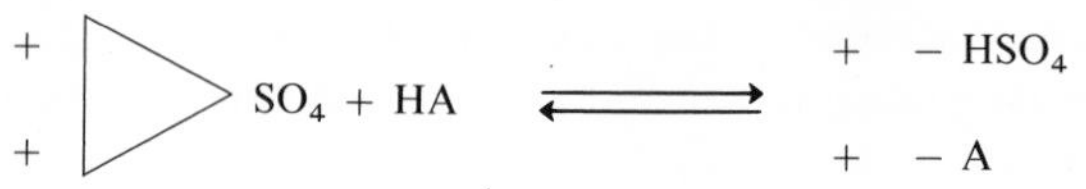

$$\begin{array}{c} + \\ + \end{array} \rhd\ SO_4 + HA \rightleftharpoons \begin{array}{c} +\ \ -\ HSO_4 \\ +\ \ -\ A \end{array} \qquad (I)$$

The mechanism, more completely illustrated, shows the uptake of bisulfates, chlorides, and nitrates on the sulfate-form resin:

$$
\begin{array}{c}
+ \\
+
\end{array}
\triangleright
\begin{array}{c}
H_2SO_4 \\
SO_4 + HCl \\
HNO_3
\end{array}
\rightleftharpoons
\begin{array}{c}
+ \quad - HSO_4 \\
+ \quad - HSO_4 \\
+ \quad - HSO_4 \\
+ \quad - Cl \\
+ \quad - HSO_4 \\
+ \quad - NO_3
\end{array}
\qquad (II)
$$

The process is controlled by the equilibrium reaction between $(HSO_4)^-$ and $(SO_4)^{2-}$:

$$
(SO_4)^{2-} + H^+ \rightleftharpoons (HSO_4)^- \qquad (III)
$$

During regeneration the rinse with water is analogous to dilution of sulfuric acid with water. This results in dissociation of monovalent bisulfate ions to divalent sulfate:

$$
\begin{array}{c}
+ \quad - HSO_4 \\
\\
+ \quad - HSO_4
\end{array}
+
\xrightarrow[\text{water}]{\text{neutr.}}
\begin{array}{c}
+ \\
\triangleright \quad SO_4 + H_2SO_4 \\
+
\end{array}
\qquad (IV)
$$

Equation I shows how the anion exchanger in sulfate form removes the acid from the effluent of the cation exchanger and is thereby converted to the bisulfate form. Sulfate ions, $(SO_4)^{2-}$, being divalent, occupy two exchange sites on the anion exchanger. During exhaustion the sulfate ions on the resin are converted to monovalent bisulfate ions, $(HSO_4)^-$, which now occupy only one of the two sites. The other site is available for adsorption of other acids, hydrochloric (HCl) and nitric (HNO$_3$), in the exhaustion reaction shown in the more complete Eq. II. The process is controlled by the equilibrium reaction between bisulfate and sulfate, $(HSO_4)^-$ and $(SO_4)^{2-}$, as given in Eq. III.

The exchange capacity of the anion resin in the sulfate–bisulfate cycle is about one half that of the normal hydroxide form of the anion resin.

The cation exchanger is regenerated with sulfuric acid, as in a conventional demineralizer. The anion exchanger, however, is not regenerated with the expensive caustic soda normally used but with raw water containing adequate alkalinity, as shown in Eq. IV. If the alkalinity of the water is too low, lime is added as a supplement. The substitution of water (plus low-cost lime, if required) for expensive caustic soda constitutes the major saving in operating cost accomplished by the SUL-biSUL process.

The regeneration converts the exhausted anion resin back to the sulfate form. This is accomplished by reducing the acidity of the anion exchanger.

Figure 12.8, which is a flow sheet of the process, shows how the regeneration is accomplished simply by rinsing with raw water (plus lime, if needed). The rinse water dilutes and neutralizes the acid on the resin, so that the monovalent bisulfate ions are dissociated to the divalent sulfate ions.

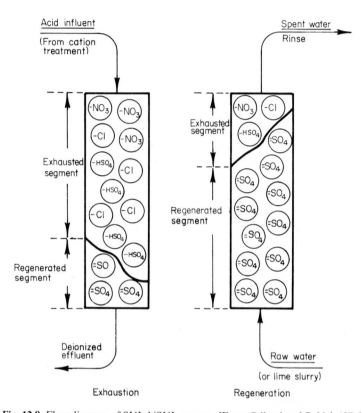

Fig. 12.8. Flow diagram of SUL-biSUL process. [From Odland and Pabich (27).]

Figure 12.9 shows a typical anion-regeneration elution curve for a raw water containing 1600 ppm total dissolved solids. The elution reduces the acidity in the regeneration effluent to zero after passing approximately 150 gal of water through a cubic foot of resin. Figure 12.10 indicates the effluent conductivity during exhaustion in three typical service runs for brackish water (892 ppm total dissolved solids) as influent.

If the raw-water alkalinity is more than 10% of the total solids, a saving in acid regenerant for the cation step may be realized by inserting a weak-acid cation exchange unit ahead of the usual strong-acid unit. The weak-acid unit can be regenerated with the excess spent acid from the strong-acid unit, both units being regenerated at the same time. With weak-acid resin in the system a unique regeneration scheme may be employed, as shown in Fig. 12.11. The

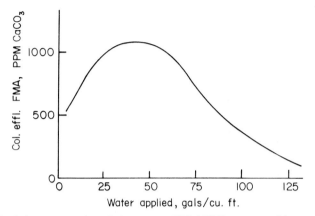

Fig. 12.9. Anion-regeneration elution curve: SUL-biSUL process with water containing 1600 ppm TDS. [From Odland and Pabich (27).]

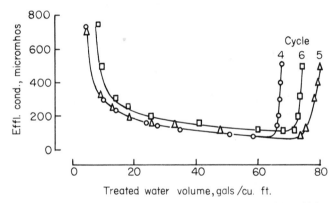

Fig. 12.10. Exhaustion of anion exchanger: SUL-biSUL process with brackish water of 892 ppm TDS. [From Odland and Pabich (27).]

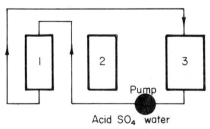

Fig. 12.11. Flow diagram of regeneration in SUL-biSUL process. (1) weak-acid cation resin, (2) strong-acid cation resin, (3) strong-base anion resin. [From Odland and Pabich (27).]

acid in the anion elution effluent is recycled through the weak-acid unit, providing suitable water for reuse as anion regenerant. This recycling can be done, however, only if the raw water has a certain minimal alkalinity. Since cation leakage is not removed by the anion unit, the final effluent quality will depend on the amount of acid used for regenerating the cation unit. The effluent quality therefore will improve with higher acid-regenerant levels. An effluent total dissolved solids of under 500 ppm may be obtained from brackish waters at operating costs, shown in Table 12.5, provided the influent alkalinity is at least 20 % of the total dissolved solids. Table 12.6 shows the effect of varying the percent alkalinity on these costs, and Table 12.7 gives approximate estimates of first cost of the equipment required.

Table 12.5

ESTIMATED OPERATING COSTS WITH SUL-biSUL PROCESS
FOR CONVERTING BRACKISH WATER TO POTABLE WATER[a]

Feed water salinity, ppm TDS	Total water cost[b], cents per 1000 gal			
	Plant capacity (1000 gal/day)			
	100	500	1000	5000
1000	129	49	38	28
2000	155	69	56	45
3000	175	87	76	65

[a] From Odland and Pabich (27).

[b] Based on 75 % capacity operation. Also includes 15 % per year facilities charge, operating labor, and space-heating expenses. Product water contains 500 ppm TDS; feedwater alkalinity, 20 %. Neutral effluents. Three-bed system.

Table 12.6

EFFECT OF ALKALINITY ON
OPERATING COSTS OF SUL-biSUL PROCESS[a]

Plant capacity, gal/day	Water cost[b], cents per 1000 gal		
	Feedwater alkalinity. %		
	0	20	40
100,000	160	155	155
500,000	74	69	68
1,000,000	63	56	55
5,000,000	51	45	44

[a] From Odland and Pabich (27).

[b] Based on 75 % capacity operation. The 20 % and 40 % alkalinity costs are for three-bed system: weak-acid, strong-acid, and strong-base. Zero-percent alkalinity costs are for two-bed system: strong-acid and strong-base. Feed and product water salinities are 2000 and 500 ppm TDS, respectively.

Table 12.7
ESTIMATED CAPITAL COSTS FOR SUL-biSUL PLANTS[a]

Feedwater		Facilities investment, × $1,000[b]		
TDS, ppm	Alk., %	50[c]	500[c]	5000[c]
1600	0	80	200	700
	20	90	220	800
	40	90	220	900
2200	0	85	215	830
	20	95	225	860
	40	95	225	910
2800	0	90	230	1000
	20	100	230	970
	40	100	230	920

[a] From Odland and Pabich (27).
[b] Does not include building, land, or well costs.
[c] In 1000 gpd.

The SUL-biSUL process and the Kunin process thus add new tools for demineralizing high-solids waters and compete with evaporators and electrodialysis plants for the conversion of brackish water to potable water.

Australian scientists have been studying the use of low cost heat, instead of expensive chemicals, for regenerating the resins for desalination (28). This work, however, needs further development before it can be applied.

REFERENCES

1. E. L. Knoedler and H. L. Walker, Feedwater make-up during drought periods using flash-type evaporation at Danskammer Station. *ASME Ann. Meeting, November 1966.*
2. S. B. Applebaum and M. C. McKeown, Boiler feedwater treatment – demineralization vs evaporation. *Wisconsin Utilities Assoc. Meeting, Milwaukee, November 1953* (reprinted in *Power Eng.* (June 1954).
3. A. B. Sisson, Three years of operation with demineralized water. *Proc. Am. Power Conf.* **15**, 653 (1953).
4. I. L. Wade, Demineralization produces plant savings. *Power* (October 1950).
5. R. M. Buchanan and A. A. Pace, Vapor purity to be expected. *Proc. Ann. Water Conf., Engrs. Soc. West Penn. 11th Ann. Conf.* (1950).
6. L. P. Aker and E. J. Connelley, Operating experiences – Louisville Gas and Elec. Co., Paddys Run Station. *Proc. Intern. Water Conf., Engrs. Soc. West Penn., October 1963.*
7. A. K. Sukumar and S. B. Applebaum, Demineralizer treating hot lime zeolite effluent replaces evaporators in Ford's River Rouge Plant. *Proc. Am. Power Conf.* (March 1958).
8. E. B. Morris and C. E. Brune, Economics, the key to evaporation vs demineralization for high pressure steam power plants. *Proc. Am. Power Conf.* **15**, 628 (1953).
9. W. P. Saunier, Discussion of Ref. 8. *Proc. Am. Power Conf.* **15**, 640 (1953).
10. E. B. Showell, Ion exchange for water treatment. *J. Am. Water Works Assoc.* **43**, No. 7 (1951).
11. T. C. Hoppe and R. A. Russell, Deionization vs evaporation of hard water supplies for boiler make-up. *Proc. Ann. Water Conf., Engrs. Soc. West Penn., 13th Ann. Conf.* (1952).

12. J. D. Yoder, W. L. Webb, and T. Baumeister, Chemical treatment, demineralization, or evaporation for make-up in high pressure by product steam plants. *ASME Ann. Meeting, 1949,* Paper 49-A-71.

13. V. J. Calise, High pressure boiler feedwater treatment, evaporation vs demineralizing and silica removal. *Proc. Ann. Water Conf., Engrs. Soc. West Penn., 11th Ann. Conf.* (1950).

14. E. F. Stalcup, E. F. Coxe, and R. L. Coit, Flash evaporators for the production of boiler make-up in power plant cycles. *ASME Ann. Meeting, Atlantic City, December 1959,* Paper 59-A-203.

15. R. L. Coit, Flash evaporators for the utility industry. *Proc. Am. Power Conf.* (March 1960).

16. M. E. Gilwood and J. G. Mack, Considerations regarding demineralization and flash evaporators of high pressure boiler make-up. *Proc. Am. Power Conf.* (March 1961).

17. B. J. Peters, Operation of a single stage flash evaporator in the heat cycle of a utility unit. *ASME Ann. Meeting, New York, November 1962.*

18. M. Liss, C. Caprara, E. F. Stalcup, W. B. Willsey, and D. Cane, Phila. Elec. Co. multi-stage flash evaporator. *Proc. Am. Power Conf.* **23** (1961).

19. G. Ostroot, Jr., Why the flash evaporator was selected. *Intern. Water Conf., Engrs. Soc. West Penn., October 1963.*

20. V. S. Ivins, Flash evaporator uses titanium to minimize corrosion and erosion. *Power Eng.* (July 1965).

21. V. F. McIlhenny, Softened sea water as a saline water conversion pretreatment. *Am. Chem. Soc. Div. Water Waste Chem. Preprints* (1962).

22. G. J. Crits, W. Y. McIntire, and D. L. Raffel, Ion exchange softening of brackish feedwater for saline conversion plant at Roswell, New Mexico. *Am. Chem. Soc. Div. Water Waste Chem. Preprints* (1965).

23. R. Kunin, Desalination of brackish waters. Rohm and Haas Co. Amber Hi-Lites, No. 89. September 1965.

24. P. Sturla, Pilot plant studies of the Kunin process. *Proc. Intern. Water Conf., Engrs. Soc. West Penn., 25th Conf. 1964.*

25. R. Kunin, Deionization of high solids water. *Ind. Water Eng.* (July 1965).

26. K. Odland and H. L. Pabich, Desalinization by the SUL-biSUL process Pt. I, The technology (by K. Odland), Pt. II, The economics (by H. L. Pabich). *Proc. Ann. Intern. Water Conf., Engrs. Soc. West Penn., 26th Conf., 1965.*

27. K. Odland and H. L. Pabich, Demineralizing brackish water. *Ind. Water Eng.* (December 1965).

28. D. E. Weiss, B. A. Bolto, R. McNeill, A. S. MacPherson, R. Siudak, E. A. Swinton, and D. Willis, The "Sirotherm" demineralization process – an ion exchange process with thermal regeneration. *Intern. Symp. Water Desalination, 1st, Washington, D.C., October 1965,* Paper SWD/10 [based on data first published by the same authors in the *J. Inst. Engrs., Australia* **37**, No. 7–8, 193–199 (1965)].

    Later papers by the same authors are:

    (a) New C.S.I.R.O. approach to water demineralization. *Proc. Roy. Australian Chem. Inst.* (1965).

    (b) An ion exchange process with thermal regeneration, Pt. II, Properties of weakly basic resins. *Australian J. Chem.* **19**, 561–587 (1966).

    (c) Pt. III, Properties of weakly acidic ion exchange resins. *Australian J. Chem.* **19**, 589–608 (1966).

    (d) Pt. IV, Equilibria in a mixed bed of weak-electrolyte resins. *Australian J. Chem.* **19**, 765–789 (1966).

    (e) Pt. V, Multistage operation. *Australian J. Chem.* **19**, 791–796 (1966).

13

Continuous Ion Exchange

The continuous technique is receiving renewed interest today as an extension of ion exchange application to the treatment of high-solids waters and other liquids. For such cases and, particularly, for large plants the continuous process may admit of an appreciable saving in investment and operating cost, in comparison with the conventional fixed-bed designs that prevail today, but to put the comparison on a more equitable basis it may be advisable to modify the fixed-bed technique so as to put its cost at a minimum.

I. Review of Past Fixed-Bed Design Criteria and Their Change

In the past in fixed-bed practice the flow direction of both the treated liquid and the regenerant solutions usually has been downward through the exchanger beds; this is called "parallel downflow." A saving in regenerant and a reduction in leakage could be realized with high-solids waters if counterflow, instead of parallel flow, were used (1); that is, the water would flow downward during exhaustion and the regenerant upward, or vice versa (see Chapter 6, Section IX A2).

The flow rates during exhaustion have been conservatively kept in the low range of 6 to 10 gal/min/ft², to limit pressure loss, but higher rates, of 15 to 25 gal/min/ft², are quite feasible and would reduce the size of the units and, accordingly, their cost.

The depth of the resin beds usually has been limited to less than 5 ft, also for the purpose of limiting the pressure loss, but for high-solids waters deeper beds, of up to 10 ft, are quite possible and would reduce the area of the shells when the resin volumes must be large.

The length of the exhaustion run often has been specified at not less than 24 hr, which reduced the frequency of regeneration. When regenerations were manually controlled, this chiefly saved operating labor, but now that reliable automatic controls are available, shorter runs, of 4 to 6 hr, are feasible, which would reduce the resin inventory drastically.

By considering these changes in the fixed-bed practice a more reasonable comparison with the continuous design may be made.

II. Description of Continuous Method

In the continuous method the whole ion exchange bed does not remain fixed in the shell, awaiting the completion of the exhaustion run but, rather, a part of the bed is always moving out in pulses, to be regenerated in another zone or in external vessels. The regenerated resin also is being transferred in pulses back to the exhaustion zone. The pulses are so frequent that the technique is called "continuous." Exhaustion and regeneration take place in different zones but at the same time, not one after the other, as in fixed-bed practice. The most exhausted parts of the resin bed are transferred and receive the regenerant counterflow, so that the "purest" (uncontaminated) regenerant contacts the "purest" (least contaminated) resin, after the resin has passed through most of the regeneration zone.

III. History of Continuous Method

Continuous ion exchange has always attracted chemical engineers because of its similarity to continuous distillation and solvent extraction. In the early nineteen-fifties many papers were presented discussing this new, possible technique. One of these, by Australian engineers, predicted wide applications of the continuous method in the metallurgical field (2). The applications included the recovery of valuable metals from mine waters, pickling and plating liquors, the refining of rare earths, the extraction of the desired metal ion from leach liquor, such as gold from a cyanide leach pump, and many others.

The method was advocated because the product stream produced would be more constant in purity and concentration, less water would be wasted in rinsing and less resin would be required, and each part of the resin, being moved out for regeneration as soon as it was exhausted, would not necessitate waiting until the whole bed was ready for regeneration.

Application of the continuous method in water treatment, however, has made slow progress. In 1954 a continuous water softener was installed in a municipal plant (3). This was an upflow fluidized-bed gravity unit (expanded by the upflow; see Chapter 6, Section VII C). Portions of the resin at the bottom of the bed were transferred by hydraulic ejector to the top of a smaller, external, downflow-regeneration vessel at frequent intervals. The regenerated resin from the bottom of the external vessel was transferred back to the top of the main softener shell by another hydraulic ejector. However, no further applications of such softeners were made, because fluidized-bed upflow exhaustion, in the design used, limited the flow rate to only about $7\ gal/min/ft^2$, to avoid resin loss by carryover and to prevent channelling and poor results. The size of the exhaustion column was therefore excessively large.

Research work with the continuous-bed, or moving-bed, technique was conducted in the nuclear field because of its possible application in separating fission products and in uranium purification. A report in 1951 gave the results of this work at Stanford Research Institute (4). The bibliography in this report includes references to many earlier papers; the subject of continuous exchange, therefore, is not new.

One of the early American workers in the field of continuous ion exchange was Higgins (5), who developed a pulsed ion exchange "contactor" applied in the production of high-purity uranyl chloride. A patent was granted to Higgins on this design, which featured compact, rather than fluidized, resin beds and a resin movement countercurrent to the liquid movement (6). The apparatus was arranged in a loop, containing different zones for the exhaustion, regeneration, and rinsing, and separated by valves. So far more than thirty of these continuous contactors have been installed, including a number of municipal water softeners.

IV. The Higgins Design*

In the Higgins design, described in an early article (7), a continuous loop is formed, as shown in Fig. 13.1. The left leg of the loop (left-hand sketch) contains two beds of resin separated by a valve. The upper bed is in the exhaustion zone, being "loaded," purifying the liquid, while the lower bed in the regeneration zone is being "stripped," or regenerated. The right leg is connected to the top and bottom of the left leg, forming a complete loop for circulation of the resin. It has two valves. A pump connected to the right leg provides surges of pressure at intervals, controlled by a timer and moving the resin around the loop. The valves shown in the figure are alternately opened and closed at proper intervals in the following three steps.

(1) The left-hand sketch shows the first step, in which the pump is idle and the impure liquid feed and regenerant are passing through the two resin beds, two valves being closed and one open. (2) After several minutes the second step, shown in the middle sketch, occurs, in which the valves are turned and the resin moves as indicated, aided by the pump; some exhausted resin enters the top of the right loop. (3) In the third step, shown in the right-hand sketch, liquid and regenerant again flow through the newly formed beds; the pulsed,

* Marketed by Chemical Separations Corporation, Oak Ridge, Tennessee.

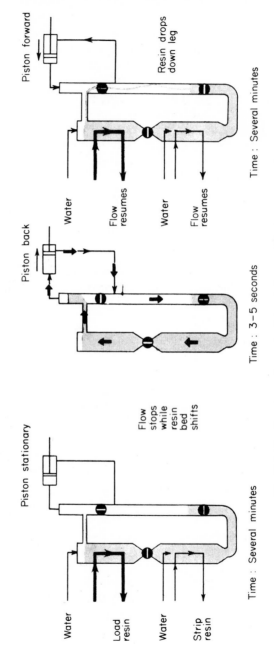

Fig. 13.1. The three operating steps of the continuous Higgins contactor.*

* Excerpted with permission from *Chemical Engineering* (July, 1957) Copyright © (1957), McGraw-Hill, Inc.

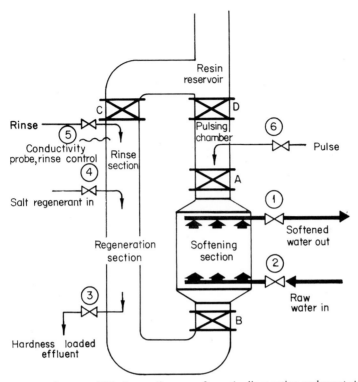

Fig. 13.2. Flow diagram of Higgins continuous softener (sodium cation exchange) showing valve operations.

Capacity, 1,000,000 gal/day; resin inventory, 90 ft^3; raw water, virtually any hardness; floor area, 7 ft $\times$ 7 ft; height, 20 ft; production rate, 40 to 90 gal/min/ft^2. The valve positions during cycles are as follows:

Run cycle (duration, 2 to 15 min)		Pulse cycle (duration, 5 to 10 sec)	
Valves open	Valves closed	Valves open	Valves closed
D	A	A	1
1	B	B	2
2	C	C	3
3	6	6	4
4			5
5			D

(Courtesy of Chemicals Separations Corp.)

exhausted resin, which was moved to the top of the right loop in step 2, now drops to the bottom of the right loop.

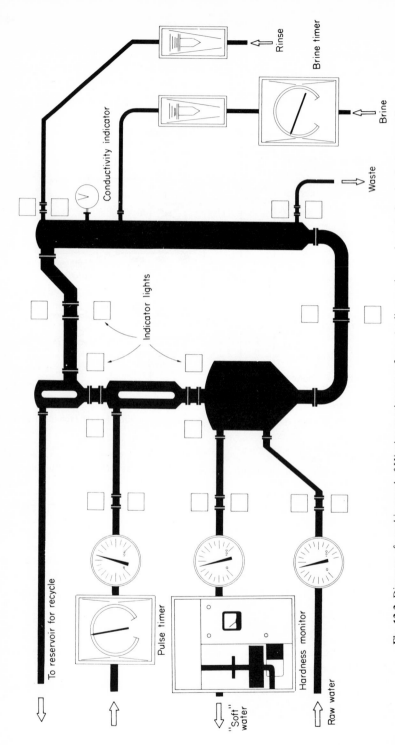

Fig. 13.3. Diagram of graphic panel of Higgins continuous softener (sodium cation exchange), showing instrumentation. (Courtesy of Chemical Separations Corp.)

The contact of the resin with the water and with the regenerant is continuous except for the few seconds of pulse during which the resin is moved, in the second step. The exhausted resin, entering the right, or return, leg, is forced around into the regeneration zone. Gradually it is advanced upward in steps, or pulses, through the open valve and into the upper exhaustion zone. The water flow during exhaustion, as shown here, is downward, but the later contactors had upflow exhaustion.

Figure 13.2 shows a flow diagram of a recently installed 1,000,000 gal/day continuous water softener of the Higgins design. The resin in this plant flows clockwise, while the water and regenerant flow counter-clockwise, around the loop; thus the latter are *countercurrent*, or *counterflow*, and the rinsing is, too. This is claimed to reduce the regeneration waste water to a fraction of that in fixed-bed practice; the amount of regenerant required is only 120 % of the equivalent hardness removed, so saving 30 to 40 % of the regenerant used in the current fixed-bed practice.

The impure liquid feed flows up through the resin bed in the exhaustion or loading zone, and the regenerant and rinse water flow down. The resin beds are not fluidized (expanded by flow) but are kept compact, without any water spaces in the zones between the valves. The loop is kept under pressure. Periodically, in short pulses lasting only several seconds, after the opening and closing of certain valves, the pressure in the loop is increased by means of a pump or a water line from a storage tank and so pushes some of the resin clockwise around the loop.

A Higgins unit, designed to soften 2850 gal/min (4,000,000 gal/day) was described in a recent article (8). The softened water will be used for boiler feed, cooling water, and drinking water. The exhaustion or loading section is 7 ft in diameter, so that the flow rate is about 75 gal/min/ft^2 in this section. The regeneration and stripping sections are 42 in. in diameter. The cation resin is in the hydrogen form, regenerated by acid; the shell is therefore rubber-lined. The valves are the Crane butterfly type, 18 in. in size. Dowex 50-W resin will be used. Instrumentation and a graphic panel usually are included, as shown in Fig. 13.3.

For two-bed demineralizers two separate loops are provided, the outlet of the cation loop being connected to the inlet of the downstream anion loop. For high-alkalinity waters, with strong-base anion resin in the demineralizer, a decarbonator is inserted between the two loops.

V. The Asahi Design*

The Asahi Chemical Industry Co., Ltd., in Japan, developed a continuous ion exchange process for the recovery of copper from a waste spinning solution

* Marketed in the U.S. by Graver Water Conditioning Company, Union, New Jersey, and by Degremont-Cottrell, Inc., Bound Brook, New Jersey.

in a rayon plant. Pilot plant tests were then made with this design in the refining of sugar juices, in water softening and demineralizing. Later some large-scale continuous plants were installed in Japan. Asahi obtained foreign patents on this system (9). The description of the design which follows, is derived from an Asahi brochure (10) and from recent papers (11, 12).*

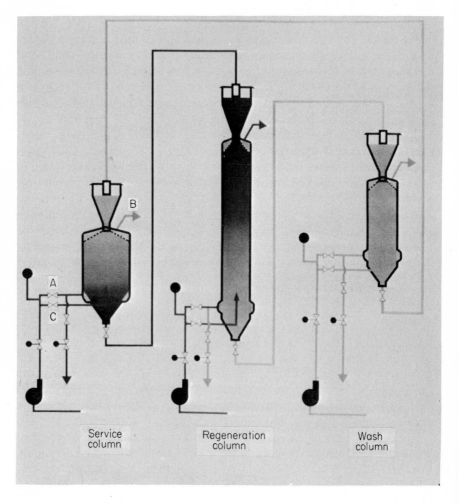

Fig. 13.4. Flow diagram of the Asahi Exchanger. [From Levendusky (11).]

Three separate columns or vessels, interconnected by piping, are used, as shown in Fig. 13.4. The vessels are called service, regeneration, and rinse (or

* Later papers on the continuous process may be found in the December 1967 *Proceedings of the Intern. Water Conf., Engrs. Soc. West. Penn.*

wash) columns. The hoppers above the three columns, mentioned below in the four operating steps, have fine horizontal screens near their tops; the screen stops the flow of resin when the resin reaches its level. By this means the volume of resin moved may be measured for each operation. The operation may be divided into four cycles: exhaustion, resin transfer, regeneration, and rinse.

A. Exhaustion

The impure liquid or feed enters the service column through the inlet valve at the bottom and leaves by the outlet valve at the top. The flow is upward through the resin bed, and the column is maintained under pressure imposed by the feed pump, shown at the left in Fig. 13.4. The resin is compacted against the upper, conical, fine screen at the top. At the bottom there is a similar screen fitted into the knuckles of the lower cone. A coarse, horizontal "baffle board" is at the bottom of the cylindrical part of the vessel, distributing the influent flow; it is coarse enough to allow resin to fall through it into the bottom cone for resin transfer. A water space exists below the compacted resin bed during the exhaustion or loading step, and a similar water space in the top of the cone below the baffle board. During exhaustion a part of the feed stream is used for transferring exhausted resin which has fallen into the bottom cone, through the open valve at the bottom apex and up into the hopper, situated above the regeneration column. This transfer is hydraulic, induced by the pressure maintained in the service column.

B. Resin Transfer

Periodically the feed inlet and outlet valves are closed, and the drain valve, connected downstream of the bottom conical screen is opened; this reduces the pressure in the service column. The resin bed then drops by gravity through the baffle board and into the lower cone. At the same time, regenerated resin, stored in the hopper above the service column, falls by gravity through a ball check valve into the top of this column. This new resin, thus introduced, replaces the exhausted resin previously transferred to the hopper above the regeneration column. The flow of feed liquid is then resumed, and the bed is again compacted upward against the top conical screen.

C. Regeneration

The regenerant solution is pumped into the bottom of the regeneration column and upflow through the compacted resin bed in this column. The operation is similar to that for the service column. The regenerated resin is transferred to the hopper located above the wash, or rinse, column.

D. Rinse

The operation of the rinse column is similar to those of the other two columns, the rinsed resin being transferred to the hopper above the service column.

VI. Economic Comparison of Continuous-Bed and Fixed-Bed Plants

A saving in capital cost and operating cost of 25 to 40 % is claimed for the continuous-bed plant as against those of the fixed-bed plant (*11*).

Table 13.1 gives an economic comparison of a continuous and a fixed-bed demineralizer plant; a two-bed continuous-bed plant is compared with a three-bed fixed-bed plant. The continuous-bed plant is designed for flow rates of 25 to 50 gal/min/ft^2, whereas the fixed-bed is designed for conservative flow rates of 6 to 12 gal/min/ft^2. The fixed-bed plant has enough resin for 10 hr cation runs and 15 hr anion runs.

If the fixed-bed units of Table 13.1 had been designed for 12 to 25 gal/min/ft^2, permitting the use of units 8 or 9 ft in diameter instead of the 12 ft 6 in. indicated, and if the runs had been shortened by about two thirds (3.3 hr cation runs and 5 hr anion runs), the resin inventory for the fixed-bed plant would have been about one third of that given in the table. The volume of cation resin for the fixed-bed plant would thus be reduced from 740 to 250 ft^3, which may be compared with the 400 ft^3 of the continuous-bed plant. The latter must include the resin volume in the regeneration and rinse vessels, which the fixed-bed plants do not need. The estimated first costs given are $182,000 for the continuous-bed equipment and $265,000 for the fixed-bed equipment, but if the latter equipment were designed for the higher flow rates and shorter runs suggested, its first cost would be the lesser of the two.

VII. Operating Problems with Continuous Beds

Offsetting the possible economic advantages of the continuous design, there are a number of problems that may be encountered in its operation. Among these are the following.

A. Excessive Resin Attrition

The continuous design is subject to difficulties caused by excessive resin attrition (*13*). The frequent forcing of the resin in pulses upward against the top fine screen and the resuming of high flow rates through the compacted bed subject the resin beads to severe strains. Indications of excessive bead breakage already have been observed abroad. Strong-base anion resin from an existing plant was tested for pressure loss after various periods of use. At flow rates of 60 gal/min/ft^2, for example, the pressure loss with new resin was 11 psi; after 1500 cycles it was 25 psi, and after 3000 cycles it reached 30 psi. This indicated the formation of considerable resin fines.

B. Need for Tougher Resins

The ion exchange resins currently available were designed for fixed-bed applications. For the moving-bed technique it may be necessary to develop a

Table 13.1

ECONOMIC COMPARISON OF CONTINUOUS-BED
AND FIXED-BED DEMINERALIZERS[a]

Design data: service flow, gal/min	1500	
Raw-water composition, as $CaCO_3$, ppm:		
Tot. cation	165	
Tot. anion	189	
Treated-water quality:		
Spec. conduct., μmhos	5 to 10	
Diss. silica, ppm	0 to 0.02	

	Continuous	Fixed bed
Basic equipment		
Dimensions, diameter		
and straight height:		
Cat. units	2–6 ft 6 in. × 6 ft	2–12 ft 6 in. × 6 ft
Cat. regen. col.	1–18 in. × 25 ft	
Cat. rinse col.	1–24 in. × 10 ft	—
Weak-base unit	none	2–12 ft 6 in. × 6 ft
Strong-base unit	2–6 ft 6 in. × 6 ft	2–12 ft 6 in. × 5 ft 6 in.
Anion regen. col.	1–24 in. × 30 ft	—
Anion rinse col.	1–36 in. × 10 ft	—
Resin inventory, ft^3:		
Cation	400	740
Weak-base anion	—	610
Strong-base anion	450	650
Regen. equipment	automat.	existing
Interconnect. pipes	yes	yes
Automatic operation	yes	yes
Structural steel	yes	—
Cost		
Est. equip., $	182,100	265,000
Est. install. $	95,000	150,000
Chem. operation, $ per yr.:		
Acid consump.	27,500	54,500
Caustic soda consump.	61,500	64,500
Cat. resin attrition	1,000	750
An. resin attrition	4,050	4,500
Total	94,050	124,250
Effluent water quality:		
Spec. conduct., μmhos-cm	5 to 10	10 to 15
Diss. salts, ppm	under 2	2 to 3
Diss. silica, ppm	0.02	0.02

[a] From Levendusky et al. (11).

family of new resins of greater physical toughness, that will withstand the increased wear and tear to which they will be subjected.

C. Maintaining Column Integrity

The resin beds in the exhaustion column must have "integrity"; that is, the nonexhausted resin must stay at the top and the exhausted resin at the bottom. The motion of the resin bed must be strictly linear. Definite resin-band displacement, or "plug flow," must be maintained properly, so that there is no upset or mixing of the exhausted and unexhausted parts of the bed. If the integrity is not maintained, the regeneration efficiency is reduced, and the effluent quality is affected adversely.

D. Accumulation of Dirt

In the resin drop step the dirtiest part of the resin at the bottom is expected to drop into the bottom cone. If this is not accomplished in a strictly linear motion, the dirt remains and accumulates in the exhaustion column, causing more pressure loss and an inferior effluent quality.

E. Availability of Components

With only one continuous column the plant will suffer from decreased availability, should any control component fail. It may therefore be advisable to install two continuous plants (one a spare) rather than to depend on a single unit.

VIII. Field of Application

The considerations discussed above lead to the conclusion that the continuous design will be most applicable for treating waters or other liquids containing high solids and, particularly, for plants handling large flows. The savings in first cost and operating costs will be most pronounced in these applications.

REFERENCES

1. P. H. Caskey and T. P. Harding, Counterflow regeneration of deionizers. *Proc. Am. Power Conf.* **19** (1957).
2. R. McNeil, E. A. Swinton and D. E. Weiss, *AIME Meeting, New York, February 1954*, Paper TP-3995P (Manuscript, December 1953).
3. A. L. Wilcox and R. D. Forger, Municipal water supply softened by continuous base exchange. *Public Works*, **85**, 70 (1954).
4. N. K. Hiester, Continuous separation of ions by means of a moving ion exchange bed. Tech. Rept. No. 6, SRI Proj. No. CU-337, Paper COO-41 (revised) covering period June 25, 1950 – January 31, 1951.
5. I. R. Higgins and J. T. Roberts, A countercurrent solid-liquid contactor for continuous ion exchange. *Chem. Eng. Progr. Symp. Ser.* **50**, 87 (1954).

6. I. R. Higgins, U.S. Patent 2,815,322 (December 1957).

7. Staff Article – ed. C. S. Cronan, Ion exchange column runs continuously. *Chem. Eng.* (July 1957).

8. Staff article, Giant sized softener. *Ind. Water Eng.* (March 1966).

9. Asahi French Patent 1,291,343 (1962).

10. Continuous ion exchange process (Asahi process), Brochure. I.E., D & E Dept., Asahi Chem. Ind. Co., Ltd., Tokyo, October 1962.

11. J. A. Levendusky, L. Limon, and L. F. Ryan, Continuous countercurrent ion exchange – A proven low cost process. *Proc. Intern. Water Conf., Engrs. Soc. West Penn., 26th Conf., 1965.*

12. J. Bouchard, Continuous flow ion exchange by the Degremont-Asahi Process. *Proc. Intern. Water Conf., Engrs. Soc. West Penn., 27th Conf., 1966.*

13. Amber-Hi-Lites, No. 62. Rohm and Haas Co., March 1961.

14

Chemical Processing by Ion Exchange

Three methods of ion exchange for the chemical processing of nonaqueous industrial liquids are discussed in this chapter. In the first the exchangers are solid and are usually regenerated with chemicals; the method is discussed in Section I, and various processes and equipment are detailed in Sections II and III. In the second the exchangers are also solid, but water elution is used without chemical regeneration; three types of this method are discussed in Section IV. In the third the exchangers are liquid rather than solid, and are regenerated with chemicals (see Section V).

I. Solid Exchangers with Chemical Regenerants

In the past the chemical processing of nonaqueous industrial liquids was accomplished by complicated refining methods, such as precipitation, sedimentation, and filtration. With the aid of exchange-resin manufacturers and liquid-treatment equipment firms the research departments of chemical, pharmaceutical, and other industrial companies began to investigate the application of simpler ion exchange techniques to chemical processing. The work involved testing, first in the laboratory and then in large pilot units, the suitability, capacity, and regeneration requirements of the various resins for the purpose of solving particular refining problems. Eventually after the parameters of design were obtained, large-scale equipment was installed in plants. Ion exchange has thus become an efficient and versatile process for the *removal of impurities* for upgrading chemical products, for the *recovery of valuable substances* from industrial liquids, and for the *purification of valuable processing liquors* for their reuse. Sections II and III following this short outline are devoted to examples, histories, and descriptions of those three applications of ion exchange.

Some examples of removing impurities for the upgrading of chemical products are as follows: decolorizing and purification of sugar solutions; purification of molasses and polyols in the production of glycerine and other products; deashing of turbid, nonaqueous, spin-baths; removal of iron from hydrochloric acid; and purification of organic solvents.

Illustrating either the recovery of valuable substances from industrial liquids or the purifying of valuable processing liquors for their reuse are the following: recovery of platinum and other precious metals from hydrochloric acid; reclamation of chromates from cooling-tower blowdown; recovery of zinc from rinse water and clarification of a spin bath in a rayon plant; reclamation of chromic acid from metal-plating bath solutions; and purification of phosphoric acid by removing its iron content, so as to permit its reuse for pickling steel.

All these examples are described in the following sections.

II. Applications: Removal of Impurities for Upgrading Products

A. Removal of Color and Impurities from Sugar Solutions

1. DECOLORIZING BY OLD METHODS

Crystal sugar is made by the evaporation of syrup, which in the natural state is highly colored. In order to produce "white crystal" sugar the syrup must be decolorized before it is evaporated.

Three decolorizing methods generally used are filtration through bonechar, the addition of powdered vegetable carbon followed by leaf filtration, and filtration through fixed granular-carbon beds.

a. Filtration through Bonechar

Bonechar is charred animal bone in granular form. The conventional bonechar filters consist of downflow towers. After exhaustion the spent char is moved from the filters to low-temperature kilns for burning off of the color bodies. Bonechar has the advantage of removing some "ash" (ionic impurities in the syrup) in addition to the color. However, it has low absorbent capacity, and therefore the volumes of bonechar and the towers required are large. These are costly and space-consuming and call for excessive operating labor, especially the manual handling of the spent bonechar to and from the kilns. Moreover, large amounts of wash water are used in the tower operations.

b. Filtration through Powdered Vegetable Carbon Coating on Leaf Filters

The powdered carbon is first added as a slurry in mixing tanks for contact with the syrup. Usually this is done in two stages in series. New carbon enters the second stage, and the once-used carbon enters the first stage; thus the flow is countercurrent. The carbon then passes out to coat the leaf filters.

Powdered-carbon plants are more efficient than bonechar towers, but they, too, have disadvantages. Regeneration of the carbon in kilns is not possible, because the carbon itself would be burned up; therefore, the carbon must be replaced at high cost. Leaf filtration likewise is complicated and requires excessive operating labor. Filter aid, also needed in this process, further increases the operating cost.

c. Filtration through Granular Carbon in Fixed Beds

Granular carbon has the advantage over powdered carbon of being regenerable in kilns, but when used in fixed beds, it has the disadvantage of low absorptive efficiency, requiring great volumes of carbon, and a considerable number of large filter units, operating in series, must be used to effect sufficient color removal.

2. DECOLORIZING BY CONTINUOUS COUNTERCURRENT MOVING BED GRANULAR-CARBON SYSTEM

The limitations of the older decolorizing methods described above led to the development of the new continuous, countercurrent, pulsed, moving-bed system with continuous carbon rejuvenation in a kiln. Figure 14.1 is a simplified flow diagram of one of these systems, installed in a new, large refinery having an annual capacity of 1,500,000 lb of sugar.

Two carbon towers about 40 ft tall are used for decolorizing the syrup, which flows upward through compact carbon beds. The lower portions of the beds therefore become exhausted first. Periodically, in short pulses, these lower, exhausted carbon layers are transferred hydraulically from the bottom to the kiln equipment. Only thin layers of the beds are removed at a time. Newly rejuvenated carbon simultaneously is transferred into the top of the towers, replacing the exhausted layer removed and so keeping the carbon columns full.

The carbon rejuvenation steps are as follows.

Sweetening off: The slurry of exhausted carbon and syrup enters a sweetening-off tank, where the syrup in the voids is separated from the carbon for reuse, and then the voids are rinsed with hot water, until the wash effluent is low in sugar content; this sweet water effluent also is reused.

Dewatering: The sweetened-off carbon slurry is discharged into a dewatering tank, where the water present is squeezed out by air.

Kiln operation: The dewatered carbon passes into the kiln, where the color, previously adsorbed by the carbon, is burned off.

Sweetening on: The rejuvenated carbon from the kiln enters the sweetening-on tank, where the voids are refilled with increasing strengths of liquid

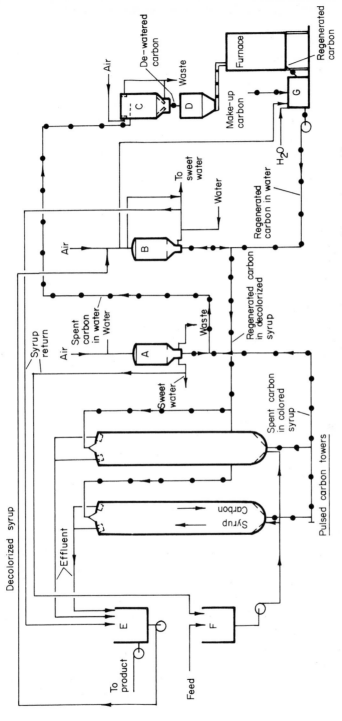

Fig. 14.1. Flow diagram of syrup decolorizer—Carbon towers with continuous kiln rejuvenation. A, sweetening-off and metering tank; B, sweetening-on tank; C, dewatering tank; D, furnace-feed hopper; E, decolorized syrup storage; F, colored syrup storage; G, quench tank; (—·—) carbon slurry lines; (——) water lines.

sugar; it is then stored in this tank, awaiting call for its use to refill the carbon towers.

This system has a number of advantages. A high degree of decolorization is obtained because of the greater efficiency of the tall, counterflow, compact carbon columns. The carbon losses and, therefore, the operating costs are comparatively low. The towers, tanks, and kilns are smaller than those used for fixed beds, reducing capital cost and space requirement. Remote, manual valve control with adequate instrumentation reduce the operating labor.

This new carbon technique is applicable in the purification of products other than sugar, such as food syrups, fine chemicals, and beverages, and in the removal of color and odor from hydrocarbons, dyes, and phenols. It is capable of removing organic impurities from heavily contaminated wastes, abating the pollution of rivers and other surface supplies.

3. TREATMENT OF DECOLORIZED CANE-SUGAR SYRUP

The decolorized syrup from the carbon towers in the sugar plant just described is passed through beds of porous strong-base type I anion resin superimposed over the cation resin in common vessels. The anion resin operates in the chloride form and is regenerated by sodium chloride brine. The anion resin exchanges its chloride for sulfates and phosphates, present in the decolorized syrup. Since the chlorides are quite soluble, they do not crystallize out with the sugar, remaining in the "mother liquor" of the evaporators. The cation resin below the anion resin, exchanges its sodium for the calcium present in the syrup; it, too, is regenerated by brine. Since sodium is much more soluble than the calcium, the final crystallized sugar contains less ionic impurities. This ion exchange treatment also adsorbs residual color left in the effluent of the carbon towers so that whiter crystal sugar is produced.

4. DELIMING OF BEET-SUGAR SYRUP

During the season when beets are the raw product instead of the more costly cane sugar the anion resin beds are removed and replaced by cation resin. The ion exchange beds then consist entirely of cation resin. The beet sugar syrup is "delimed" by the cation resin, so that its calcium content is replaced by the more soluble sodium exchanged from the resin. Reduction of the calcium content prevents the formation of calcium carbonate deposits in the evaporator and so saves costly outages and operating labor for its cleaning.

B. Purification of Molasses and Polyols in the Manufacture of Glycerine and Other Products

1. THE PLANT

Several years ago a large chemical company developed a new process for making synthetic glycerine, ethylene, and other glycols from agricultural raw materials. Previously these alcohol compounds were made mostly from petroleum chemicals. A new plant was built, with an annual capacity of 50,000,000 lb of glycerine and related products.

The raw material for this process had to be low in cost and pure enough to avoid poisoning the catalysts added. Invert molasses proved to be the best raw product for meeting these requirements. The process involves both hydrogenation and hydrogenolysis of the carbohydrates. Many reagents and catalysts are added for the conversion of the sucrose sugar, first to invert sugar, and then to glycerine and other polyols. Ion exchange was selected as the method of reducing the impurities in the liquor at the various stages of the process. The impurities must be removed to facilitate subsequent processing steps and to give the desired purity to the final products.

Figure 14.2 is a simplified flow diagram of the plant and indicates the various ion exchanger units installed. For molasses deashing the demineralizing plant consists of two primary cation exchangers, operating in parallel and regenerated with sulfuric acid. These are followed by three primary weak-base anion exchangers, two of which operate in series while the third is being regenerated with caustic soda. Finally, there is a secondary pair of cation and weak-base anion exchanger units. For polyol purification the demineralizer has two trains of cation and strong-base anion units, followed by a single weak-base anion unit. For softening the water used in regeneration and sweetening-off three sodium zeolite softeners are included.

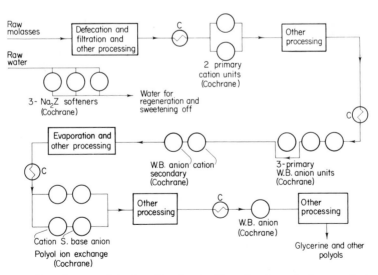

Fig. 14.2. Flow diagram of demineralizer for deashing of molasses in the manufacture of glycerine and other polyols. (C, cooler.)

2. RESULTS OF ION EXCHANGE

The molasses, after "defecation" pretreatment, contains mineral impurities, or ash, besides color and other organic matter. The cationic impurities, consisting of calcium, magnesium, sodium, and potassium, are removed by the primary cation units. Because the calcium content is high, a five-step sulfuric acid regeneration is used, to avoid forming calcium sulfate precipitates that would foul the exchange resin during regeneration. The acids in the effluent of the cation exchange step, formed from the gluconates, aconitates, and amino acids present, are removed by the primary anion exchangers. The primary demineralizer thus reduces the ash in the defecated molasses from 4% to an average of 0.5% (called ash leakage). The secondary demineralizer (cation and anion units) reduces this ash leakage (plus some impurities added in further processing steps between the primary and secondary demineralizers) to 0.05%. The polyol dual demineralizer removes this remaining ash (plus some traces of metals and other constituents added in the further processing) to 0.005%; this is equivalent to 50 ppm. The final weak-base anion unit removes small amounts of acidity.

C. Deashing of Turbid, Nonaqueous, Spin-Bath Solvent Solution

The spin-bath solvent solution in the case chosen for review here contained ionic impurities which a synthetic-fiber textile plant wished removed by demineralization, so that it could manufacture a final product of greater purity. However, the solvent also contained a high amount of valuable suspended materials, which were to pass through the demineralizer unaffected.

The solvent solution was an equal mixture of methylene chloride and methanol. The total ions (ash) present amounted to about 5 ppm, of which calcium and sodium acetates were the main constituents. The demineralizer was installed, to reduce the 5 ppm of ionic impurities to 0.3 ppm, decreasing the conductivity from 0.9 to 0.3 μmhos.

The valuable suspended matter present in the solvent consisted mainly of cellulose acetate. About 1000 ppm of this suspended matter were present, together with some oil. This posed a difficult problem in ion exchange, because conventional downflow exchanger beds would be rapidly clogged. A special upflow fluidized-bed technique had to be developed.

A demineralizer pilot plant was first installed for treating about 50 gal of solvent per minute. It had a mixture of cation and strong-base anion resins in upflow units. The results were sufficiently encouraging so that a plant was installed for treating 1000 gal/min. The large-scale demineralizer plant consisted of six units, each 72 in. in diameter and 144 in. high. Each unit contained 48 ft^3 of Dowex HCR-W cation exchanger and 72 ft^3 of Dowex SBR-P (porous strong-base type I anion exchanger). The flow of solvent was upward through this resin bed, and the flow rate was less than 7 gal/min/ft^2. At this flow rate the resin bed was expanded and fluidized, allowing the suspended matter to pass through. However, the bed remained compact enough to effect good exchange capacity. For regeneration the resin was periodically sluiced out of one exchange unit at a time into an external regeneration vessel 48 in. in diameter and 18 ft high. Sulfuric acid (in two steps) and caustic soda were the regenerants.

Softened water was used for the regeneration steps in the external vessel. No water was allowed to enter the main columns (72 in. in diameter). The resin was sluiced out of the main columns in an alcohol slurry into the external regenerating vessel. There the resin was sweetened off, to recover the alcohol in the voids, and then regenerated. After regeneration the resin was sweetened on, to replace the water in the voids with alcohol before returning it to the main columns. Regenerations were infrequent (once in two days).

Besides being regenerated the resin in the main shells received a cleansing treatment with methylene chloride several times daily. The effluent methylene chloride was recovered for reuse. Instrumentation and remotely operated manual valves simplified the operations.

There was some initial difficulty with the fouling of the upper, fine screens near the outlet of the main columns. Special jets were installed, to keep the screen washed and unclogged. A similar application of fluidized upflow resin beds containing suspended materials was reported by a drug manufacturer for the isolation of streptomycin from a broth (*1*). In that case a motor-driven agitator prevented the plugging of the top outlet screen.

D. Removal of Iron from Hydrochloric Acid

The muriatic acid facilities of a petrochemical company wanted to remove iron from their 36% hydrochloric acid in order to produce a more refined grade of acid. This would extend their acid market to the food and pharmaceutical fields. The amount of iron present was 8 ppm (as Fe), and a 90% reduction was desired.

The iron is present as a complex anion $(FeCl_4)^-$. Strong-base Type I anion resin is used for removing the ferrous chloride, and in this exceptional case chemicals were not required for regeneration; city water alone suffices for stripping the iron from the resin. This is explained by the fact that the complex anion $(FeCl_4)^-$ can exist only in strong acids. When the city water is passed through the resin, it dilutes the strong acid present, whereupon the complex anion $(FeCl_4)^-$ breaks down to a neutral salt, $FeCl_3$, which is rinsed out of the resin to waste.

E. Removal of Impurities from Organic Solvents

A large pharmaceutical manufacturer installed ion exchangers to purify mixed organic solvents: methanol, acetone, and methyl ethyl ketones. The impurities consisted mainly of calcium compounds, and 90% removal was required.

The ion exchange equipment installed consists of three systems, as follows.

System 1. This system includes three cation downflow columns containing Amberlite 200, a macroreticular strong-acid cation exchange resin. There are six regeneration steps: sweetening off, backwash, regeneration with brine, regeneration with sulfuric acid, rinse, and sweetening on.

System 2. This system consists of two upflow columns containing Amberlyst 15, a special Rohm and Haas Company macroreticular strong-acid cation resin for nonaqueous applications. Upflow exhaustion is used for fluidizing the resin bed, because the liquid solvent contains valuable organic crystals that are not to be removed. The columns are conical in shape, 4 ft 6 in. in diameter at the bottom and 8 ft 0 in. in diameter at the top and 12 ft 0 in. high. The conical shape, by reducing the velocity at the top, helps prevent the escape of the resin. The shells and internal distributors are of stainless steel. Regeneration is pushbutton automatic, with brine for removing the calcium. The resin is then rinsed, and caustic soda is passed through, to remove organic foulants. Finally, sulfuric acid is passed through the resin, to convert it to the hydrogen form. The usual sweetening-off and sweetening-on steps are also included. The product flow is 450 gal/min through one column while the other is being regenerated.

System 3. This system consists of two downflow columns, each 5 ft 0 in. in diameter and 9 ft 0 in. in height, containing macroreticular weak-base anion resin Amberlite IRA-93. The shells, internal and external piping, and valves are of stainless steel. The two columns operate mostly in series, but when one of the columns is being regenerated, the other is operated alone, and the regenerated column then becomes the first one in the series train on the next run. The anion to be removed is mostly sulfuric acid. The pH value of the solvent is raised to 7.0 by the anion resin. Regeneration (pushbutton automatic) is accomplished first with acid and then with caustic soda. The sweetening-off and sweetening-on steps are included. The flow of solvent treated is 200 gal/min.

III. Applications: Recovery of Valuable Substances and Purification of Liquors for Reuse

A. *Recovery of Platinum and Other Precious Metals from Concentrated Hydrochloric Acid*

A smelting and refining company wanted to use ion exchange to recover certain precious metals from concentrated hydrochloric acid. A pilot unit was installed and found to be effective.

The metals are present as complex anions, so that anion resin can remove them. Platinum, for example, is present as metal chloride ions $(PtCl_6)^{2-}$, called chloroplatinate. Anion resin has a strong affinity for these complex molecules, even when other anions are present. In this particular case the anion resin has a potential capacity of 3.0 milliequivalents of platinum per gram of resin. Translated to economic terms, each cubic foot of anion resin has a potential capacity for recovering 9.7 lb of platinum, worth $12,500 (in 1960).

The feed solution also contained considerable gold, rhodium, and copper and traces of silver. Copper does not form a complex chloride ion to any significant degree, nor does silver in the presence of a strong hydrochloric acid solution. Gold and rhodium do form chloride complex ions and are absorbed by the resin, too. However, the presence of these other metals reduced the actual platinum exchange capacity, so that only about $3000 worth of platinum was removed by each cubic foot of resin.

Since it was impractical to remove the stable complexes from the resin in the concentrated form, the usual regeneration with chemicals was not employed in this case. Final recovery of the platinum was accomplished by burning the resin and reclaiming the metal in molten form. The resin was thus expendable in this application.

The equipment installed consisted of an exchanger column, designed to withstand concentrated hydrochloric acid, with facilities for transferring the resin conveniently to the external furnace. No regeneration equipment was used. Fully regenerated anion resin only replaced the exhausted resin.

In operation the end of the exhaustion was determined by the color, verified by chemical analysis, of the precious-metal content of the effluent. It was essential that the feed solution be kept free from acids other than hydrochloric acid, because the ability of the anion resin to absorb precious metals is seriously reduced by the other acids.

B. Reclaiming of Chromates from Cooling-Tower Blowdown

Industrial cooling systems for heat exchangers use cooling towers wherever water is too scarce for once-through cooling. The warm cooling water is recirculated over the tower, and the water is recooled by evaporation in the tower and reused. The evaporation causes the dissolved impurities to concentrate. When the concentration reaches the solubility limit of the salts in question, precipitates form, which deposit on heat-exchange surfaces. To avoid such deposits, the concentration is limited by blowing off some of the concentrated water and replacing it with fresh, unconcentrated makeup water. Water is also lost from the tower by "windage," and this loss, too, must be made up.

Chromates, polyphosphates, or zinc, or both the latter two, are often added to the recirculated cooling water, to act as inhibitors for the protection of the heat-exchanger surfaces from corrosion. The chromates are lost in the tower blowdown water and must be replaced and, since they are toxic, the tower blowdown water cannot be discharged into surface-water supplies without causing a serious pollution problem.

Ion exchange proved a convenient solution of this problem. Research into the development of the proper regeneration procedure was described in two papers (2, 3). A Type I strong-base anion resin is used, and sodium chloride plus caustic soda are used for regeneration. Greater chromate-removal capacity of the anion resin is obtained if the pH value of the cooling-water influent is depressed to 4.5 or 5.0 by the addition of acid. The exchange capacity then is about 4 lb of chromate (as CrO_4) removed per cubic foot of anion resin, when the resin is regenerated with 2 lb of caustic soda plus 6 or 7 lb of sodium chloride. The permissible flow rate through the resin bed is 4 gal/min/ft^3. The chromate is recovered from the elution water during regeneration and is reused.

Another solution of this problem has been the demineralizing of the makeup for the cooling tower. The demineralized makeup is so free from dissolved solids that no buildup by concentration takes place; therefore the tower does not have to be blown down at all, and no chromate is lost. This permits the use of chromates for corrosion inhibition without causing a pollution problem. Several cooling-water makeup demineralizers have been installed for this purpose.

C. Recovery of Zinc from Rinse Water and Clarification of Spin-Bath Liquor

The case chosen for description here is a viscose rayon process, starting with cellulose sheets and ending with the filament winding operation; see Fig. 14.3.

The spin bath contains about 150 ppm polysulfide suspended matter, which is to be removed. The flow of the filtered spin-bath solution is 1200 gal/min, and three pressure filters, each 96 in. in diameter, are used. The spin bath is acid, and the chemicals present damage ordinary rubber linings. Special lining was therefore required for the shell and piping. Sweetening-off and sweetening-on steps are required during backwashing of the filters, to avoid dilution of the spin bath.

The zinc recovery from the acid rinse water is accomplished, as shown in Fig. 14.3, with two cation exchange columns, regenerated either with acid or glauber salts (Na_2SO_4) obtained from the crystallizer. The zinc-rich product, eluted from the cation resin during regeneration, is returned to the evaporator for concentration and, finally, to the spin bath for reuse.

D. Recovery of Chromic Acid from Plating Baths

The plating of metal objects protects them from corrosion and enhances their appearance. Plating is done by depositing a thin layer of a nobler metal

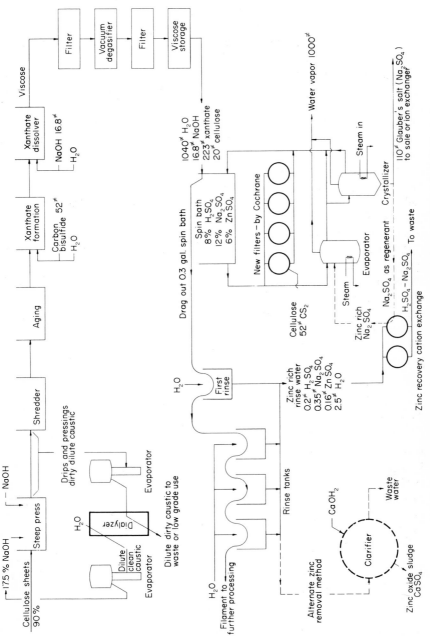

Fig. 14.3. Flow diagram of filters for removing suspended matter from spin-bath liquor in a viscose rayon plant and of cation exchanger plant for recovering zinc from acid rinse water.

on the base metal. Examples of noble metals are copper, cadmium, nickel, and chromium.

In the plating process the base metal parts (called "work") are immersed in the plating solutions, through which an electric current is passed. The work acts as one of the electrodes. The current causes the nobler metal to migrate and deposit on the work. The work is then withdrawn, allowed to drip off, and rinsed. Some of the plating solution adheres to the metal surfaces; the adhering solution is called "drag-out." It must be thoroughly rinsed off, to avoid interfering with later finishing steps.

The plating baths in time become contaminated by metallic and other impurities and must be dumped to waste or cleaned up by chemical means. The dumping of the plating solutions causes a pollution problem, because many plating waste waters contain toxic chemicals such as cyanides and chromic acid. Most antipollution regulations limit cyanide to 0.5 ppm and chromic acid to 1.0 ppm in the waste waters to be discharged into rivers or other surface supplies.

Ion exchange was adopted, to remove these chemicals from rinse waters following chromic acid baths. Figure 14.4 shows a typical flow sheet of chromic acid recovery. The cation exchanger removes iron, trichrome, and other metallic cation impurities. The anion exchanger removes chromate and other anions, and its effluent becomes the demineralized rinse water, recovering valuable water. The demineralized water used for rinsing avoids the introduction of additional contaminants into the cycle.

The toxic chromate (hexavalent chrome) removed by the anion resin is stripped from the resin by the caustic soda regeneration. The two passes of regenerant caustic soda through the anion exchangers, illustrated in Fig. 14.4, enrich it to a concentrated (3% by weight) alkaline solution of sodium chromate. The latter is then passed through the cation exchanger, where it is converted to chromic acid. The cation regenerant effluent often is further concentrated by evaporation (up to 30%) for reuse in the plating bath. Either a vacuum or an atmospheric evaporator (as indicated in Fig. 14.4) may be used for this purpose. Thus, both the chromic acid and the rinse waters are recovered, resulting in appreciable savings and at the same time avoiding a pollution problem.

E. Removal of Iron from Phosphoric Acid for Pickling Steel

Phosphoric acid is a good metal-pickling agent because it produces an adherent, rust-resistant coating on the steel surfaces. The pickling operation is carried out with a 15 to 20% strength of the acid at 190°F in a spray chamber. Some steel, dissolved in the pickling process, accumulates in the phosphoric acid and reduces its efficiency.

When the iron concentration in the phosphoric acid reaches about

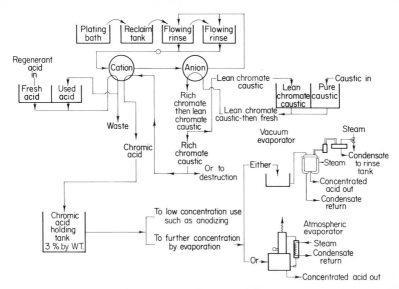

Fig. 14.4. Flow diagram of ion exchangers for recovering chromic acid and rinse water in plating plants.

1/16 lb/gal, the iron begins to precipitate. At that point the phosphoric acid used to be dumped to waste. Because this was costly and also caused a pollution problem, hydrogen cation exchange columns were installed for removing the iron from the phosphoric acid and replacing it with hydrogen. The treated phosphoric acid is thereby recoverable and is returned to the pickling operation for reuse.

Sulfuric acid is used for regeneration at a cost of about 10¢ for each pound of iron removed. High regeneration efficiency is obtained by four cation exchange columns, two operating in series and the other two regenerating in series. The runs are short, so that the volumes of resin and the size of the exchanger vessels are small. Capital and operating costs thus are kept low.

IV. Solid Exchangers with Water Elution and No Chemical Regenerants

The three water-elution methods described in the following paragraphs—ion exclusion, ion retardation, and acid retardation—are the most economical separation processes, since they do not require chemical regenerants. However, in certain cases the separation may not be sufficiently sharp and complete, and undesirable side effects may occur, such as excessive dilution. Then it may be necessary to follow the water-elution process with a process of ion exchange that involves regeneration with chemicals, which completes the separation.

Ion exclusion and ion retardation are compared in the paragraphs on ion retardation. Acid retardation is similar to ion retardation.

A. Ion Exclusion

The ion exclusion process was developed by the Dow Chemical Company in the early nineteen-fifties and two patents were granted (4, 5). A paper published in 1956 describes the process as follows (6): "Basically ion exclusion is a method for the fractionation of electrolytes from non-electrolytes, both present in aqueous solution, by the use of ion exchange resins, but without chemical regeneration." As the authors of a later paper put it (7), "If a solution containing ionic and non-ionic components is placed on top of a bed of resin and forced down through the column with water, the ionic material will be eluted first since it only has to displace the solution in the voids. The non-ionic solution must displace both the liquid in the voids and resin liquid and will appear in the effluent after the ionic material has passed out of the column."

Figure 14.5 shows the sharp separation of sodium chloride from ethylene glycol. Another application of ion exclusion is the purification of sugar solutions (8, 9). It was reported that spent sulfite liquor also can be split by ion exclusion into sugar and lignin sulfonates (10).

B. Ion Retardation

The Dow Chemical Company also developed ion retardation, which is very similar to ion exclusion (11). In both processes the separation of solution components "is based upon the differences in their degree of adsorption on the resin. Likewise, both employ water as an eluant; and finally, both are applicable to the fractionation of mixtures of organic and inorganic materials."

The differences between the two processes are as follows.

(a) In ion exclusion the resins are conventional ones, whereas in ion retardation the resins are a special kind, called "retardion resins." These are "amphoteric snake-cage polyelectrolytes made by chemical modification of ordinary ion-exchange resins" (11).

(b) In ion exclusion the separation of electrolytes from large, organic molecules is dependent upon the diffusion of the organic molecule into the resin pores, and for this reason pore size is a limiting factor. Therefore, separation may not be possible by ion exclusion if the molecular weight of the organic component is greater than several hundred. In such cases ion retardation is applicable.

(c) Ion exclusion will not fractionate mixtures of highly ionized substances, such as two salts, whereas ion retardation frequently can accomplish this.

In processes now involving dialysis, fractional crystallization, or ion exchange the ion-retardation technique may achieve improved performance.

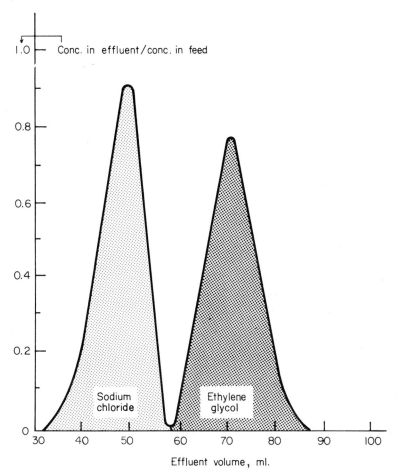

Fig. 14.5. Separation of sodium chloride from ethylene glycol by ion exclusion. [From Seamster and Wheaton (7).]

Some possible applications are the separation of ionic materials from non-ionic, such as chloride from sucrose, and the fractionation of ionic mixtures, when the cost of eluant and regenerants in other ion exchange processes would be too high. Examples of the latter are the separation of sodium sulfate from sodium chloride, of zinc chloride from ammonium chloride, and of ferrous sulfate from zinc sulfate.

C. Acid Retardation

Acid retardation is similar to ion retardation but is used for separating strong acids from their salts (12). The strong acids are retarded relative to the movement of the salts, when the acid solution is passed through a bed of Type I strong-base anion resin.

Examples of the applications of acid retardation for the removal of salts or metals from various acids are the following (*12*): the separation of ferrous chloride or sodium chloride from hydrochloric acid, of ferric nitrate from nitric acid, of copper and iron from nitric acid, of magnesium from acetic acid, and of ferric sulfate from sulfuric pickling acid. Acid retardation also has separated sulfonic acids from sulfuric acids (*13*) and recovered sulfuric acids or nitric acids from ore leach and from metal-pickling liquors.

V. Liquid Exchangers

As new fields of application for ion exchange appear on the scene, the development of new techniques is stimulated by the limitations of existing methods. For example, solid ion exchangers are not well suited for extraction applications where high concentrations of the ions are to be absorbed. The recent production of organic liquids with ion exchange properties presented the possibility of a continuous liquid–liquid technique for overcoming this limitation of solid resins. The development of liquid ion exchange was derived from the suggestion of two English chemists, Smith and Page (*13a*), of employing long-chain high-molecular-weight aliphatic amines as acid-binding extractants. Kunin compares the new liquid–liquid technique with the older solvent extraction as follows (*14*): "Solvent extraction is based upon the relative solubility of a solute in two immersible solvents. Liquid ion exchange, however, depends upon extraction, with a reaction or energy of binding between the solute and the extractant phase.... the extraction of uranyl nitrate from an aqueous nitric acid solution by tributyl phosphate is an example of solvent extraction, since only solubilities are involved." He cites an example of liquid ion exchange: "The extraction of an acid from water by a water soluble amine, dissolved in an inert solvent, involves the removal of the acid from the aqueous phase and its transfer to the organic phase, accompanied by a distinct chemical reaction with the amine, to form an amine salt."

Conventional solid–liquid and liquid–liquid ion exchanges are compared as follows (*14*):

"The analogy of conventional ion exchange involving solids exchangers and liquid ion exchange is most striking. For the extraction of an acid from an aqueous solution, one may write the same equation for both systems.

$$RNH_2 + HX \rightarrow RNH_3X$$

R represents either the backbone polymer of the conventional ion exchange resin or a long chain, oil soluble radical of the liquid exchanger.

"Since salt formation is involved in both the liquid and conventional ion exchange systems, the distribution coefficients or selectivity coefficients are usually much higher for the ion exchange systems than for the solvent extraction systems. Although the overall chemistry involved in liquid ion exchange is almost identical with that of conventional ion exchange resins, the role of moisture or water is different in the two systems. Whereas conventional solid exchangers are highly hydrated, the liquid ion exchangers are essentially anhydrous throughout the entire exchange process. Yet their effectiveness is unhindered. Conventional ion exchangers are normally ineffective unless they are highly hydrated."

The Rohm and Haas Company announced the production of two weak-base anion liquid ion exchangers, Amberlite LA-1 and LA-2. They are high-molecular-weight water-insoluble liquid secondary amines. Five requirements are given for good liquid ion exchangers (14): "(1) low solubility; (2) high selectivity; (3) good miscibility in cheap diluents; (4) freedom from emulsion-forming tendencies; and (5) ability to be stripped or regenerated in cyclic processes."

The equipment used for liquid ion exchange is the same as for solvent extraction, namely "mixer settlers, centrifugal contactors and the various pulsed and non-pulsed extraction columns" (14). Generally the mixer settlers are preferred.

Liquid exchangers may be used for the extraction of acids and bases or for the simple exchange of cations and anions. They are, in turn, regenerated or stripped in the same way as solid exchangers. For example, a liquid exchanger that has been loaded with hydrochloric acid may be stripped by ammonia, as follows:

$$RNH_2Cl + NH_4OH \rightarrow RNH + NH_4Cl + H_2O$$

Likewise, an exchanger loaded with nitrate ions may be stripped by brine, thus:

$$RNH_2NO_3 + NaCl \rightleftharpoons RNH_2Cl + NaNO_3$$

The liquid exchanger extractant is best dissolved in an inert solvent, facilitating separation of the organic and aqueous phases and minimizing solubility and entrainment losses. Examples of good inert solvents are kerosene and benzene. The usual concentration of the liquid exchanger in the diluent ranges from 2.5 to 12.5% by volume.

A. Advantages

The following advantages are listed for liquid ion exchangers (14): "continuous operation; ease in changing flow conditions to counteract changes in feed compositions; ease of stripping the exhausted liquid exchanger; ease of adjustment of exchange capacity; fast rate of exchange; few extraction or stripping stages; low consumption of reagents; minimal rinse and dilution problems; and the availability of simple and readily available industrial equipment."

B. Applications

Liquid exchangers are mainly applicable in recovery and purification operations in the field of hydrometallurgy. An example is uranium recovered from low-grade ores. The liquid exchanger, dissolved in a kerosene diluent, contacts an acid sulfate leach liquor, in which the uranium is present as uranyl sulfate anion. After extracting the uranium, the liquid exchangers are stripped with solutions of salt or sodium carbonate.

Other substances may be extracted from concentrated hydrochloric acid, such as traces of ferric chloride, impurities from aluminium chloride, and iron, cobalt, and nickel.

Waste process waters can be purified by liquid ion exchangers; the removal of impurities abates pollution, and at the same time valuable products are recovered.

C. Disadvantages

Lewis confirmed the applicability of liquid ion exchangers for treating waste water but cited certain disadvantages (15):

(a) The operating costs are high owing to "loss of expensive extraction reagent as the result of its water solubility, spillage or mechanical entrainment." Further, human error in operation may permit the liquid to "go down the drain." Since liquid exchangers cost $1 to $2 per pound, these losses may be too costly.

(b) The operating cost is high owing to the tendency of liquid ion exchangers to "wet and adhere to solids in the system."

(c) Objectionable odors and tastes are in the waste stream; they are due to the kerosene or hydrocarbon. They may have to be removed by expensive supplementary adsorption.

D. General Mills Process

The Chemical Division of General Mills, Inc., Minneapolis, developed a number of liquid ion exchangers (16); water-insoluble LIX reagents, the tertiary amine Alamine 336 and the quaternary amine Aliquat 336. These were used for the concentration and purification of uranium and vanadium. Figure 14.6 is a diagram of vanadium extraction.

Recently LIX-64 was developed for the recovery of copper from acidic dump leach liquor (17). Figure 14.7 is a diagram of the new process. The following advantages are claimed for LIX-64 in this application: it can be

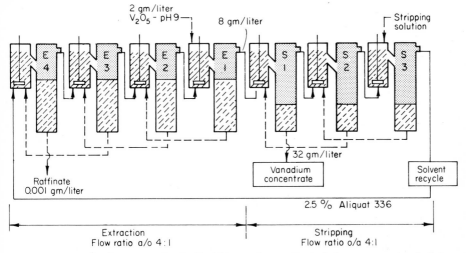

Fig. 14.6. Vanadium extraction by liquid ion exchange. Unshaded areas, organic; shaded areas, aqueous. [From an article (*16*).]

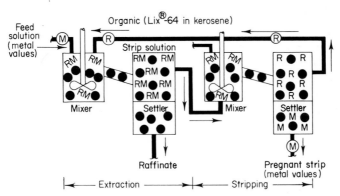

Fig. 14.7. General Mills process of recovering copper from leach liquor by liquid ion exchange. [Reprinted from *Chem. Eng. News*, October 18, 1965, with the permission of the Am. Chem. Soc. and General Mills, Inc.]

used without any chemical treatment of the liquor prior to extraction, the recovery ranges from 96 to 99.9 % of the copper in the dilute liquor, it is stable and is easily stripped with sulfuric acid, and it rejects essentially both ferric and ferrous ions.

LIX-64 must compete with two existing means for this application: powdered iron or finely divided sponge iron, which precipitates the copper from leach waters, and the cementation process, most widely used for copper extraction. LIX-64, operating in the hydrogen cycle, extracts the copper by forming an organic-soluble complex with the metal. It does not form complexes with other contaminants, such as ferric iron, although some ferric iron does dissolve in the organic phase.

Sulfuric acid solution (200 g/lit strength) is used as the stripping solution. It reacts with the copper in the organic phase to form copper sulfate solution. The latter is pumped to an electrolysis unit, and the copper-free organic phase is recycled back to the extraction unit. The electrolysis unit causes the copper to plate out in a more than 99 % purity. The sulfuric acid regenerated by the operation is recycled back to the stripping stage.

Extraction is usually done in four mixer-settler tanks operating in series (only one is shown in Fig. 14.7). The organic and aqueous solutions are pumped into the mixer tanks, agitated, and then allowed to separate in the settlers. The organic-extractant solution flows through the four mixer-settlers countercurrent to the aqueous feed solution. The copper content increases from one tank to the next. The raffinate (liquor minus the copper) is discharged from the first settler tank.

The organic phase is a 10 % (by volume) solution of LIX-64 in kerosene. The aqueous phase is the leach liquor, which usually contains 0.85 to 1.5 g of copper per liter of solution and 2 to 10 g of ferric iron per liter. The pH of the liquor varies from 1.75 to 2.75.

REFERENCES

1. C. R. Bartels, G. Kleiman, J. N. Korzun, and D. B. Irish, A novel ion-exchange method for the isolation of streptomycin. *Chem. Eng. Progr.* **54**, No. 8, 49 (1958).
2. L. Sloan. An ion exchange method of recovery and re-use of chromate inhibitor from cooling tower blowdown water. *Cooling Tower Inst. Ann. Spring Meeting, New York, June 1964.*
3. J. C. Hesler, P. R. Puckorius, and N. B. Farnsworth, Recovery and re-use of chromates from cooling tower blowdown. *Intern. Water Conf., Engrs. Soc. West Penn., September 1964.*
4. W. C. Bauman, U.S. Patent 2,684,331 (1954).
5. D. W. Simpson and W. C. Bauman, U.S. Patent 2,771,193 (1956).
6. R. M. Wheaton, New uses for ion exchange resins. *Chem. Eng. Progr.* (October 1956).
7. A. H. Seamster and R. M. Wheaton, Ion exchange becomes powerful processing tool. *Chem. Eng.* (August 22, 1960).
8. D. R. Asher, Sugar purification by ion exclusion. *Ind. Eng. Chem.* **48**, 1465 (1956).
9. A. C. Reents and H. W. Keller, U.S. Patent 2,937,959 (1960).
10. V. F. Feleicatta, M. Lung, and J. L. McCarthy, Sugar-lignin sulfonate separations using ion exchange resins. *Tappi* **42**, No. 6, 496 (1959).
11. Ion retardation. Dow Catalog, April 1957 (reprinted with additions November 1957), Dow Chemical Co.
12. M. J. Hatch and J. A. Dillon, Acid retardation: A simple physical method for separation of strong acids from their salts. *Ind. Eng. Chem. Process Design Develop.* **2**, No. 4, 253 (1963).
13. R. C. Glogau, D. O. Halvorson, and W. J. Sloan, Separate sulfonic and sulfuric acids with an ion exchange resin. *Ind. Eng. Chem.* **53**, No. 4, 275 (1961).
13a.E. L. Smith and J. E. Page, Acid binding properties of long-chain aliphatic amines. *J. Soc. Chem. Ind.* **67**, 48 (1948).

14. R. Kunin, Liquid ion exchangers – a new phase of ion exchange technology. Rohm and Haas Co. Amber Hi-Lites, No. 62, March 1961, No. 63, May 1961.
15. C. J. Lewis, Liquid-liquid extraction for ion exchange recovery or treatment of industrial wastes. *Ind. Wastes* (September 1957) (from *Ind. Waste Conf., 12th, Purdue Univ., Lafayette, Indiana*).
16. Staff Article, Liquid ion exchange – promising union of solvent extraction and ion exchange. *Chem. Process* (June 1961).
17. Staff Article, New ion exchange resin for solvent extraction increases copper recovery. *Chem. Eng. News* (October 18, 1965).

Author Index

Numbers in parentheses are reference numbers and indicate that an author's work is referred to, although his name is not cited in the text. Numbers in italics show the page on which the complete reference is listed.

A

Abrams, I. M., 161(23), *171*
Adams, B. A., 4(6), *6*
Adams, R. C., 201(2), *224*
Aker, L. P., 321(6), *339*
Allen, Y. T., 106(25), *107*, 290(30), 291(30), *296*
Alling, S. F., 52(11), *66*
Angele, G. J., 115(2), *130*, 209(4), *225*
Angelo, J., 261(1), *294*
Applebaum, S. B., 33(2), 38(4, 5, 6), 50(10), 54(12), 60(17), 61(18), *66, 67*, 94(9), 100 (14, 16), 106(25), *106, 107*, 115(2), *130*, 146(9), 159(18), 164(25), *170, 171*, 197(1), 209(4), *224, 225*, 261(2), 276(10), 288(25), 290(28, 30, 31), 291(30, 32), 292(33), *294, 295, 296*, 303(9), *317*, 319(2), 321(7), 322 (2), *339*
Asher, D. R., 368(8), *374*

B

Banks, C. D., 102(20), *107*, 267(8), *295*
Bartels, C. R., 361(1), *374*
Bauman, W. C., 54(12a), *66*, 368(4, 5), *374*
Baumeister, T., 322(12), *340*
Beohner, H. L., 74, 142(3), *170*

Bogin, G. J., 294(41), *296*
Bolto, B. A., 339(28), *340*
Booher, B. L., 146(10), 160(10), *170*, 188(3), *195*
Bouchard, J., 348(12), *353*
Brooks, R. M., 219(9), *225*
Brune, C. E., 321(8), *339*
Brush, G. W., 115(2), *130*, 209(4), *225*
Brutschy, F. J., 309(11), *318*
Buchanan, R. M., 320(5), *339*

C

Caddell, J. R., 273(12), *295*
Calise, V. J., 60(16a), *67*, 105(23a), *107*, 276(11), *295*, 322(13), *340*
Calmon, C., *6*, 165(26), *171*
Camp, T. R., *22*
Cane, D., 326(18), *340*
Caprara, C., 326(18), *340*
Caskey, P. H., 152(14), *170*, 290(29), *296*, 341(1), *352*
Clark, T., 24(1), *66*
Coit, R. L., 322(14), 323(14, 15), 324 (14), *340*
Conley, W. R., 77(3, 4, 5, 6), 78(6), 98(3, 4, 5, 6), *106*
Connelley, E. J., 321(6), *339*
Cotton, K. C., 261(1), *294*
Coxe, E. F., 322(14), 323(14), 324(14), *340*

377

Subject Index